ANTIBIOTICS MONOGRAPHS NO. 2

Under the Editorial Direction of
Henry Welch, PH.D., *and* Félix Martí-Ibáñez, M.D.

ASSAY METHODS OF ANTIBIOTICS

A Laboratory Manual

By Donald C. Grove, PH.D., *and*

William A. Randall, PH.D.

Division of Antibiotics, Food and Drug Administration,
U. S. Department of Health, Education, and Welfare

FOREWORD

By Henry Welch, PH.D., *and* Félix Martí-Ibáñez, M.D.

A Publication of

MEDICAL ENCYCLOPEDIA, INC.

30 EAST 60TH STREET, NEW YORK 22, N. Y.

Copyright 1955 by Medical Encyclopedia, Inc., New York, N. Y.

Distributors outside U.S.A.: Interscience Publishers, New York–London.

CONTENTS

Section D. Determination of penicillin in body fluids and other substances.

FOREWORD

Ever since Pasteur introduced the microbial doctrine and Ehrlich's Chromo-therapy ushered in the era of modern chemotherapy, the laboratory has been the main battleground of Medicine. Gone are the days of philosophical investigation in the "pristine and serene" atmosphere of the laboratory. In today's laboratory the most important branch of Therapeutics was born and clinical diagnosis is each day brought to completion. If the clinician orients diagnosis on the basis of the exploration of the patient, in the laboratory the diagnosis is pinned to a basis so precise as to be sometimes almost mathematical, and it is confirmed or rejected. This is also the place where an infinite number of substances endowed with chemotherapeutic powers have been tested or discovered. If the hospital is art, the laboratory is science, and there the research worker, aided by his test tubes, often announces whether the patient will live or die.

In the hospital the physician struggles with symptoms and signs; in the laboratory the research worker zealously pursues the microbial or biochemical etiology of disease until he corners it like an animal at bay and then turns it over to the relentless pack of dogs of modern chemotherapeutic agents.

It was the physician's daily chores that gave historical rise to early clinical medicine. The laboratory came much later and was the fruit of the research man's wish to carry his understanding of the patient one step beyond what his senses could reveal. If the clinic is the expression of man seeking the truth about disease with his senses, the laboratory represents the historical yearn to plumb the abyssal mysteries of organic cells and humors; it is an attempt to extend, with the help of the clear hard pupil of the microscope, the search for the invisible cause of disease beyond the limits of what can be seen with the naked eye.

Antibiotics, perhaps the greatest accomplishment of modern research, have, since their inception, imparted to the laboratory a tremendous importance in Medicine. No longer is the mission of the laboratory to investigate some simple diagnostic tests. The laboratory must now produce constantly new curative weapons, and it must identify, isolate, measure, and stabilize them, determine their purity, and also act as wise adviser and mentor to the clinic. Without the laboratory, there would be no Antibiotic Era, and Therapeutics could not aspire to anything loftier than the empirical application of remedies extracted from Nature. In the laboratory, man, with the help of methods, instruments, and reactives, discovers and imprisons in his brain the immutable laws that rule the world of chemotherapeutics.

Since 1942 literally thousands of antibiotic substances have been isolated in laboratories. Many, in fact the great majority, have been discarded because of poor antimicrobial activity or high toxicity. There are now available on the American pharmaceutical market 17 useful antibiotics and hundreds of preparations of penicillin, tyrothricin, streptomycin, dihydrostreptomycin, bacitracin, chloramphenicol, chlortetracycline, oxytetracycline, tetracycline, polymyxin, viomycin, neomycin, erythromycin, carbomycin, fumagillin, nystatin, and anisomycin.

The useful methods for analysis of all these antibiotic preparations are included in this monograph, the second in a series dedicated to present a concise and accurate picture of each of the principal antibiotics and its application in clinical medicine.

This monograph is the first and only source in which useful and practical methods for the assay of all these antibiotic preparations are described. Many of the methods are "official" in that they are the ones used by the Food and Drug Administration in determining the identity, strength, quality, and purity of the so-called "certifiable" antibiotics. However, the others are not neglected and the most useful and acceptable methods for those antibiotics not certified by the Government are also included.

The first 15 chapters of this book describe the methods used for determining the potency of the salts of the 17 basic antibiotics. The various methods for preparations, such as tablets, troches, and ointments, are also given. In addition, where applicable, methods of analysis of body fluids and tissue are described. Assay of mixtures of antibiotics in pharmaceutical dosage forms are detailed in Chapter 16, while Chapters 17 and 18 describe methods of identification and the tests for toxicity, pyrogens, histamine, and sterility. Methods of determining bacterial sensitivity to the antibiotics are given in Chapter 19, and special methods are described in Chapter 20. All media, solutions, reagents, and apparatus are grouped in the final chapter of this comprehensive volume.

The authors of this monograph have had wide experience in the field of antibiotics. Doctor Grove as assistant director of the Division of Antibiotics of the Food and Drug Administration has kept close contact with the development of antibiotic methods through supervision of a large group of bacteriologists and chemists who analyze daily hundreds of antibiotic dosage forms. Doctor Randall as director of the research group in the same Division has been responsible for the development or modification and improvement of many of the methods included in this monograph. It is an interesting historical point that the first official assays of crude penicillin were carried out in 1943 in his laboratory.

The correlation of this large group of methods has been a monumental task and is so extremely well done that this book will be of great value to laboratory technicians and research workers in the antibiotic field. Industrial laboratories, where thousands of analyses of these drugs are made daily, and hospital, state, and municipal agencies will find this book a rich and rewarding source of useful information. This Manual is written in the clear, terse style that has become the characteristic idiom—chary of word, rich in meaning—of laboratory investigators. For the research man has beaten out for himself a sort of scientific shorthand. Methods, instruments, and systems are grouped on the pages of this book with the precision of soldiers lined up for the most exacting inspection. Indeed, since a laboratory manual is always the most eloquent of scientific books, it teaches us the art of saying a maximum of useful things with a minimum of verbiage, thus providing a supreme vehicle for the transmission of scientific knowledge. The clinician and the research man welcomes books like this Manual, on the pages of which the laboratory holds high its historical mission of seeker of scientific truth.

HENRY WELCH, PH.D.

Director, Division of Antibiotics, Food and Drug Administration;
Editor-in-Chief, ANTIBIOTICS & CHEMOTHERAPY and ANTIBIOTIC MEDICINE;

FELIX MARTI-IBAÑEZ, M.D.

International Editor, ANTIBIOTICS & CHEMOTHERAPY;
Associate Editor, ANTIBIOTIC MEDICINE

PREFACE

The value of antibiotics in the treatment of infectious diseases of man and the impact they have had on public health is well known by everyone today. The use of antibiotics in the treatment of animal diseases and in animal feeds for growth development has also become commonplace. The more recent use of these drugs for plant diseases further demonstrates their ubiquity. It is exceedingly important therefore to have accurate means of testing and controlling this outstanding class of drugs. Many methods of assay have been described in the scientific literature and there are many unpublished methods or modifications of methods. However, there is not available a compilation of tested and proved procedures for all of the antibiotics commonly distributed today. It is believed therefore that a real need for such a book exists.

The official regulations, promulgated under section 507 of the Federal Food, Drug, and Cosmetic Act, contain tests and methods of assay for penicillin, streptomycin, dihydrostreptomycin, chlortetracycline, tetracycline, chloramphenicol, bacitracin, and also a few of these antibiotics combined with polymyxin or neomycin. However, these regulations do not contain methods for various other antibiotics nor methods for determining antibiotics in body fluids, tissues, animal feeds, or milk. The regulations also do not contain methods for determining the sensitivity of an organism to an antibiotic or identification tests.

The present book gives practical tests and methods of assay for all of the antibiotics that are being distributed commercially in the United States today and for the various preparations and substances in which they may occur. Because of the tremendous amount of research being conducted to find new antibiotics, this book will probably not be published very long before some new ones will be introduced for clinical or other use, further adding to the list of these important drugs. It is believed, however, that such a wide variety of methods are presented that it will be a relatively simple matter to adapt them to any new antibiotics that may come along. It is hoped that this book will be of value not only to those who are engaged in the testing of antibiotics, but to students and teachers whose field of interest embraces this important and useful class of drugs.

The authors wish to express their sincere appreciation to Dr. Henry Welch, Dr. William Wright, and Mr. Amiel Kirshbaum for their helpful suggestions and review of the manuscript. We also wish to thank Dr. Joseph DiLorenzo for preparing the various charts and figures in the book.

DONALD C. GROVE, PH.D.
Assistant Director, Division of Antibiotics
Food and Drug Administration;

WILLIAM A. RANDALL, PH.D.
Director of Research, Division of Antibiotics
Food and Drug Administration

1 INTRODUCTION

The methods for testing antibiotics presented in the following chapters are largely those used in the laboratories of the Food and Drug Administration. Many of these methods were developed in these laboratories, while others were devised by the manufacturers of antibiotics and other investigators. No attempt has been made to present all of the methods available for testing antibiotics, and there are other methods available which no doubt will work just as satisfactorily as those given here. However, for general usefulness, accuracy, sensitivity, ease of preparation, and reproducibility, the methods described are recommended. No literature references are given for microbiologic assays, since the methods given have gone through so many modifications and variations of early published procedures that it would be difficult to give deserved credit to all of the investigators involved.

Assay methods are given only for the antibiotics that are actually distributed commercially in the United States at this time. A chapter is devoted to each antibiotic in most instances. Streptomycin and dihydrostreptomycin are discussed in the same chapter because of their close chemical structure and properties. Similarly, chlortetracycline, oxytetracycline, and tetracycline are also grouped in one chapter. Each chapter on an individual antibiotic has been arranged, where applicable and where the information is available, into four sections: a section for microbiologic assays, a section for chemical assays, a section for assays of the various pharmaceutical dosage forms, and a section dealing with the assay of the antibiotic in body fluids and in other substances, such as animal feeds. An attempt has been made to have each chapter on an individual antibiotic as complete as possible in itself with respect to assay instructions in order to keep cross references from one chapter to another at a minimum.

Following the chapters on individual antibiotics are chapters on the assay of mixtures of antibiotics; identification of antibiotics; methods for toxicity, pyrogen, histamine, and sterility testing; methods for determining the sensitivity of bacteria to antibiotics; miscellaneous tests, such as determination of penicillin G and moisture determinations; and a final chapter containing the formulas for various media and buffers and other information concerning equipment or reagents used.

General Comments on Microbiologic Assays. The "double-dose cylinder-plate method" given in Chapter 2 for estimating the potency of penicillin can also be applied to other antibiotics, although ratios other than 1:2 or 1:4 may be necessary. The method using the single concentration as the reference point is the most convenient and widely used. After some experience, and when a number of daily standard curves have been made, these daily curves can be matched, and, if their slope is seen to be generally similar, a composite standard curve can be constructed. Thereafter it is not necessary to run a daily curve, since potencies can be determined from the composite standard curve. It is desirable, however, to set up a curve from time to time in order to check the slope and accuracy of the master standard curve, or the slope of the master standard curve may be checked daily by preparing three plates using a double-dose method.

In the determination of potency by cylinder-plate methods it will be noted that the standard is placed on each plate along with the unknown sample. This is a most important part of the procedure, because numerous factors may affect the zone size, but, if something is operating to depress the zone size of the standard, it will likewise affect the unknown. Thus, if the zone size of the 1 unit/ml. standard on a given plate is smaller than the average of all of the 1 unit/ml. zones on all of the plates, it is assumed that something has also depressed the unknown and this is taken into account in the calculation of potency. This would be impossible unless the standard was placed on each plate.

The glass Petri dishes used are 20 by 100 mm. The 20 mm. depth is used so that the 10 mm. cylinders resting on the agar surface will not touch the cover. Also, the covers used are porcelain covers glazed on the outside but not inside. The unglazed under surface absorbs water of syneresis during incubation. Special aluminum Petri dish tops are also available and satisfactory for use provided they contain a cardboard liner that absorbs moisture.

When the melted media is poured in the dishes, it is important that this be done on a level surface, since variation in the thickness of the agar can affect the sensitivity of the test as well as the reproducibility of the zones of inhibition. It is also very important when the test culture is added to the melted agar to be sure that the agar has cooled to the temperature specified in the method. If the agar is too hot, very sparse growth or no growth at all may be obtained on the plates.

Stainless steel cylinders are recommended in place of glass or porcelain because they do not chip and are of the right weight to seat properly on the surface of the medium. The cylinders (cups) are placed on the surface of the seeded plates in a certain prescribed, regular fashion so that they are at approximately 60 degree intervals on a 2.8 cm. radius. This may be accomplished in several ways. First a cardboard template may be made the size of the Petri dish and marked with ink in the spaces where the cylinders should fall. The seeded plate is then placed over this marked board and the cylinders dropped with forceps into the proper position. Secondly, a plastic (lucite) template can be made to fit on top of the open Petri dish with holes bored of the proper size and interval. The depth of the plastic template should be sufficient to guide the cylinder straight to the surface of the seeded agar. A five hole template is described in the literature [1] and can easily be adapted for six holes. A mechanical metal dropping device [2] has been used for many years in our laboratories and also by others. This latter cylinder dropping device can hold as many as six tubes each containing about 50 cylinders and is recommended when assays are run routinely.

Many laboratories prefer to use filter paper discs instead of cylinders. Under properly controlled conditions these discs may be used satisfactorily. However, under certain circumstances the filter paper disc may act as a paper chromatogram of the solution being tested and irregular zone sizes may be obtained. Also with substances like sera, protein binding by absorption may occur so that the antibiotic does not diffuse into the agar medium.

The simplest way of measuring the diameter of the zone of inhibition is by inverting the plate over a suitable light source and measuring with a millimeter ruler. A refinement of this is to use a bacterial colony counter in which the scored plate for counting bacteria is removed and replaced by one having a millimeter scale etched on the surface of the glass. Other convenient instruments are the Fisher-Lilly zone reader, an apparatus especially designed for reading zone sizes, and the Bausch and Lomb Model B O H Balopticon, which can be adapted by mounting a Petri dish carrier on the chassis for projecting an enlarged image of the plate on a screen or wall on which is inscribed an enlarged millimeter scale. This latter system is the best for reading large numbers of plates as eye strain is greatly reduced. Electronic devices have been designed, which are satisfactory and in limited use. When these latter instruments break down, however, they require the services of expert electronic engineers for their repair and therefore are not practical at present.

In the adjustment of the culture inoculum of the test organism for the seed layer, it is necessary to try to standardize it so that essentially the same density of suspension is used from day to day. This is usually done by adjusting the suspension so that it will give a certain per cent light transmission when measured in a photoelectric colorimeter at a chosen wave length. It has been found that the per cent light transmission obtained will depend upon the type and thickness of the cell used and the narrowness of the filter or wave length selector of the particular instrument used. One instrument might give an 80 per cent light transmission reading, whereas another on the same suspension might read 40 per cent. Any instrument may be used as long as it is known which per cent light transmission on that instrument will give a suspension of satisfactory characteristics for the assay. Another method of standardizing the culture suspension is to make an actual viable microorganism count and adjust the suspension to contain a definite number of microorganisms. In either case, test plates should be run to determine the quantity of the standardized suspension to be added to each 100 ml. of seed agar to give clear, sharp, inhibitory zones of appropriate size.

Serial dilution methods suffer the disadvantage of measuring only between two concentrations of the dilution series. Thus if growth occurs in, for example, the sixth tube in a twofold dilution series and not in the fifth tube, this means that the concentration of the antibiotic has been increased by 100 per cent for complete inhibition. In order to obtain a more precise estimation of the minimal inhibitory concentration of the drug, it would be necessary to use narrower increments in the dilution series, which results in greater labor and time expenditure. The serial dilution method suffers from still another disadvantage. There are many unknown inhibitory substances in blood, urine, tissue, and milk, which will inhibit the test organisms in a liquid medium but which do not diffuse in the agar medium and hence do not interfere in the cylinder-plate assay procedure. Also, rigid sterility conditions must be maintained in serial dilution tests, which are not necessary in the plate assay technique. Further, the assay of turbid material may obscure the exact end point. In spite of these drawbacks, the serial dilution method is still a very useful means for determining the potency of antibiotics in body fluids, as well as in certain other substances. All of the bacterial species used in the plate assays described are suitable for use in the serial dilution assay. A suitable dilution of the test organism is selected by determining the sensitivity of various dilutions to the standard antibiotic. The final volume of medium for most serial dilution tests is either 1 or 2 ml. When samples are assayed the standard antibiotic is made up in the same or similar material (i.e., serum if it is being assayed) and diluted in the culture medium selected.

Turbidimetric methods for the assay of antibiotics are quite accurate and have the advantage in most cases of a shorter incubation period for the growth of the test organism, usually three to four hours. Thus, results are obtained on the same day of the test. In such methods, however, it is usually necessary to run a standard curve each day. The presence of solvent residues or other inhibitory substances are more likely to affect turbidimetric assays than the cylinder-plate methods. Further, cloudy or turbid preparations will cause interference in the turbidimetric methods.

In the turbidimetric microbiologic assay it is necessary to read the turbidity of the tubes at the end of the incubation period. We have found the Lumetron photoelectric colorimeter, Model 402-E, to be readily adaptable for such use. The instrument was designed for reading the light transmission of colored solutions, and it is described for such use as a bridge circuit instrument with balance cell, with the galvanometer as zero indicator, and with the readings to be taken on the slide wire dial. It may be also used as a direct reading instrument whereby the readings are taken on the galvanometer scale rather than on the slide wire. This direct reading method is recommended for reading the turbidities obtained in the turbidimetric microbiologic methods because it has the advantage of greater speed of operation. In addition, it is possible to utilize the balance cell of the instrument for the purpose of "zero suppression." The instrument can be set so that one end of the galvanometer scale corresponds to the most turbid solution of the standard tubes and the other end to the least turbid solution. In this way, the total range of turbidity that is of interest is spread over the galvanometer scale and it is possible to measure small differences in turbidity. A special drain tube adapter may be purchased which remains stationary in the instrument. In this way, the same tube is used for all measurements, avoiding errors due to differences in diameters of tubes. The tube may be flushed out and washed between each reading without removing it from the instrument.

In addition to the Lumetron instrument just mentioned, we have also used the Beckman Model B Spectrophotometer to measure the turbidities with satisfactory results. With this instrument, the wave length is selected which gives the maximum spread in optical density readings between the most turbid and least turbid solutions of the standard tubes. Undoubtedly, other spectrophotometers can also be suitably adapted for the measurement of the turbidities obtained in turbidimetric assays.

The assay of antibiotics in blood serum and other substances presents certain features not encountered in testing for the drug in the relatively high concentrations found in most products. Most antibiotics are bound to a certain extent by proteinaceous material and hence the standard must be made up in the same vehicle as the antibiotic being tested. In most cases, the quantities of antibiotic present are small and the assay technique must be modified to make it more sensitive. This can be done by using an organism of greater sensitivity, by reducing the inoculum in the seed layer, by reducing the depth of nutrient agar in the base layer, by lowering the temperature of incubation to slow down the growth of the test organism while the antibiotic diffuses, or by adding small quantities of a substance, such as a sulfa drug, to the medium that while not in itself inhibitory acts in a synergistic way with the antibiotic to be tested. Many other factors may affect the sensitivity of assays, such as pH of medium and buffer, concentration of buffer, and percentage of the agar. By using one or more of these modifications, most standard plate assay methods can be adapted for the detection of minute quantities of drug which usually cannot be determined by chemical methods. Such exquisitely sensitive biologic tests must be carefully controlled to make sure that substances other than the antibiotic tested for are not active. Normal inhibitory substances may sometimes be found in blood, tissue extracts, urine, and other natural products. In determining blood and urine concentrations of antibiotics, controls taken before medication will detect natural inhibitory substances and also indicate whether or not the subject has received previous antibiotic treatment and is still excreting the drug.

In the determination of serum concentrations of antibiotics, fraction V bovine albumin can often be substituted for serum for making up the standard antibiotic for the standard curve and test plates. Bovine albumin cannot be used with neomycin because of its excessive binding power nor with carbomycin because it enhances its diffusability. If serum is used, it must be tested for the presence of inhibitory substances and the pH adjusted to pH 7.4 before use, since the loss of carbon dioxide on standing causes an increase in pH. The concentration of bovine albumin solution is tested in parallel tests with normal serum so that the concentration used is equal to the binding power of normal serum. This is usually 7 per cent except in the case of the tetracyclines where it is 3.5 per cent. Bovine albumin is a more standard product than serum and is very useful as a substitute because of the difficulty in obtaining sufficient amounts of pooled serum free of inhibitory substances.

In the assay of antibiotics in blood serum, milk, and other substances, we find that very small concentrations of some antibiotics, such as streptomycin in milk and the tetracyclines in milk and serum, are inactive when added to assay plates undiluted but reveal activity when diluted. For example, when streptomycin is placed in milk in the concentrations prescribed for the standard curve, we find that the 0.1 μg./ml. concentration will not give a zone of inhibition while the 0.3 μg./ml. concentration will give a very small zone. If, however, we add to these concentrations in milk equal parts of phosphate buffer no. 3, pH 8, we find that we now obtain a definite zone of inhibition in the lower 0.1μg./ml. concentration even though the concentration of streptomycin has been halved, and the 0.3 μg./ml. concentration now gives a larger zone than before even though the actual concentration is only 0.15 μg./ml. Thus by diluting the milk sample with an equal volume of buffer, we are able to detect a level of streptomycin that would have been recorded as negative if tested undiluted. This phenomenon occurs when streptomycin is assayed in milk but not in the assay in serum, while the tetracyclines must be diluted 1:3 with phosphate buffer no. 4, *p*H 4.5, in both milk and serum. Since each antibiotic may act differently in different substrates, they must be tested for this property when assays are made in different types of substances.

General Comments on Chemical Assay Methods. When one demonstrates the ability of an antibiotic to kill or inhibit the growth of a living microorganism as is done in the microbiologic assay, a direct measure of the activity or potency of the antibiotic is obtained. In order for a chemical assay method to be of value therefore, it must be able to give results that will correlate well with those obtained by microbiologic assays. The chemical or physical methods of assay presented in the following chapters have been shown to give results in good agreement with those obtained by bioassay. Further comments on the individual methods are given in the respective chapters.

Chemical methods are usually more precise and less time consuming than microbiologic assay methods and may be substituted for the microbiologic methods for the assay of relatively pure antibiotics when thorough study has shown agreement between the two methods. Care should be exercised in the use of chemical methods for long-term stability studies of antibiotics or preparations containing antibiotics. Occasionally, degradation products may be formed, which are measured as active drug by chemical methods. Because of this, microbiologic assay methods are preferred for such stability studies, or at least should be used as a confirmatory check on the chemical method.

2 PENICILLIN

Section A: **Microbiologic Assay Methods for Penicillin**

Two cylinder-plate methods are described, one using *Micrococcus pyogenes* var. *aureus* and the other *Sarcina lutea* as the test organisms. A two dose and a one dose procedure are given using *M. pyogenes* var. *aureus*. If it is desirable to determine the error of the assay, the two dose method should be utilized. However, in laboratories in which standardized conditions are used routinely, the standard curve (one dose) procedure has been found to give entirely satisfactory results. In the laboratories of the Food and Drug Administration such a procedure has been found to be so reproducible that a composite standard curve can be used, and it is only necessary to run a standard curve for check purposes once a month.

The *S. lutea* method is used primarily for the testing of serum, tissues, and other substances, where the concentration of penicillin is likely to be small. This test organism is capable of measuring penicillin concentrations as low as 0.005 unit/ml. It will be noted in the *S. lutea* method that only 10 ml. of medium is used for the base layer compared to the 21 ml. used in the *M. pyogenes* var. *aureus* method. This is done to make the assay more sensitive. When the depth of the medium is reduced, the zone sizes are increased.

METHOD 1: Cylinder-plate Method Using *Micrococcus pyogenes* var. *aureus* as the Test Organism. (ATCC 6538P.)

Two Dose Procedure. CYLINDERS (CUPS). Use stainless steel cylinders with an outside diameter of 8 mm. (±0.1 mm.), an inside diameter of 6 mm. (±0.1 mm.), and a length of 10 mm. (±0.1 mm.).

CULTURE MEDIA. Use agar medium no. 1 for both the seed layer and for carrying the test organism. Use agar medium no. 2 for the base layer.

WORKING STANDARD. Keep the working standard at room temperature in tightly stoppered vials, which in turn are kept in larger stoppered tubes containing a suitable desiccant. Weigh out carefully, in an atmosphere of 50 per cent relative humidity or less, between 4 and 5 mg. of the working standard and dilute with sterile phosphate buffer no. 1, *p*H 6, to make a stock solution of any convenient concentration. Keep this solution at a temperature of about 10 C. and use for two days only. From this stock solution, make appropriate working dilutions in phosphate buffer no. 1, *p*H 6.

PREPARATION OF SAMPLE. The method of preparing samples of the various preparations to be tested is described under the individual penicillin dosage forms in Section C of this Chapter.

PREPARATION OF TEST ORGANISM. Maintain the organism on agar slants (medium no. 1) and transfer to a fresh agar slant once a week. The inoculum for the plates may be prepared as follows: Grow the organism on an agar slant and incubate for 24 hours at 32 to 35 C. Further incubate for 24 hours at room temperature and wash with 2.0 ml. of sterile physiologic saline onto a large agar surface such as that provided by a Roux bottle containing 300 ml. of agar medium no. 1. Spread the suspension of organisms over the entire agar surface with the aid of sterile glass beads. Incubate 24 hours at 32 to 35 C. and store for 24 hours at room temperature. Wash the resulting growth from the agar surface with about 50 ml. of sterile physiologic saline. Standardize this suspension by determining the dilution that will give 20 per cent light transmission through a filter at 6,500 Å. units in a Lumetron 400-A photoelectric colorimeter. (In the preparation of the suspension of the test organism on Roux bottles, the 24 hour storage period at room temperature may be omitted if the suspension will permit 20 per cent light transmission through a filter at 6,500 Å. units in the photoelectric colorimeter.) This standardized suspension is used to prepare the inoculum for the plates. The bulk suspension may be kept refrigerated for several months. Run test plates to determine the quantity of this standardized suspension to be added to each 100 ml. of agar medium no. 1 to give clear, sharp, inhibitory zones of appropriate size. This quantity is usually 1.5 to 2 ml.

PREPARATION OF PLATES. Add 21 ml. of melted agar medium no. 2 to each Petri dish (20 by 100 mm.). Distribute the agar evenly in the plates, cover with porcelain covers glazed only on the outside or other suitable covers, and allow to harden. Use the plates the same day they are prepared. Melt sufficient agar medium no. 1, cool to 48 C., add the proper amount of standardized suspension, mix thoroughly, and add 4 ml. to each of the plates containing the 21 ml. of the uninoculated agar. Tilt the plates back and forth to spread the inoculated agar evenly over the surface. Place four cylinders on the agar surface so that they are at approximately 90 degree intervals on a 2.8 cm. radius.

ASSAY. Use four plates for each sample. Fill one cylinder on each plate with a 1.0 unit/ml. concentration, and one with 0.25 unit/ml. concentration of the working standard. Add the estimated concentrations of 1.0 unit/ml. and 0.25 unit/ml. of the sample under test to the remaining two cylinders on each plate. Carefully place the plates in racks and incubate 16 to 18 hours at 32 to 35 C. After incubation, measure the diameter of each circle of inhibition.

ESTIMATION OF POTENCY AND ERROR. Use the accompanying chart (fig. 1) and nomograph (fig. 2) for estimating the potency and its error. To use the chart for estimating potency two values, namely V and W, are required. For each plate, calculate two values.

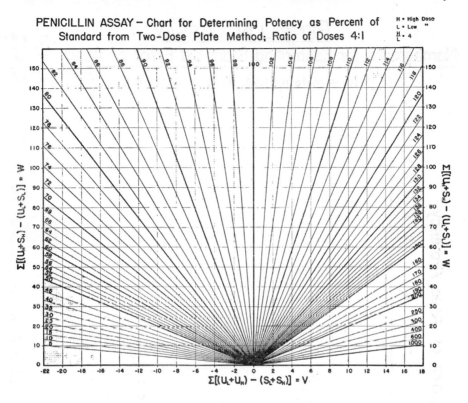

PENICILLIN ASSAY – Chart for Determining Potency as Percent of Standard from Two-Dose Plate Method; Ratio of Doses 4:1

Fig. 1. Penicillin assay. Chart for determining potency as per cent of standard from two dose plate method. Ratio of doses, 4:1. H, high dose; L, low dose; H/L, 4.

$$v = (u_L + u_H) - (s_L + s_H)$$

and

$$w = (u_H + s_H) - (u_L + s_L)$$

where s_H and s_L are the diameters of the zones of inhibition in millimeters of the 1.0 unit and 0.25 unit concentrations of the standard, respectively, and u_H and u_L refer similarly to the corresponding concentrations of the sample under test. The value V is the sum of the v values for all plates and W is the sum of the w values for all plates. To estimate the potency, locate the point on the chart corresponding to the values of V and W, and the potency can be read from the radial lines on the chart.

The error of the assay is estimated by using the nomograph which requires five values, namely, the potency, V, W, Rv, and Rw. Rv (the range of the v's) is the highest value of v minus the lowest value of v obtained from the individual plates. Similarly, Rw is the difference between the highest and lowest w values. After obtaining these five values, connect with a straightedge the points corresponding to v and w on the respective scales on the right side of the nomograph. Mark with a pin or sharp-pointed pencil the intersection of

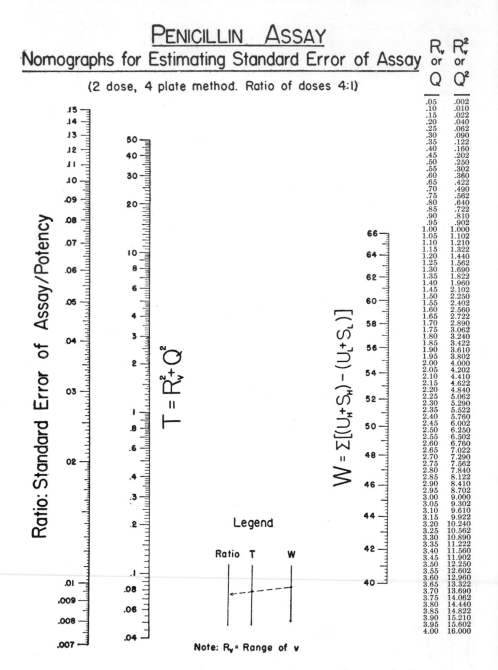

Fig. 2. Penicillin assay. Nomographs for estimating standard error of assay. Two dose, four plate method. Ratio of doses, 4:1.

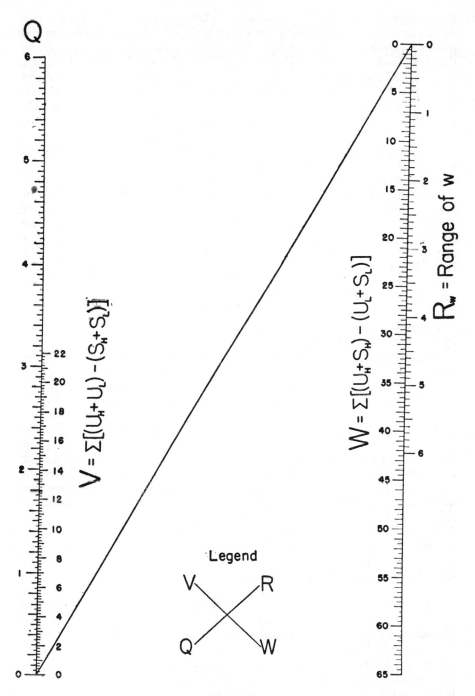

Figure 2.

the straightedge and the diagonal line of the nomograph. Move the straightedge so that it connects the value of Rw on its scale and the diagonal line at the point of the pin. The value for Q is thus determined by the scale value where the straightedge crosses the line labeled "Q." T is obtained by adding the squares of Q and Rv. On the left side of the chart connect the values of T and W with the straightedge and read the value of the ratio (error of assay potency) where the straightedge intersects the scale of values for the ratio. This value multiplied by the potency equals the percentage error of the assay. The error of the assay calculated here estimates only how closely one assayist can check himself on any given set of dilutions of unknown and standard. It does not include any errors of weighing or errors owing to variations in materials or subdivisions of a lot of penicillin.

The chart for determining potency should not be used for determinations of potency lower than 50 per cent or higher than 150 per cent of the standard. If the potency lies outside these limits, the assay should be repeated using a higher or lower dilution. The radial lines on the chart beyond these limits permit a rough estimation of potency from as low as 5 per cent to as high as 1,000 per cent when low values of W are found. If the value of V or W falls outside the limits of the chart, divide both V and W by the same proper number to bring them into the range of the chart and read the potency from the radial lines as before. If 11.4 Rw is greater than W, the slope of the assay does not differ significantly from zero and the assay is invalid. (The figure 11.4 was obtained by use of Student's "t" test for determining the significance of a slope.)

In certain laboratories it has been noted that with the 4 to 1 ratio, involving concentrations of 0.25 unit for the low dose, the zone of inhibition given by this dose may either be too small for accurate reading or have edges that are poorly defined. In order to permit the use of a higher concentration of penicillin for the low dose, the third of the attached charts (fig. 3) may be used in assays in which the ratio of doses is 2 to 1, i.e., the high dose (s_H) is twice the low dose (s_L). As in the preceding chart (fig. 1), if the potency lies outside the limits of 50 to 150 per cent the assay should be repeated, using a lower or higher dilution. The potencies beyond these limits are to be used for rough estimation purposes only. These extensions can also be used for four (or more) plate assays if both V and W are divided by the same proper number to bring them into the range of the chart. The error of the assay using the ratio of doses 2 to 1 is estimated by using the nomograph (fig. 2) in the same manner as described for the 4 to 1 ratio of doses. However, the resultant error of the assay derived in this manner must be divided by 2 to give the correct error of the assay for the 2 to 1 ratio of doses.

One Dose Procedure. The potency of the sample may also be determined by the standard-curve technique, using a single dose of standard and unknown. Cylinders, culture media, working standard, preparation of organism suspension, and preparation of plates are the same as for the two dose procedure. In the standard-curve technique, dilute the sample to be tested to 1.0 unit/ml. (estimated) in phosphate buffer no. 1, *p*H 6. Place six cylinders on the inoculated agar surface so that they are at approximately 60 degree intervals on a 2.8 cm. radius. Use three plates for each sample. Fill three cylinders on each plate with the 1.0 unit/ml. standard and three cylinders with the 1.0 unit/ml.

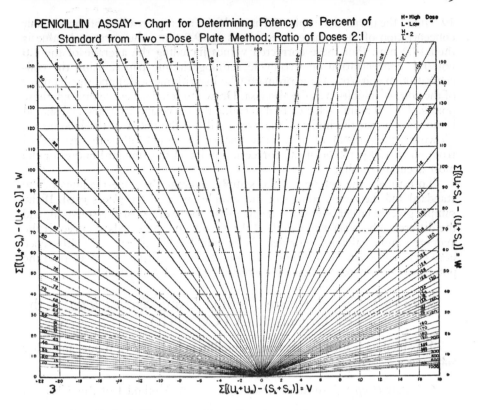

Fig. 3. Penicillin assay. Chart for determining potency as per cent of standard from two dose plate method. Ratio of doses, 2:1. H, high dose; L, low dose; H/L, 2.

(estimated) sample, alternating standard and sample. At the same time, prepare a standard curve using concentrations of the standard of 0.6, 0.7, 0.8, 0.9, 1.0, 1.1, 1.2, 1.3, 1.4, and 1.5 units/ml. in sterile phosphate buffer no. 1, pH 6. Use three plates for the determination of each point on the curve except the 1 unit/ml. concentration, a total of 27 plates. On each of three plates fill three cylinders with the 1.0 unit/ml. standard and the other three cylinders with the concentration under test. Thus there will be 81 of the 1 unit determinations and nine determinations for each of the other concentrations on the curve. Incubate the plates for 16 to 18 hours at 32 to 35 C. and measure the diameter of each circle of inhibition. Average the readings of the 1.0 unit/ml. concentration and the readings of the concentration tested for each set of three plates and average also all 81 readings of the 1.0 unit/ml. concentration. The average of the 81 readings of the 1.0 unit/ml. concentration is the correction point for the curve. Correct the average value obtained for each concentration to the figure it would be if the 1.0 unit/ml. reading for that set of three plates were the same as the correction point. Thus, if in correcting the 0.8 unit concentration, the average of the 81 readings of the 1.0 unit concentration is 20.0 mm., and the average of the 1.0 unit concentration of this set of three plates is

19.8 mm., the correction is plus 0.2 mm. If the average reading of the 0.8 unit concentration of these same three plates is 19.0 mm., the corrected value is then 19.2 mm. Plot these corrected values including the average of the 1.0 unit/ml. concentration on two-cycle semilogarithmic paper, using the concentration in units/ml. as the ordinate (the logarithmic scale) and the diameter of the zone of inhibition as the abscissa. Draw the standard curve through these points. The 10 points selected to determine the curve are arbitrary and should be so chosen that the limits of the curve will fill the needs of the laboratory. However, the potency of the sample under test should fall in the interval of from 60 to 150 per cent of the correction point of the standard curve for the most accurate results.

To estimate the potency of the sample, average the zone readings of the standard and the zone readings of the sample on the three plates used. If the sample gives a larger average zone size than the average of the standard, add the difference between them to the 1.0 unit zone on the standard curve. If the average sample value is lower than the standard value, subtract the difference between them from the 1.0 unit value on the curve. From the curve read the potencies corresponding to these corrected values of zone sizes.

METHOD 2: Cylinder-plate Method Using *Sarcina lutea* as the Test Organism. (ATCC 9341.)

This method is used for assaying penicillin in body fluids, tissue, and other substances.

Cylinders (Cups). Use the same cylinders as in Method 1 of this Chapter.

Culture Media. Use agar medium no. 1 for carrying the test organism and for the base layer. Use agar medium no. 4 for the seed layer and use broth medium no. 3 for preparing an inoculum of the test organism.

Working Standard. Use the same standard and stock solution described in Method 1 of this Chapter. From this stock solution make a dilution to 10.0 units/ml. using phosphate buffer no. 1, pH 6. From this, further dilutions are made as directed in Section D of this Chapter.

Preparation of Sample. The preparation of the various samples of blood, tissue, etc., are described in Section D of this Chapter.

Preparation of Test Organism. Maintain the test organism on agar slants (medium no. 1) and transfer to a fresh agar slant about once every two weeks, incubating overnight at 32 to 35 C. Prepare an inoculum for the plates by washing the culture from the agar slant into 100 ml. of broth medium no. 3 with 2 to 3 ml. of distilled water. Incubate this broth for 48 hours by continuous shaking on a shaking machine at room temperature. This culture when refrigerated may be used for at least two weeks. Determine per cent of inoculum to be used by determination of the best zones of inhibition obtained on test plates. Generally, this will be obtained within a range of 2 to 5 per cent inoculum.

An alternate method and the one usually used in preparing the test suspension is as follows: Maintain the test organism on slants of agar medium no. 1 and transfer to a fresh agar slant once a week. Streak an agar slant heavily with the test organism and incubate for 24 hours at 26 C. Wash the growth off with 3 ml. of broth medium no. 3. Use the suspension so obtained to inoculate the surface of a Roux bottle containing 300 ml. of agar medium no. 1. Spread the suspension over the entire surface with the aid of sterile glass beads. Incubate for 24 hours at 26 C. Wash growth from the agar surface with 15 ml. of broth medium no. 3. If an aliquot of this bulk suspension, when diluted with broth medium no. 3, 1:10, gives 10 per cent light transmission in a Lumetron 400-A photoelectric colorimeter equipped with a filter having a wave length of 6,500 Å. units, the bulk suspension is satisfactory for use. It may be necessary to adjust the bulk suspension by dilution so that an aliquot of the adjusted suspension diluted 1:10 gives 10 per cent light transmission. (The adjusted bulk suspension only and not the 1:10 dilution of it is used in preparing the seed layer.) The bulk suspension may be used for several months or longer. The adjusted suspension is usually used in the proportion of 0.3 to 0.5 ml. of suspension for every 100 ml. of seed layer agar.

Preparation of Plates. Add 10 ml. of agar medium no. 1 to each Petri dish (20 by 100 mm.). Distribute the agar evenly in the plates, cover with porcelain covers glazed only on the outside or other suitable covers, and allow it to harden. Use the plates the same day they are prepared. Add the appropriate amount (as determined in paragraph "Preparation of test organism") of the broth culture or suspension to each 100 ml. of seed agar medium no. 4, which has been melted and cooled to 48 C. Mix the culture and agar thoroughly and add 4 ml. to each of the plates containing the 10 ml. of the uninoculated base agar. Tilt the plates back and forth to spread the inoculated agar evenly over the surface.

Standard Curve and Assay Procedure. STANDARD CURVE. Place six cylinders on the inoculated agar surface so that they are at approximately 60 degree intervals on a 2.8 cm. radius. Use one or more plates for each sample. Fill three cylinders on each plate with the 0.1 unit/ml. standard and three cylinders with sample, alternating standard and sample. At the same time, prepare a standard curve using concentrations of the standard (unless otherwise directed in Section D of this Chapter) of 0.03, 0.05, 0.10, 0.20, 0.30, and 0.40 unit/ml. in the diluent directed in Section D of this Chapter. The 0.1 unit/ml. concentration is the reference point. Use three plates for the determination of each concentration on the curve except the 0.1 unit/ml. concentration, a total of 15 plates. On each of three plates, fill three cylinders with the concentration under test. Thus, there will be 45 of the 0.1 unit determinations and nine determinations for each of the other concentrations on the curve. Incubate the plates for 16 to 18 hours at 26 C. and measure the diameter of each circle of inhibition. Average the readings of 0.1 unit/ml. concentration and the readings of the point tested for each set of three plates and average also all 45 readings of the 0.1 unit/ml. concentration. The average of the 45 readings of the 0.1 unit/ml. concentration is the correction point for the curve. Correct the average value obtained for each concentration to the figure it would be if the 0.1

unit/ml. reading for that set of three plates were the same as the correction point. Thus, if in correcting the 0.05 unit concentration, the average of the 45 readings of the 0.1 unit concentration is 20.0 mm., and the average of the 0.1 unit concentration of this set of three plates is 19.8 mm., the correction is + 0.2 mm. If the average reading of the 0.05 unit concentration of these same three plates is 17.0 mm., the corrected value is then 17.2 mm. Plot these corrected values including the average of the 0.1 unit/ml. concentration on two-cycle semilogarithmic paper, using the concentration in units/ml. as the ordinate (the logarithmic scale) and the diameter of the zone of inhibition as the abscissa. Draw the standard curve through these points. To estimate the concentration of the sample, average the zone readings of the standard and the zone readings of the sample on the plates used. If the sample gives a larger average zone size than the average of the standard, add the difference between them to the 0.1 unit zone on the standard curve. If the average sample value is lower than the standard value, subtract the difference between them from the 0.1 unit value on the curve. From the curve, read the concentrations corresponding to these corrected values of zone sizes.

Section B: Chemical Method for Penicillin

Of all the chemical methods developed for penicillin, only the iodometric method is described, since it is the most generally applicable method. The iodometric method is based on the fact that the intact (active) penicillin molecule does not absorb iodine, while the alkali inactivation product, sodium penicilloate, does absorb iodine. Since a blank determination is run before inactivation with alkali, the method actually measures active penicillin and gives results that are in excellent agreement with the biologic methods of assay.

It has been shown that benzylpenicillin (penicillin G) when inactivated with alkali absorbs nine atoms of iodine per mole of penicillin. However, in actual practice this amount may vary from 8.5 to 9.0 atoms depending upon the particular conditions of the experiment. Temperature, time, pH, concentration of the iodine solution, and other factors will have an effect on the absorption. Because of these possible variations, instead of using a definite chemical factor to obtain the quantity of penicillin present from the titration, the sodium penicillin G working standard is titrated along with the unknown sample under the same conditions and the results are calculated on the basis of the value obtained on the standard.

In order to use the iodometric method for determining the potency of penicillin O, which absorbs more iodine than penicillin G because it possesses an allylmercaptomethyl group, it is necessary to standardize the titrating solutions against the penicillin O working standard to obtain the factor F and use the figure 1612 to convert to units.

The iodometric method is easy to carry out, requires no special apparatus, and can be used to determine the penicillin potency of most of the pharmaceutical dosage forms. Large amounts of starch or sugars often found in tablets and oral powders may cause interference in this method, but in general it is applicable to a wide variety of preparations containing penicillin.

Penicillin may also be assayed by titrating a second carboxy group formed when the β-lactam ring is broken by means of the enzyme penicillinase or by alkali. Both of these methods are based on titration of the liberated acid group, and are satisfactory for relatively pure samples of penicillin; however, the presence of buffer substances interferes with the titration and these methods are therefore limited in scope.

Another chemical method depends on the reaction between penicillin and hydroxylamine to give a hydroxamic acid, which then forms a purple-colored complex with ferric ion. The reaction is not specific, since many esters, anhydrides, and amides also react with the reagent to produce hydroxamic acids. Hydroxylamine can also react with aldehydes or ketones to give oximes that form colored complexes with ferric ion. The hydroxylamine method for penicillin also has a disadvantage in that the color formed is unstable.

The Iodometric Titration Method. This method was adapted from Alicino[3] and Mundell et al.[4] Dilute a weighed sample (approximately 30 mg.) with phosphate buffer no. 1, pH 6, to a concentration of approximately 1.2 mg./ml. (2,000 units/ml.). Add 2.0 ml. aliquots to each of two 125 ml. glass stoppered Erlenmeyer or iodine flasks. To one add 2.0 ml. of 1 N sodium hydroxide and allow to stand at room temperature for 15 minutes. At the end of this time, add 2.0 ml. of 1.2 N hydrochloric acid and 10 ml. of 0.01 N iodine (prepared from 0.1 N iodine, U.S.P.). After 15 minutes, titrate the excess iodine, using 0.01 N sodium thiosulfate (prepared from 0.1 N sodium thiosulfate) standardized accurately against potassium iodate. Toward the end of the titration, add one drop of starch solution or about 5.0 ml. of carbon tetrachloride. Continue the titration by the addition of 0.01 to 0.02 ml. portions of 0.01 N sodium thiosulfate, shaking vigorously after each addition. The end point is reached when the blue color of the starch iodine complex is discharged or when the carbon tetrachloride layer becomes colorless. To the second flask, add 10 ml. of 0.01 N iodine and titrate immediately with 0.01 N sodium thiosulfate for the blank determination. Divide the difference in titers by a factor, F, which is the number of milliliters of 0.01 N iodine absorbed by 1.0 mg. of sodium penicillin G working standard, to obtain the milligrams of penicillin sodium salt. Determine the factor F by actual standardization against the sodium penicillin G working standard, using the method that was just mentioned.

$$\text{Units of penicillin G per milligram} = \frac{\text{Difference in titers} \times \text{potency of working standard in u./mg.}}{\text{Milligrams of sample in 2.0 ml.} \times \text{F}}$$

Section C: Assay of Penicillin Salts and Pharmaceutical Dosage Forms

Sodium, Potassium, and Calcium Penicillins. The structural formula for benzylpenicillin (penicillin G) salts is as follows:

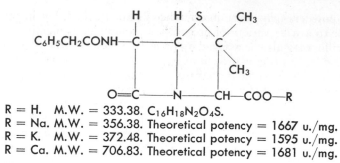

R = H.   M.W. = 333.38. $C_{16}H_{18}N_2O_4S$.
R = Na. M.W. = 356.38. Theoretical potency = 1667 u./mg.
R = K.   M.W. = 372.48. Theoretical potency = 1595 u./mg.
R = Ca. M.W. = 706.83. Theoretical potency = 1681 u./mg.

To assay, these water-soluble salts are simply dissolved in water to give an appropriate stock solution. An aliquot of the stock solution is then diluted with phosphate buffer no. 1, *p*H 6, to 1.0 unit/ml. (estimated) and assayed by the microbiologic assay in Method 1, Section A of this Chapter.

The chemical assay method Section B of this Chapter may also be used, in which case the stock solution is diluted with phosphate buffer no. 1, *p*H 6, to a concentration of 2,000 units/ml.

Aluminum Penicillin. The exact formula for this salt of penicillin is not known. The potency of the usual commercial preparations is about 1,100 units/mg. Because of the insolubility of aluminum penicillin in water or phosphate buffer, a citrate buffer is used in the assay. The sample is dissolved in citrate buffer no. 2, *p*H 6.3, to give a concentration of 1.0 unit/ml. (estimated) for the microbiologic assay in Method 1, Section A, or to 2,000 units/ml. for the chemical method, Section B of this Chapter. If the microbiologic assay method is used, the citrate buffer must also be used in preparing the solutions of the penicillin working standard instead of the phosphate buffer.

Procaine Penicillin G. Diethylaminoethyl-*p*-aminobenzoate penicillin G.

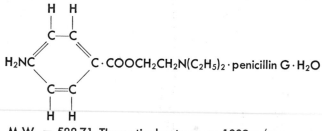

M.W. = 588.71. Theoretical potency = 1009 u./mg.

This salt of penicillin has a solubility in water of about 6,000 to 7,000 units/ml. (6 to 7 mg.). For assay purposes, small quantities can be dissolved directly in phosphate buffer no. 1, *p*H 6. However, a more rapid method of dissolving and one usually followed is to dissolve about 50 mg. in 2 ml. of redistilled methanol and further dilute with phosphate buffer no. 1, *p*H 6, to a concentration of 1.0 unit/ml. (estimated) for microbiologic assay in Method 1, Section A, or to 2,000 units/ml. for the chemical method, Section B of this Chapter.

Ephedrine Penicillin G. 1-phenyl-2-methylaminopropanol penicillin G.

$$C_6H_5CH \cdot CH \cdot N \cdot CH_3 \cdot \text{penicillin G}$$
$$\hspace{1.2cm} | \hspace{0.6cm} | \hspace{0.3cm} |$$
$$\hspace{1.0cm} OH \hspace{0.2cm} CH_3 \hspace{0.1cm} H$$

M.W. = 499.62. Theoretical potency = 1189 u./mg.

To assay, dissolve the salt in sufficient phosphate buffer no. 1, *p*H 6, to give a concentration of 1.0 unit/ml. (estimated) for microbiologic assay in Method 1, Section A, or to 2,000 units/ml. for the chemical method, Section B of this Chapter.

l-Ephenamine Penicillin G. l-N-methyl 1,2 diphenyl-2-hydroxyethylamine penicillin G.

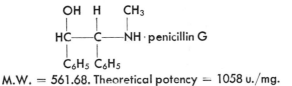

M.W. = 561.68. Theoretical potency = 1058 u./mg.

This salt has a solubility in water of approximately 1,000 units/ml. To assay, dissolve about 50 mg. in 5 ml. of redistilled methanol and further dilute with phosphate buffer no. 1, *p*H 6, to a concentration of 1.0 unit/ml. (estimated) for microbiologic assay in Method 1, Section A, or to 2,000 units/ml. for the chemical method, Section B of this chapter.

Benzathine Penicillin G. N,N'-dibenzylethylenediamine dipenicillin G.

$$\hspace{1.2cm} H \hspace{0.8cm} H$$
$$\hspace{1.2cm} | \hspace{0.8cm} |$$
$$\hspace{0.8cm} HC\text{———}CH \hspace{1.2cm} \cdot (\text{penicillin G})_2 \cdot 4\,H_2O$$
$$\hspace{1.2cm} | \hspace{1.2cm} |$$
$$C_6H_5CH_2NH \hspace{0.3cm} HNCH_2C_6H_5$$

M.W. = 981.18. Theoretical potency = 1211 u./mg.

This salt has a solubility in water of about 200 units/ml. (0.16 mg.). It is very soluble in formamide or dimethylformamide. These solvents may be used first to dissolve the salt and then further dilute with phosphate buffer no. 1, *p*H 6, for the bioassay. Usually 30 to 50 mg. are dissolved in about 20 ml. of formamide, or dimethylformamide, and then diluted with phosphate buffer no. 1, *p*H 6, to 1.0 unit/ml. (estimated) and assayed by microbiologic assay in Method 1 of Section A of this Chapter. The formamide or dimethylformamide used should always be tested for *p*H. These solvents have a tendency to develop free ammonia on aging and the presence of too much ammonia will destroy penicillin activity. If the *p*H is more than 6, add concentrated sulfuric acid to adjust the *p*H to 6. Concentrated acid is used to avoid dilution of the reagent with water.

The iodometric chemical assay method in Section B of this Chapter may be used by running the blank on a suspension of the salt containing 2.0 mg./ml. in phosphate buffer no. 1, *p*H 6, and preparing the solution for inactivation as follows: Dissolve a weighed sample (30 to 60 mg.) in sufficient 1 *N* sodium hydroxide to give 2.0 mg./ml. Pipette a 2.0 ml. aliquot into a 125 ml. glass stoppered Erlenmeyer flask and after 15 minutes add 2.0 ml. of 1.2 *N* hydrochloric acid and 10 ml. of 0.01 *N* iodine. Allow to stand 15 minutes and titrate the excess iodine with 0.01 *N* sodium thiosulfate.

In the chemical method, the salt is not soluble enough in water to give the usual 2,000 units/ml. concentration required. The benzathine penicillin is, however, soluble in sodium hydroxide solution and this can be used as both solvent and inactivator in the method.

Penethamate. Diethylaminoethyl ester penicillin G hydriodide.

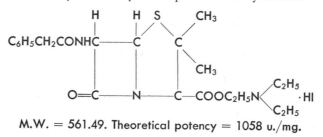

M.W. = 561.49. Theoretical potency = 1058 u./mg.

This ester of penicillin has no activity per se but, on hydrolysis, gives active penicillin. In the bioassay of the ester, it is therefore necessary first to hydrolyze to free penicillin. The hydrolysis must be gentle so that the liberated penicillin is not destroyed. The method used is as follows: Dissolve the sample in phosphate buffer no. 3, *p*H 8, to make a stock solution of 100 units/ml. (estimated). Allow to stand at room temperature for not less than one and a half hours and not more than two hours, then dilute an aliquot with phosphate buffer no. 1, *p*H 6, to 1.0 unit/ml. (estimated) and assay by microbiologic assay in Method 1, Section A of this Chapter.

The ester may also be assayed by the chemical method Section B of this Chapter by dissolving approximately 50 mg. in 2.0 ml. of redistilled methanol and further diluting in phosphate buffer no. 1, *p*H 6, to 2,000 units/ml.

Sodium and Potassium Penicillin O. Penicillin O differs from penicillin G by having an allylmercaptomethyl group instead of the benzyl group. The structural formula is as follows:

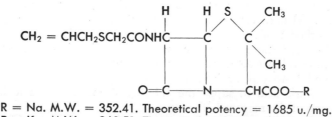

R = Na. M.W. = 352.41. Theoretical potency = 1685 u./mg.
R = K.   M.W. = 368.51. Theoretical potency = 1612 u./mg.

The sodium and potassium salts of penicillin O are very soluble in water and solutions of these salts may be assayed in the same manner as described for the sodium and potassium salts of penicillin G, Section C of this Chapter.

2-Chloro-procaine Penicillin O.

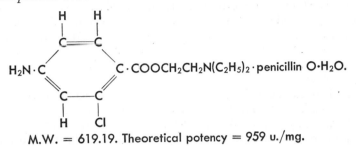

M.W. = 619.19. Theoretical potency = 959 u./mg.

This salt of penicillin O has about the same solubility in water as procaine penicillin G and may be assayed in the same manner as described for procaine penicillin G, Section C of this Chapter.

Dibenzylamine Penicillin.

$$C_6H_5CH_2$$

$$NH \cdot penicillin\ G \cdot H_2O$$

$$C_6H_5CH_2$$

M.W. = 549.65. Theoretical potency = 1085 u./mg.

This salt has a solubility of about 4,000 to 5,000 units/ml. (4 to 5 mg.) and may be assayed in the same manner as described for procaine penicillin, Section C of this Chapter.

Hydrabamine Dipenicillin G. N,N′-bis′(dehydroabietyl)-ethylenediamine dipenicillin G.

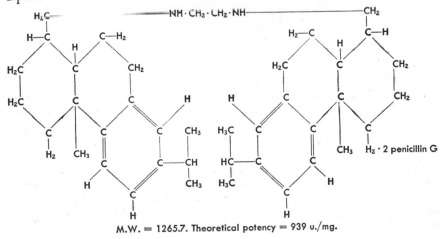

M.W. = 1265.7. Theoretical potency = 939 u./mg.

This salt has a solubility in water of about 10 units/ml. (about 0.01 mg.). It is soluble in methanol and chloroform.

To assay, dissolve an accurately weighed sample in methanol and dilute with methanol to 1,000 units/ml. (estimated). By means of a volumetric pipette, add a 1.0 ml. aliquot to a 1,000 ml. volumetric flask containing approximately 800 ml. of phosphate buffer no. 1, *p*H 6, constantly swirling the flask during the addition. Make to a volume of 1,000 ml. with phosphate buffer no. 1, *p*H 6, and assay by the microbiologic assay in Method 1, Section A of this Chapter. (Note that because of the insolubility of this compound, it is necessary to make the dilutions in the sequence given in order to prevent precipitation.)

The chemical method given in Section B of this Chapter may be used with suitable modifications. The procedure is as follows: Accurately weigh 30 to 50 mg. of the sample in a 50 ml. Erlenmeyer flask and dissolve in sufficient chloroform to give a concentration of 2.0 mg./ml. Pipette 2.0 ml. of this solution into a 125 ml. glass stoppered Erlenmeyer flask, add 10 ml. of 0.01 *N* iodine and titrate immediately with 0.01 *N* sodium thiosulfate for the blank determination. Toward the end of the titration, add one drop of starch solution or about 5 ml. of carbon tetrachloride. Continue the titration by the addition of 0.01 to 0.02 ml. portions of 0.01 *N* sodium thiosulfate, shaking vigorously after each addition. The end point is reached when the blue color of the starch-iodine complex is discharged or when the carbon tetrachloride layer becomes colorless. Prepare the solution of inactivated penicillin as follows: To 10 ml. of the original chloroform solution add 10 ml. of 1 *N* sodium hydroxide and shake well immediately and five minutes later. Fifteen minutes after the initial shaking, pipette 2.0 ml. of the upper sodium hydroxide layer into a 125 ml. glass stoppered Erlenmeyer flask, add 2.0 ml. of 1.2 *N* hydrochloric acid and 10 ml. of 0.01 *N* iodine. Stopper the flask. After 15 minutes titrate the excess iodine with 0.01 *N* sodium thiosulfate.

Units of hydrabamine penicillin G per mg. =
$$\frac{\text{Difference in titers} \times \text{potency of working standard in u./mg.}}{4 \times F}$$

Where F = the number of ml. of 0.01 *N* iodine absorbed for each 1.0 mg. of the sodium penicillin G working standard.

Penicillin Ointment. Accurately weigh the container and contents and place 0.5 to 1.0 Gm. (estimated) into a separatory funnel containing approximately 50 ml. of peroxide-free ether. Reweigh the container to obtain weight of ointment used in the test. Shake ointment and ether until homogeneous. Shake with a 25 ml. portion of phosphate buffer no. 1, *p*H 6. Remove the buffer layer and repeat the extraction with three 25 ml. quantities of buffer. Combine the extracts and make the proper estimated dilutions in phosphate buffer no. 1, *p*H 6.

The sample may also be prepared by placing an accurately weighed sample consisting of 0.5 to 1.0 Gm. of the ointment into a glass blending jar containing 100 ml. of phosphate buffer no. 1, *p*H 6. Using a high-speed blender, blend the mixture for two minutes and make the proper estimated dilutions in phosphate buffer no. 1, *p*H 6.

The extracted penicillin is assayed by the microbiologic assay in Method 1, Section A of this Chapter.

. Quite often penicillin ointments are used in veterinary practice for the treatment of mastitis in cattle. In this case, the entire contents of the tube or container are used as a single dose. To assay such preparations, squeeze or express the entire contents into a separatory funnel and use correspondingly larger volumes of ether and buffer depending upon the quantity of ointment. Usually four extractions with buffer will remove all of the penicillin; however, it is always wise to make a fifth extraction and test it to be sure all of the antibiotic has been extracted.

Penicillin Tablets. Penicillin tablets may contain, in addition to the penicillin, various other drugs, such as sulfonamides, antihistaminics, and aspirin. None of these other drugs so far encountered will interfere in the microbiologic assay for penicillin.

Place 12 tablets in a mortar and add approximately 20 ml. of phosphate buffer no. 1, pH 6. Disintegrate the tablets by grinding with a pestle. Transfer with the aid of small portions of the buffer solution to a 500 ml. volumetric flask and make to 500 ml. by adding sufficient phosphate buffer no. 1, pH 6. Make the proper estimated dilutions in phosphate buffer no. 1, pH 6.

The sample may also be prepared as follows: Place 12 tablets in a blending jar and add thereto approximately 200 ml. of a 500 ml. quantity of phosphate buffer no. 1, pH 6. After blending for one minute with a high-speed blender, add the remainder of the 500 ml. of buffer. Blend again for one minute and make the proper estimated dilutions in phosphate buffer no. 1, pH 6.

If the tablets contain the benzathine salt of penicillin, which is only sparingly soluble in water or buffer, proceed as follows: Place six tablets in a flask and add enough formamide or dimethylformamide to give a concentration of no more than 15,000 units/ml. Shake well and allow to stand for one hour. Dilute to 1.0 unit/ml. with phosphate buffer no. 1, pH 6.

The penicillin solution thus prepared may be assayed by either the microbiologic assay in Method 1, Section A, or by the chemical method, Section B of this Chapter. If the iodometric chemical method is used, it should be first ascertained that no interfering substances are present.

Penicillin Troches (Pastilles, Lozenges). Two types of penicillin troches are manufactured. One type is meant to be held in the mouth until it slowly dissolves away while the other contains a masticatory substance, such as paraffin or gum, and is meant to be chewed.

If the troche does not contain a masticatory substance, it is assayed by the same procedure used for penicillin tablets, Section C of this Chapter.

If the troche contains paraffin as a masticatory substance, place five troches in a separatory funnel containing 75 ml. of n-hexane; shake until the troches are dissolved. Shake with a 25 ml. portion of phosphate buffer no. 1, pH 6. Remove the buffer layer and repeat the extraction with three 25 ml. quantities of buffer. Combine the extracts and make the proper estimated dilutions in phosphate buffer no. 1, pH 6. Assay by the microbiologic assay in Method 1, Section A of this Chapter.

If the troche contains gum as a masticatory substance, cut each of five troches into fine pieces and place in a glass blending jar containing 100 ml. of a 50 per cent acetone-water solution. Using a high-speed blender, blend for three to five minutes. Add an additional 100 ml. of a 50 per cent acetone-water solution to the blender and blend for an additional three to five minutes and then make the proper estimated dilutions in phosphate buffer no. 1, *p*H 6. Assay by the microbiologic assay in Method 1, Section A of this Chapter.

Penicillin Dental Cones. Follow the same procedure used for penicillin tablets, Section C of this Chapter.

Penicillin with Vasoconstrictor (Nose Drops). This preparation may be encountered as a tablet containing the penicillin plus the vasoconstrictor and suitable buffering substances, binders, etc., or it may be a soluble penicillin tablet that is to be mixed with a liquid diluent containing the vasoconstrictor. It may also be manufactured as a penicillin powder preparation to be mixed with water or a suitable vasoconstrictor diluent. The preparation is also made as a capsule containing penicillin and a vasoconstrictor.

If the preparation to be assayed is a tablet or capsule, assay by the same procedure used for penicillin tablets, Section C of this Chapter.

If the preparation is a powder, use the same procedure as for soluble salts of penicillin, sodium, potassium, and calcium, Section C of this Chapter.

Penicillin Tablets Containing Aluminum Penicillin. Because of the insolubility of aluminum penicillin in water or phosphate buffer, a citrate buffer is used to dissolve the sample. Aluminum penicillin tablets are assayed by the same procedure used for penicillin tablets, Section C of this Chapter, except citrate buffer no. 2, *p*H 6.3, is used instead of phosphate buffer. Also, citrate buffer must be used in preparing the solutions of the penicillin working standard instead of phosphate buffer.

Penicillin Sulfonamide Powder. Take about 0.5 Gm. from each of 12 containers, accurately weigh the combined powder, add 100 ml. of distilled water, and shake thoroughly to dissolve the penicillin. Use an aliquot of the solution, make the proper estimated dilutions in phosphate buffer no. 1, *p*H 6, and assay by the microbiologic assay of Method 1, Section A of this Chapter.

Penicillin Vaginal Suppositories. Use five suppositories and follow the separatory funnel extraction method for penicillin ointment, Section C of this Chapter, using 150 ml. of ether to dissolve the suppositories. The blender method described under penicillin ointment may also be used in which case 200 ml. of phosphate buffer no. 1, *p*H 6, is used in the blender for the five suppositories.

Penicillin Bougies. Assay by the same procedure used for penicillin tablets, Section C of this Chapter.

Procaine Penicillin in Oil. Introduce 1 ml. of the well-shaken sample by means of a 2 ml. hypodermic syringe, into a 50 ml. volumetric flask. Add 3 to 4 ml. of chloroform, shake the flask well, and make to 50 ml. with absolute ethyl alcohol. Mix thoroughly, withdraw a 1 ml. aliquot, and make the proper estimated dilutions in phosphate buffer no. 1, pH 6. The sample may also be prepared as follows: Introduce 1 ml. of the well-shaken sample by means of a 2.0 ml. hypodermic syringe into a blending jar containing 98 ml. of phosphate buffer no. 1, pH 6, and 1.0 ml. of a 10 per cent aqueous solution of polysorbate 80 (Tween 80). Using a high-speed blender, blend the mixture for one minute and make the proper estimated dilution in phosphate buffer no. 1, pH 6.

Assay by microbiologic assay in Method 1, Section A, or by the chemical assay method, Section B of this Chapter.

Penicillin for Inhalation Therapy. These preparations contain finely powdered penicillin salts and are inhaled as a dust. A weighed sample of the powder or the contents of one or more containers is dissolved in phosphate buffer no. 1, pH 6, and assayed by microbiologic assay in Method 1, Section A, or by the chemical assay method, Section B of this Chapter.

Procaine Penicillin for Aqueous Injection. This preparation exists in two forms, one a dry powder and the other an aqueous suspension of procaine penicillin. Both are assayed in the same manner except that in the case of the dry powder, a suspension is prepared by adding the quantity of water recommended in the labeling by means of an accurately standardized hypodermic syringe. Shake the suspension thoroughly and remove 1.0 ml. or other suitable aliquot with an accurately standardized hypodermic syringe. Dissolve in phosphate buffer no. 1, pH 6, and assay by the microbiologic assay in Method 1, Section A, or by the chemical assay method, Section B of this Chapter.

Procaine Penicillin and Buffered Crystalline Sodium or Potassium Penicillin for Aqueous Injection. TOTAL POTENCY (MULTIPLE DOSE CONTAINERS). Add the amount of distilled water recommended in the labeling to the contents of a vial by means of an accurately standardized hypodermic syringe and shake well. Withdraw 1.0 ml. or other suitable aliquot with an accurately standardized hypodermic syringe, dilute with phosphate buffer no. 1, pH 6, and assay by the microbiologic assay in Method 1, Section A, or by the chemical assay method, Section B of this Chapter.

FOR CONTENT OF BUFFERED CRYSTALLINE SODIUM OR POTASSIUM PENICILLIN. Use a second 1.0 ml. or other suitable aliquot of the suspension prepared under "total potency" and place in a 10 ml. volumetric flask. Add 20 per cent sodium sulfate solution almost to the mark, shake well, centrifuge sufficiently to see the meniscus, make to volume with 20 per cent sodium sulfate solution, shake well, and centrifuge to obtain a clear or reasonably clear solution.

Dilute a 5.0 ml. aliquot of the centrifuged solution to 50 ml. with phosphate buffer no. 1, pH 6. Determine the total quantity of penicillin in a 2.0 ml. aliquot of this solution by the chemical assay method, Section B of this Chapter.

Determine the small quantity of procaine penicillin in another aliquot of this solution by the following method and using solutions of sodium nitrate, ammonium sulfamate, N-(1-naphthyl)-ethylenediamine, and 4 N hydrochloric acid.

Dissolve 0.1 Gm of sodium nitrate in 100 ml. of distilled water. Prepare a fresh solution every week and store under refrigeration. Dissolve 0.5 Gm. of ammonium sulfamate in 100 ml. of distilled water and store under refrigeration. Dissolve 0.1 Gm. of N-(1-naphthyl)-ethylenediamine dihydrochloride in 100 ml. of distilled water. Prepare a fresh solution every week and store under refrigeration.

Standard curve. Prepare a standard solution containing 27.55 mg. of procaine hydrochloride U.S.P. in a liter of distilled water (each ml. of the standard solution is equivalent to the procaine content of 60 units of procaine penicillin). Transfer, respectively, 1.0, 2.0, 3.0, 4.0, and 5.0 ml. of the standard solution and 5.0 ml. of distilled water to each of six 50 ml. volumetric flasks. Add 4.0, 3.0, 2.0, and 1.0 ml. of water to the first four flasks, respectively, to give each a volume of 5.0 ml. To each flask add 0.5 ml. of 4 *N* hydrochloric acid, 1.0 ml. of the sodium nitrite solution, 1.0 ml. of the ammonium sulfamate, and 1.0 ml. of the N-(1-naphthyl)-ethylenediamine solution, with mixing after each addition. Make each flask to volume of 50 ml. with distilled water. Read the per cent light transmission of the colored solutions using a 2.0 cm. cell and a 550 mμ filter in a suitable photoelectric colorimeter. The instrument is balanced so that the zero concentration reads 100 per cent light transmission. Prepare a standard curve on semilogarithmic paper, plotting the per cent light transmission on the logarithmic ordinate scale and the concentration of units of procaine penicillin on the abscissa.

Procedure. Transfer another 2.0 ml. aliquot of the solution that was prepared by diluting 5.0 ml. of the centrifuged solution to 50 ml. with phosphate buffer no. 1, *p*H 6, to a 50 ml. volumetric flask, add 0.5 ml. of 4 *N* hydrochloric acid, 1.0 ml. of the sodium nitrate solution, 1.0 ml. of the ammonium sulfamate solution, and 1.0 ml. N-(1-naphthyl)-ethylenediamine solution, with mixing after each addition. Make to 50 ml. with distilled water. Set the colorimeter at 100 per cent light transmission with the zero per cent concentration blank as described under "standard curve" and obtain the per cent light transmission of the sample. The concentration obtained directly from the standard curve corresponding to the per cent light transmission of the sample equals the concentration of procaine penicillin in the 2 ml. aliquot. The content of buffered crystalline penicillin in 1.0 ml. of the suspension is equal to the difference between the total number of units of penicillin in 2.0 ml. of the solution as determined by the chemical assay method and the total number of units of procaine penicillin in 2.0 ml. of this same solution as just determined multiplied by 50.

PROCAINE PENICILLIN CONTENT. The procaine penicillin content of the preparation is the difference between the total potency determined by the method described under "total potency" or under "one dose container" and the content of the buffered crystalline penicillin that was determined by the method just described.

(ONE DOSE CONTAINER). *For content of buffered crystalline sodium or potassium penicillin.* Add the quantity of distilled water recommended in the labeling, shake well, withdraw as much of the contents as possible with a hypodermic syringe and add to a 10 ml. volumetric flask. Add 20 per cent sodium sulfate solution and proceed as already described for multiple dose containers.

Total potency. Wash into a 250 ml. volumetric flask the material remaining in the 10 ml. volumetric flask referred to in the last paragraph, make to volume with phosphate buffer no. 1, *p*H 6, and assay by the chemical assay method, Section B of this Chapter. Obtain the total potency by adding the number of units found in the 250 ml. of solution to 25 times the number of units found in the 2.0 ml. of solution assayed by the chemical assay method, Section B, as directed for "content of buffered crystalline sodium or potassium penicillin" in multiple dose containers.

Procaine penicillin content. The procaine penicillin content is the difference between the total penicillin determined in the last paragraph and the buffered penicillin content determined under paragraph covering content of buffered crystalline sodium or potassium penicillin, one dose container.

The buffered crystalline penicillin used in this preparation is either sodium or potassium penicillin with sodium citrate. A 20 per cent sodium sulfate solution is used to dissolve the sodium or potassium penicillin and at the same time to decrease still further the solubility of the procaine penicillin. The sodium sulfate solution will contain all of the sodium or potassium penicillin in the sample plus about 200 units/ml. of procaine penicillin. Since these preparations contain a minimum of 100,000 units of sodium or potassium penicillin in each ml. of aqueous suspension, this quantity of procaine penicillin could almost be disregarded. However, it is determined by measuring the procaine portion of the procaine penicillin colorimetrically and subtracting the procaine penicillin so determined from the total penicillin content of the sodium sulfate solution.

Some prefer to measure the procaine penicillin content of this preparation by completely dissolving it and determining the total procaine content by the N-(1-naphthyl)-ethylenediamine colorimetric method. The procaine penicillin found is then subtracted from the total penicillin to obtain the sodium or potassium penicillin content. It has been our experience that the colorimetric measurement of procaine penicillin is subject to errors that multiply themselves, and the sodium or potassium penicillin result obtained by difference may be quite variable.

Procaine Penicillin and Crystalline Sodium or Potassium Penicillin in Oil. TOTAL POTENCY. The total potency may be determined by microbiologic assay in Method 1, Section A, or the chemical method, Section B of this Chapter, after extracting a 1 ml. portion of the oil in the same manner as for procaine penicillin in oil, Section C of this Chapter.

CONTENT OF CRYSTALLINE SODIUM OR POTASSIUM PENICILLIN. Introduce 1 ml. or other suitable aliquot of the well-shaken sample by means of an accurately standardized hypodermic syringe into a 30 ml. centrifuge tube equipped with a screw cap. Add 10 ml. of chloroform and 10 ml. of a 20 per cent sodium sulfate solution, shake well for about one minute and centrifuge to obtain a clear upper layer. Proceed as directed under procaine penicillin and buffered crystalline penicillin for aqueous injection, Section C, for multiple dose containers.

PROCAINE PENICILLIN CONTENT. The difference between the total penicillin and the crystalline penicillin as already determined represents the procaine penicillin.

l-Ephenamine Penicillin G for Aqueous Injection. Add the quantity of water recommended in the labeling by means of an accurately standardized hypodermic syringe, shake the suspension thoroughly, remove 1.0 ml., dissolve in phosphate buffer no. 1, *p*H 6, and assay the buffer solution by microbiologic assay in Method 1, Section A, or by the chemical method, Section B of this Chapter.

l-Ephenamine Penicillin G in Oil. Follow the same procedure used for procaine penicillin in oil, Section C of this Chapter.

Benzathine Penicillin G Oral Suspension. Dissolve 1.0 ml. of the suspension in 20 ml. of formamide or dimethylformamide, dilute with phosphate buffer no. 1, *p*H 6, and assay by microbiologic assay in Method 1, Section A of this Chapter. The chemical method, Section B of this Chapter, may also be used by running the blank on a suspension prepared by diluting 1.0 ml. of the preparation with phosphate buffer no. 1, *p*H 6, to give a concentration of 2,000 units/ml. of benzathine penicillin G. In preparing the solution for inactivation, dissolve 1.0 ml. of the preparation in 20 ml. of 0.5 *N* sodium hydroxide. Allow to stand 15 minutes. Dilute with distilled water to a volume to give 2,000 units/ml. Pipette a 2 ml. aliquot into a 125 ml. glass stoppered Erlenmeyer flask, add 2.0 ml. of 1.2 *N* hydrochloric acid, 10 ml. of 0.01 *N* iodine, etc.

Benzathine Penicillin G for Aqueous Injection. If the preparation is the dry powder form, add the quantity of water recommended in the labeling by means of an accurately standardized hypodermic syringe. Shake the suspension thoroughly, remove 1.0 ml., dissolve in 50 ml. of formamide or dimethylformamide, dilute with phosphate buffer no. 1, *p*H 6, and assay by microbiologic assay in Method 1, Section A of this Chapter. If the preparation is the suspension in water, use 1.0 ml. of the well-shaken suspension and proceed as previously.
The chemical method may also be used by following the same procedure given under benzathine penicillin G oral suspension, Section C of this Chapter.

Benzathine Penicillin G and Buffered Crystalline Sodium or Potassium Penicillin for Aqueous Injection. TOTAL POTENCY. Follow the same procedure given under benzathine penicillin G for aqueous injection, Section C of this Chapter.

BUFFERED CRYSTALLINE SODIUM OR POTASSIUM PENICILLIN CONTENT. Place 1.0 ml. of the preparation in a 10 ml. volumetric flask and add 20 per cent sodium sulfate solution to make 10 ml. Shake well and centrifuge to obtain a clear, or reasonably clear, solution. Dilute a 5 ml. aliquot with phosphate buffer no. 1, *p*H 6, and assay by microbiologic assay in Method 1, Section A, or by chemical method, Section B of this Chapter. (Note that because of the sparing solubility of the benzathine penicillin, only negligible quantities of it are dissolved in the sodium sulfate solution and no correction need be made for it.)

BENZATHINE PENICILLIN G CONTENT. The difference between the total potency and the buffered crystalline penicillin content represents the quantity of benzathine penicillin present.

Benzathine Penicillin G, Procaine Penicillin, and Buffered Crystalline Sodium or Potassium Penicillin for Aqueous Injection. TOTAL POTENCY. Add the quantity of water recommended in the labeling by means of an accurately standardized hypodermic syringe. Shake the suspension thoroughly, remove 1.0 ml., dissolve in 50 ml. of formamide or dimethylformamide, dilute with phosphate buffer no. 1, *p*H 6, and assay by microbiologic assay in Method 1, Section A of this Chapter.

The chemical assay method, Section B of this Chapter, may also be used to determine the total potency as follows.

Using a standardized hypodermic syringe, withdraw 2.0 ml. or one dose of the suspension, place in a 500 ml. volumetric flask and make to volume with distilled water. Use an aliquot of this suspension as the blank.

Withdraw another 2.0 ml. or one dose of the suspension, place in a 500 ml. volumetric flask, add 40 ml. 0.5 *N* sodium hydroxide, mix well, being sure all penicillin is in solution, and allow to stand for 15 minutes. Add 20 ml. 1.2 *N* hydrochloric acid, mix, and dilute to volume with distilled water. Remove an aliquot containing approximately 2,000 units of penicillin, add 10 ml. of 0.01 *N* iodine, allow to stand 15 minutes, and titrate with 0.01 *N* sodium thiosulfate as in the chemical assay method, Section B of this Chapter.

PROCAINE PENICILLIN CONTENT. Place a 10 ml. aliquot of the 500 ml. of solution prepared as noted in last paragraph in a 100 ml. volumetric flask and make to volume with water. Determine the procaine penicillin content of this solution by the colorimetric N-(l-naphthyl)-ethylenediamine method described under procaine penicillin and buffered crystalline penicillin for aqueous injection, Section C, multiple dose containers, of this chapter.

BUFFERED CRYSTALLINE SODIUM OR POTASSIUM PENICILLIN CONTENT. Follow the procedure given for the buffered crystalline sodium or potassium penicillin content of procaine penicillin and buffered crystalline sodium or potassium penicillin for aqueous injection, Section C, under multiple dose containers, of this Chapter.

BENZATHINE PENICILLIN G CONTENT. The sum of the procaine penicillin content and the buffered crystalline sodium or potassium penicillin content as already determined, subtracted from the total potency represents the benzathine penicillin G content.

Ephedrine Penicillin Tablets. Follow the same procedure used for penicillin tablets, Section C of this Chapter.

Buffered Penicillin Powder. This is an oral preparation and is usually sold in two forms. One is a combination package containing the penicillin in one bottle and an aqueous flavored vehicle in another bottle. The penicillin is dissolved in the vehicle before dispensing. The other form is a dry powder containing penicillin plus sugar, buffer, and flavorings to which water is added before dispensing. Determine the penicillin content of either preparation by dissolving or suspending as directed in the labeling, diluting a suitable aliquot of the solution or suspension with phosphate buffer no. 1, *p*H 6, and assay by microbiologic assay in Method 1, Section A, or by the chemical method, Section B of this Chapter.

Penicillin Tooth Powder. Prepare a suspension of the preparation, using a weighed sample, in phosphate buffer no. 1, *p*H 6, and assay by microbiologic assay in Method 1, Section A, or by the chemical assay method, Section B of this Chapter.

Penethamate (Diethylaminoethyl Ester Penicillin G Hydriodide) for Aqueous Injection. Add the quantity of water recommended in the labeling by means of an accurately standardized hypodermic syringe. Shake the suspension thoroughly, remove 1.0 ml., or one dose, and dissolve in phosphate buffer no. 3, *p*H 8, to make a stock solution of 100 units/ml. (estimated). Allow to stand at room temperature for not less than one and a half hours and not more than two hours and then dilute an aliquot with phosphate buffer no. 1, *p*H 6, to 1.0 unit (estimated) and assay by the microbiologic assay in Method 1, Section A of this Chapter.

The chemical method of assay, Section B of this Chapter, may be used by dissolving 1.0 ml. or one dose of the prepared preparation in 2 to 3 ml. of redistilled methanol and further diluting with phosphate buffer no. 1, *p*H 6, to a concentration of 2,000 units/ml. (estimated).

Chloroprocaine Penicillin O for Aqueous Injection. Follow the same procedure used for procaine penicillin for aqueous injection, Section C of this Chapter.

Hydrabamine Penicillin Oral Suspension. Place 1.0 ml. of the thoroughly shaken suspension in a 100 ml. volumetric flask and dilute to volume with methanol. By means of a volumetric pipette, add a 1.0 ml. aliquot of this solution to a sufficient volume of phosphate buffer no. 1, *p*H 6, to give a solution having a concentration of 1 unit/ml. (constantly swirling the flask during the addition), and assay by the microbiologic assay in Method 1, Section A of this Chapter.

The chemical assay method may also be used, in which case proceed as follows: Dilute 1.0 ml. of the sample with sufficient phosphate buffer no. 1, *p*H 6, to produce a suspension containing 2,000 units/ml. (estimated). Mix and pipette 2.0 ml. into a 125 ml. glass stoppered Erlenmeyer flask. Add 10 ml. of 0.01 N iodine and titrate immediately with 0.01 N sodium thiosulfate for the blank determination. Dilute a second 1.0 ml. portion of the sample with 1 N sodium hydroxide to produce a suspension containing 2,000 units/ml. (estimated) and add approximately half that amount of chloroform U.S.P. Shake immediately and again after five minutes. Fifteen minutes after the initial shaking, pipette 2.0 ml. of the upper sodium hydroxide layer into a

125 ml. glass stoppered Erlenmeyer flask and add 2.0 ml. of 1.2 N hydrochloric acid and 10 ml. of 0.01 N iodine. After 15 minutes titrate the excess iodine with 0.01 N sodium thiosulfate.

Units of penicillin per ml. of suspension =
  Difference in titers $\times$ potency of working standard in units/mg. $\times$ volume of
2,000 units/ml. suspension

$$\overline{F \times 2.}$$

Where F = the number of ml. of 0.01 N iodine absorbed by 1.0 mg. of the sodium penicillin G working standard.

Penicillin Capsules. These are hard gelatin capsules containing crystalline sodium or potassium penicillin with suitable buffers, diluents, etc. To assay, dissolve the contents of 12 capsules in distilled water to give an appropriate stock solution. An aliquot of the stock solution is then diluted with phosphate buffer no. 1, pH 6, to 1.0 unit/ml. (estimated) and assayed by the microbiologic assay in Method 1, Section A of this Chapter.

Penicillin Oral Suspension. This preparation contains crystalline sodium or potassium penicillin emulsified in an oily vehicle. By means of an accurately standardized hypodermic syringe, introduce 5 ml. of the well-shaken test sample into a high speed blender jar containing 244 ml. of phosphate buffer no. 1, pH 6, and 1.0 ml. of a 10 per cent aqueous solution of polysorbate 80. Blend the mixture for three to five minutes. Make the proper estimated dilutions in phosphate buffer no. 1, pH 6, and assay by the microbiologic assay in Method 1, Section A of this Chapter.

Section D: Determination of Penicillin in Body Fluids and Other Substances

Blood Serum. Use the *S. lutea* plate microbiologic assay in Method 2, Section A of this Chapter. Dilute the penicillin standard to a concentration of 10 units/ml. in phosphate buffer no. 1, pH 6, and from this make dilutions of 0.03, 0.05, 0.10, 0.20, 0.30, and 0.40 for the standard curve, using 7.0 per cent bovine albumin solution (Chapter 21) as a diluent. The reference point for the standard curve is the 0.1 unit/ml. concentration. Normal serum may be used in place of the albumin solution; however, it tends to become alkaline on standing and the pH should be readjusted to 7.4 before using. Great care must be taken to insure that the serum is prepared from the blood of individuals who have not been treated with penicillin or other antibiotics that might cause inhibition of the test organism. The bovine albumin solution is used in a concentration that has the same binding power as normal human serum and is a more standard and reproducible diluent.

PREPARATION OF SAMPLE. Draw 5 ml. of blood aseptically into a tube and allow to clot. Centrifuge the blood and transfer serum immediately to a sterile tube. If the tests cannot be made the same day the blood is drawn, the serum should be kept frozen in a carbon dioxide ice chest or a deep freeze refrigerator at

—20 C. or less until used. When ready for use, the serum is placed on test undiluted unless a concentration greater than 0.4 unit/ml. is expected. In this case, the sample should be diluted to an estimated 0.1 unit/ml. with bovine albumin solution. One or more plates are used depending on the quantity of serum available.

Urine. Either microbiologic assay in Methods 1 or 2, Section A of this Chapter, may be used for the determination of penicillin in urine. About 20 per cent of an orally administered dose is excreted in the urine and 50 to 80 per cent of an injected dose. In either case, the urine is appropriately diluted in phosphate buffer no. 1, *p*H 6, for assay. The concentration of penicillin in the urine is usually so high that no special diluent is needed for the standard, which is diluted in phosphate buffer no. 1, *p*H 6. If Method 1 is used, dilute the urine to contain an estimated 1.0 unit/ml.; if Method 2 is employed, dilute to an estimated 0.05 unit/ml. and prepare the standard curve using concentrations of penicillin to contain 0.01, 0.02, 0.03, 0.05 (reference point), 0.10, 0.20, and 0.30 unit/ml.

Tissue. The tissue to be examined for penicillin concentration is removed and any extraneous blood or adhering fascia removed by dissecting and washing with water. Weigh the tissue (heart, lung, spleen, brain, muscle) and dilute 1 to 6 or greater depending on its estimated antibiotic content on a Gm. /volume basis with phosphate buffer no. 1, *p*H 6. Thoroughly homogenize in a blender. Allow the tissue debris to settle and assay the supernatant using microbiologic assay in Method 2, Section A of this Chapter. The standard curve and the reference point for the test samples is the same as described under "Urine." It is especially important when testing organs and tissues to test normal untreated controls as well, because of the possible presence of inhibitory substances sometimes normally present. While this applies especially to body tissues, it is also equally true of any other test substance.

Milk. Use microbiologic assay in Method 2, Section A of this Chapter. Dilute the penicillin standard to a concentration of 10 units/ml. in phosphate buffer no. 1, *p*H 6, and from this make dilutions for the standard curve in normal milk. The milk used for preparing the standard curve must have been previously tested and shown to be free of inhibitory substances. Add the milk sample to be tested to the cups undiluted unless a concentration greater than 0.4 unit/ml. is anticipated, in which case dilute the milk sample to an estimated 0.1 unit/ml., using the same milk used for diluting the standard.

Animal Feed Supplements and (Mixed) Final Feeds. FEED SUPPLEMENT. Add 3 Gm. of the supplement to a glass stoppered graduated cylinder containing 25 ml. phosphate buffer no. 1, *p*H 6. Shake the cylinder for two minutes and allow the material to settle. Decant supernatant into a centrifuge tube. Add 25 ml. of buffer to cylinder, shake two minutes, allow to settle, and add supernatant to first washing. Rinse cylinder with 50 ml. of buffer and add to prior washings. Centrifuge for approximately 15 minutes at 2,000 r.p.m. Remove 1 ml. of supernatant and dilute to an estimated penicillin concentration of 0.05 unit with phosphate buffer no. 1, *p*H 6.

When supplements contain more than 100 Gm. procaine penicillin activity per pound, add 1 Gm. of supplement and proceed as previously.

FINAL FEED. Add 10 Gm. of feed to a glass stoppered graduated cylinder containing 35 ml. of phosphate buffer no. 1, pH 6. Shake for two minutes, allow to settle, and decant supernatant into centrifuge tube. Add 35 ml. of buffer, shake two minutes, allow to settle, and combine supernatant with first washing. Rinse graduate with 30 ml. of buffer and combine with prior washings. Centrifuge, dilute, and assay as previously.

For both methods described under feed supplements and mixed feeds, assay the final dilutions obtained by microbiologic assay in Method 2, Section A of this Chapter. The standard curve is prepared in phosphate buffer no. 1, pH 6, using penicillin concentrations of 0.01, 0.02, 0.03, 0.05 (reference point), 0.10, 0.20, and 0.30 unit/ml.

Penicillin may be assayed in a variety of other substances by slight modifications of the examples given. For example, the following substances have been tested for their penicillin content: Cheese, butter, dried milk, evaporated milk, and eggs. The S. lutea plate method is the more generally useful because of its sensitivity and, if the material under test contains substantial amounts of the antibiotic, the dilution necessary will tend to eliminate many substances that might cause false positive zones of inhibition on the assay plates.

Penicillin is unique among the currently used antibiotics in that we have a specific enzyme, penicillinase, which will inactivate it (see Chapter 21). Therefore, if it is necessary to prove that the activity shown by a given sample is due to penicillin and not to some other inhibitory substance, the sample can be divided into two parts, one part with and the other without penicillinase. If the penicillinase-treated sample gives no inhibitory zones on the test plates while the untreated one does, it can be stated with reasonable assurance that the inhibitory substance is penicillin.

3 STREPTOMYCIN AND DIHYDROSTREPTOMYCIN

Section A: Microbiologic Assay Methods for Streptomycin and Dihydrostreptomycin

Two methods are described, a cylinder-plate method using *B. subtilis* and a *K. pneumoniae* turbidimetric method. A large series of tests on identical samples showed that the turbidimetric method was the more accurate and less subject to biologic variation than the plate method and in the absence of interfering substances is preferred. In the assay of streptomycin or dihydrostreptomycin in certain pharmaceutical preparations, blood, body fluids, and other substances, the turbidimetric method cannot be used because of the light transmission interference caused by coloring matter and turbidities of the substances tested, which do not affect the plate method. For these reasons, the cylinder-plate method of assay was retained as an official method, and slightly modified for the assay of streptomycin and dihydrostreptomycin in blood serum and other substances.

METHOD 1: Cylinder-Plate Method Using *Bacillus subtilis* as the Test Organism. (ATCC 6633.)

Cylinders (Cups). Use stainless steel cylinders with an outside diameter of 8 mm. (±0.1 mm.), an inside diameter of 6 mm. (±0.1 mm.), and a length of 10 mm. (±0.1 mm.).

Culture Media. Use agar medium no. 5 for both the seed and base layers. Maintain the test organism on agar medium no. 1.

Working Standard. If streptomycin is to be assayed, use a streptomycin sulfate working standard. If dihydrostreptomycin is to be assayed, use a dihydrostreptomycin sulfate working standard. Both standards may be kept at room temperature in tightly stoppered vials, which in turn are kept in larger stoppered vials containing a suitable desiccant. Both standards are hygroscopic and should be dried at 60 C. for three hours under vacuum before using. Dissolve a weighed sample of the dried standard in water to obtain a concentration of 1,000 μg./ml. Keep this stock solution at a temperature of 15 C. or less and do not use later than 30 days after it is made.

Preparation of Sample. The method of preparing samples of the various preparations to be tested is described under the individual dosage forms in Section C of this Chapter.

Preparation of Test Organism. Prepare a spore suspension by growing the organism in Roux bottles on agar medium no. 1, for one week at 37 C. Suspend the spores in sterile distilled water and heat for 30 minutes at 65 C. Wash the spore suspension three times with sterile distilled water, heat again for 30 minutes at 65 C., and resuspend in sterile distilled water. Maintain the spore suspension at approximately 15 C. Determine by appropriate tests the quantity of spore suspension to be added to each 100 ml. of agar medium no. 5 (usually 0.5 to 1.0 ml.) for the secondary layer that will give sharp, clear zones of inhibition. This spore suspension will keep for months.

An equally satisfactory suspension may be prepared by growing the organism in liquid medium no. 6 containing manganese, which induces spore formation. Inoculate medium no. 6 from a stock slant of *B. subtilis* and incubate at 26 C. for four to six days on a mechanical shaking apparatus (reciprocal shaker). Determine the degree of sporulation by direct smear and stain. If 80 per cent or more of the cells are in the spore state, centrifuge the culture, remove the supernatant, and reconstitute the cells to 30 per cent of the original broth volume with sterile saline. Heat shock the spore suspension by immersing in a water bath at 70 C. for 30 minutes and store under refrigeration. Run test plates to determine the quantity of this suspension to be added to each 100 ml. of agar medium no. 5 to give clear, sharp, inhibitory zones of appropriate size. This quantity is usually 0.5 to 1.0 ml.

Preparation of Plates. Add 21 ml. of melted agar medium no. 5 to each Petri dish (20 by 100 mm.). Distribute the agar evenly in the plates, cover with porcelain covers glazed only on the outside or other suitable covers, and allow it to harden. Use the plates the same day they are prepared. Melt the agar medium no. 5 to be used for the secondary (seed) layer, cool to 55 to 60 C., and add the spore suspension. Mix thoroughly and add 4 ml. of this seeded medium to the hardened base layer. Tilt the plates back and forth to spread the inoculated medium evenly over the surface. After this seed layer hardens, place six cylinders on the inoculated agar surface so that they are at approximately 60 degree intervals on a 2.8 cm. radius.

Standard Curve and Assay Procedure. STANDARD CURVE. Prepare daily in phosphate buffer no. 3, *p*H 8, from the stock standard solution concentrations of 0.6, 0.7, 0.8, 0.9, 1.0, 1.1, 1.2, 1.3, 1.4, and 1.5 μg./ml. solutions. A total of 27 plates is used in the preparation of the standard curve, three plates for each solution except the 1.0 μg./ml. solution. This latter concentration is the reference point and is included on each plate. On each of three plates fill three cylinders with the 1.0 μg./ml. standard and the other three cylinders with the concentration under test. Thus, there will be 81 of the 1.0 μg. determinations and nine determinations for each of the other points on the curve. Incubate the plates for 16 to 18 hours at 37 C. and measure the diameter of each circle of inhibition. Average the readings of the 1.0 μg./ml. concentration and the readings of the concentration tested for each set of three plates and average also all

81 readings of the 1.0 μg./ml. concentration. The average of the 81 readings of the 1.0 μg./ml. concentration is the correction point for the curve. Correct the average value obtained for each concentration to the figure it would be if the 1.0 μg./ml. reading for that set of three plates were the same as the correction point. Thus, if in correcting the 0.8 μg./ml. concentration, the average of the 81 readings of the 1.0 μg./ml. concentration is 16.5 mm. and the average of the 1.0 μg./ml. concentration of this set of three plates is 16.3 mm., the correction is +0.2 mm. If the average readings of the 0.8 μg./ml. concentration of these same three plates is 15.9 mm., the corrected value is then 16.1 mm. Plot these corrected values, including the average of the 81 concentrations of 1.0 μg./ml., on two-cycle semilogarithmic paper using the concentration in μg./ml. as the ordinate (the logarithmic scale) and the diameter of the zone of inhibition as the abscissa. Draw the standard curve through these points. The 10 points selected to determine the curve are arbitrary and should be so chosen that the limits of the curve will fill the needs of the laboratory. However, the potency of the sample under test should fall in the interval of from 60 to 150 per cent of the correction point of the standard curve.

ASSAY OF SAMPLE. Use one or more (usually three) plates for each sample. Fill three cylinders on each plate with the 1.0 μg./ml. standard and three cylinders with the 1.0 μg./ml. (estimated) sample, alternating standard and sample. Incubate the plates for 16 to 18 hours at 37 C. and measure the diameter of each zone of inhibition. Average the zone readings of the standard and average the zone readings of the sample on the three plates used. If the sample gives a larger zone size than the average of the standard, add the difference between them to the 1.0 μg. zone size of the standard curve. If the average sample zone size is lower than the standard value, subtract the difference between them from the 1.0 μg. value of the curve. From the curve, read the concentrations corresponding to these corrected values of zone sizes.

METHOD 2: Turbidimetric Method Using *Klebsiella pneumoniae* as the Test Organism. (ATCC 10031.)

Test Culture and Media. Employ agar medium no. 7 for maintaining the test organism. Transfer stock cultures every two weeks for test purposes. Transfer the organism to fresh agar medium no. 7 slants and incubate overnight at 37 C. Suspend the growth from two or three of these slants in sterile distilled water and add approximately 5 ml. of culture suspension to each of two Roux bottles containing agar medium no. 7. Incubate the bottles overnight at 37 C., harvest the growth, and suspend in sufficient sterile distilled water to give a light transmission reading of 65 per cent, using a filter of 6,500 Å. units in a Lumetron 400-A photoelectric colorimeter. Keep the resulting suspension of organisms in the refrigerator and use for a period not to exceed two weeks. Prepare a daily inoculum by adding 6.0 ml. of this suspension to each 100 ml. broth medium no. 3 cooled to a temperature of approximately 15 C.

WORKING STANDARD SOLUTIONS. Add the required quantities of the 1,000 μg./ml. stock solution of the standard described in Method 1 of this Chapter to 100 ml. volumetric flasks containing sterile distilled water and bring to volume to give working stock solutions containing 60, 70, 80, 90, 100, 110, 120, 130, and 140 µg./ml. (see table I). These nine flasks, if well stoppered, will remain stable when maintained at 15 C. for one month. Prepare the final dilutions daily by adding 4.2 ml. of each of these nine working stock solutions to 9.6 ml. of sterile distilled water. Add 1.0 ml. of each final dilution to each of six, 16 by 125 mm. (outside dimensions) tubes (total 54 tubes). Add 9.0 ml. of the inoculated broth to each tube and place immediately (all at the same time) in a 37 C. water bath for three to four hours. The final concentration of streptomycin or dihydrostreptomycin per ml. of broth is also included in table I.

TABLE I: *Working Standard Solutions*

Amount of standard solution (1000 µg./ml.)	Working concentration µg./ml. (also per cent concentration)	Final concentration µg./ml. after addition of distilled water and broth
6.0	60	1.8
7.0	70	2.1
8.0	80	2.4
9.0	90	2.7
10.0	100	3.0
11.0	110	3.3
12.0	120	3.6
13.0	130	3.9
14.0	140	4.2

Preparation of Sample. Dilute the sample under test with sterile distilled water to contain 100 µg./ml. (estimated). To 4.2 ml. of this sample dilution, add 9.6 ml. sterile distilled water. Add 1.0 ml. of this dilution to each of six of the 16 by 125 mm. tubes (outside dimensions). Add 9.0 ml. of the inoculated broth to each tube and place immediately in a 37 C. water bath for three to four hours. A control tube containing 1.0 ml. of distilled water and 9.0 ml. of the inoculated broth is similarly incubated. After incubation, add 0.5 ml. of formalin diluted 1:3 to each tube and read the light transmission in a Lumetron 402-E photoelectric colorimeter, using a broad-band filter having a wave length of 5,300 Å. units. Other suitable photoelectric colorimeters may also be used.

Estimation of Potency. Set the slide wire scale of the Lumetron photoelectric colorimeter at 80. Adjust the instrument so that the galvanometer scale reads about 90 using the pooled contents of the six tubes containing the highest amount of the standard (4.2 µg./ml. final concentration) and to about 10 using the pooled contents of the six tubes containing the lowest concentration (1.8 µg./ml.). Read and average the galvanometer readings for each six tubes of the intermediate concentrations. Plot these values on cross section paper, employing average galvanometer readings as the ordinate and streptomycin or dihydrostreptomycin concentration per ml. of broth as the abscissa. Prepare the standard curve by connecting successive points with a straightedge. Since the final concentration of antibiotic per ml. of broth is equivalent to the concentration per ml. of the working stock solution, the latter concentrations for each concentration level of the standard may be expressed as per cent and substituted on the abscissa of the standard curve. If this is done, the per cent potency of the sample under test may be read directly from the standard curve. Determine the galvanometer reading of each of the six tubes of the sample under test, average the six figures obtained, and determine the potency on the standard curve already described. It is essential to run the standard curve simultaneously with the test samples.

METHOD 3: Modified Cylinder-plate Assay Method Using *Bacillus subtilis.*

This method was adapted from Method 1 and used for the determination of streptomycin or dihydrostreptomycin in body fluids, tissues, milk, and other substances.

Proceed as directed in the microbiologic assay in Method 1 of this Chapter except that only 10 ml. of agar medium no. 5 is used for the base layer. The standard curve and assay procedure are the same as described in Method 1, except the concentrations for the standard curve are made to contain 0.10, 0.30, 0.50, 1.0 (reference point), 2.0, and 4.0 μg./ml. of streptomycin or dihydrostreptomycin, whichever is under test. Special diluents for the standard curve, which may be required, are described under the individual test substances in Section D of this Chapter.

Section B: Chemical Methods for Streptomycin and Dihydrostreptomycin

The success of any chemical method for determining the potency of an antibiotic depends upon its ability to correlate well with microbiologic potency tests. In the early days of streptomycin production, two types of antibiotics were commonly produced, streptomycin and mannosidostreptomycin (streptomycin B). The potency of mannosidostreptomycin when measured by microbiologic methods is about 20 to 30 per cent that of streptomycin. Chemically, the only difference between these two compounds is that mannosidostreptomycin has a mannose group not possessed by streptomycin. Since the difference in the molecular weights of these two compounds (581.6 and 743.4) is not so great as the difference in their microbiologic activity, it is to be expected that no one chemical assay method will give values on mixtures that will agree with the microbiologic method unless the quantity of mannosidostreptomycin present is small. Because of the low activity of mannosidostreptomycin, manufacturers of streptomycin have selected cultures of *Streptomyces griseus* capable of producing high yields of streptomycin and minimal quantities of mannosidostreptomycin. They have also been able to reduce mannosidostreptomycin to a marked degree during the extraction and purification processes. Recent analyses of commercial samples of streptomycin and dihydrostreptomycin have shown the mannosidostreptomycin or mannosidodihydrostreptomycin content to be usually 1 per cent or less. Therefore, we need to be concerned only with determining one type of streptomycin or dihydrostreptomycin and chemical and biologic methods should give good agreement. This has been found to be true with the drugs being produced today.

When streptomycin is heated with sodium hydroxide, maltol (2-methyl-3-hydroxy-γ-pyrone) is formed. Maltol has characteristic absorption maximums in both alkaline and acid solutions and reacts with ferric chloride to give a purplish-red color that is stable in acid solution. Maltol also gives a color with the Folin and Ciocalteu phenol reagent. In analyzing relatively pure samples of streptomycin by the maltol method, the maltol may be measured without separation from the reaction mixture. With impure preparations, it may be desirable to separate the maltol. This can be accomplished by extracting the maltol into organic solvents, such as chloroform, or by steam distillation.

The colorimetric maltol method given in detail under Method 1, Section B, has been found to agree satisfactorily with microbiologic assay methods and is useful for the testing of relatively pure samples of streptomycin. Parenteral streptomycin solutions oftentimes contain phenol or bisulfite as a preservative. If these ingredients are present, interference with the color test may occur. For such preparations, it is advisable to measure the maltol formed by means of the ultraviolet spectrophotometer procedure under Method 1, Section B, of this Chapter.

When streptomycin is hydrogenated, the aldehyde group is reduced to an alcohol group and dihydrostreptomycin is formed. Dihydrostreptomycin heated with alkali does not form maltol. The maltol test therefore is specific for streptomycin and may be used to determine streptomycin in the presence of dihydrostreptomycin.

Of the several chemical methods available, it is believed that for convenience, specificity, and accuracy the ultraviolet spectrophotometric, Method 2 of Section B, is the method of choice in determining the potency of dihydrostreptomycin. Streptomycin will not interfere unless present in large amounts. Commercial dihydrostreptomycin is not permitted to contain more than 3 per cent of streptomycin. This small quantity of streptomycin does not interfere in the method. The method is based upon the fact that dihydrostreptomycin when heated with acid exhibits an absorption maximum at 265 mμ, while streptomycin shows maximums at 245 and 315 mμ.

Another chemical method suitable for measuring the potency of either streptomycin or dihydrostreptomycin is based upon a reaction of the guanidino groups, which are common to both compounds. On the addition of an alkaline solution of sodium nitroprusside and potassium ferricyanide to a dilute aqueous solution of streptomycin or dihydrostreptomycin an orange-red color, with an absorption maximum at 490 mμ, is produced that is proportional to the concentration. This reaction is the basis for the colorimetric procedure described under Method 3. One disadvantage of this method is that streptidine (1,3-diguanido-2,4,5,6-tetrahydroxycyclohexane), a degradation product of both streptomycin and dihydrostreptomycin, also gives the same color reaction. There is no way to run a blank determination to correct for any free streptidine that may be present. However, as streptidine has only a sparing solubility in water, it should not be present to any appreciable extent. The presence of methanol may interfere in the method. Also the presence of sodium chloride in excess of 0.5 per cent or sodium sulfate reduces the color intensity of this reaction.

METHOD 1: Maltol Method for Streptomycin.[5,6]

Colorimetric Procedure. REAGENTS. Ten per cent ferric chloride stock solution. Dissolve 5 Gm. of ferric chloride in 50 ml. 0.1 N hydrochloric acid.

A 0.25 per cent ferric chloride solution. Dilute 2.5 ml. of the 10 per cent ferric chloride to 100 ml. with 0.01 N hydrochloric acid. Prepare the solution fresh daily.

Solutions of 1 N sodium hydroxide and 1.2 N hydrochloric acid.

PREPARATION OF STANDARD. Prepare a stock aqueous solution of the streptomycin working standard to contain 1.0 mg./ml. of streptomycin base. Store this standard solution in the refrigerator and use for no longer than two weeks. Transfer 1.0, 2.0, 3.0, 4.0, 5.0, 6.0, and 7.0 ml. of this standard solution to 25 ml. volumetric flasks. Add 9.0, 8.0, 7.0, 6.0, 5.0, 4.0, and 3.0 ml. of distilled water to the flasks respectively to give each a total volume of 10.0 ml.

PREPARATION OF SAMPLE. Dilute the sample to be tested with distilled water to a concentration of 0.5 mg./ml. of streptomycin base (estimated). Transfer 10 ml. of this solution to a 25 ml. volumetric flask.

BLANK. Transfer 10 ml. of distilled water to a 25 ml. volumetric flask.

PROCEDURE. To each of the 25 ml. volumetric flasks containing standard, sample, and blank, add 2.0 ml. of 1 N sodium hydroxide and heat in boiling water bath for 10 minutes. Cool in ice water for three minutes and add 2.0 ml. 1.2 N hydrochloric acid. Add 5.0 ml. of 0.25 per cent ferric chloride reagent. Make to volume with distilled water. Transfer each of the colored solutions to a 2.0 cm. absorption cell and measure the transmittance at 550 mμ in a suitable photoelectric colorimeter. Set the colorimeter at 100 per cent transmittance with the blank and then obtain the transmittance of the standards and sample. Prepare a standard curve of the transmittances obtained on the standard solutions on semilogarithmic paper, plotting the transmittance on the logarithmic ordinate scale and the concentration of streptomycin base on the abscissa. Calculate the streptomycin content of the sample under test from the standard curve.

Spectrophotometric Ultraviolet Procedure. REAGENTS. A 0.1 N sodium hydroxide (freshly prepared from 1 N sodium hydroxide) is needed.

PREPARATION OF STANDARD. Prepare an aqueous solution of the streptomycin working standard to contain 0.25 mg./ml. of streptomycin base. Transfer 1.0, 1.5, and 2.0 ml. aliquots to test tubes (approximately 16 by 150 mm.). Add 1.0, 0.5, and 0 ml. of distilled water to give each a 2.0 ml. volume.

PREPARATION OF SAMPLE. Dilute the sample to be tested to a concentration of 0.25 mg./ml. streptomycin (estimated). Transfer 2.0 ml. to a test tube.

BLANK. Use 2.0 ml. of distilled water.

PROCEDURE. To each tube of the standard and sample containing 2.0 ml. add, in turn, 8.0 ml. of 0.1 N sodium hydroxide, mix thoroughly, and immediately determine the absorbance at 325 mμ in a suitable spectrophotometer. Set the spectrophotometer at zero absorbance for the blank similarly treated. Return the solution to the test tube, heat in a boiling water bath for 10 minutes, cool in an ice bath for three minutes, and allow to come to room temperature. Determine the absorbance at 325 mμ. The difference in reading before and after heating is the absorbance of the maltol formed. Prepare a standard curve of these absorbance differences obtained on the standard solutions. The streptomycin content of the sample under test is calculated from the standard curve.

METHOD 2: Ultraviolet Spectrophotometric Method for Dihydrostreptomycin.

This method adapted from Hiscox.[7]

Preparation of Standard. Prepare an aqueous solution of the dihydrostreptomycin working standard to contain 0.75 mg./ml. of dihydrostreptomycin base. Transfer 1.0, 2.0, and 3.0 ml. aliquots to test tubes (approximately 25 by 200 mm.) fitted with ground glass joints. Add 2.0, 1.0, and 0 ml. of distilled water to give each a 3.0 ml. volume.

Preparation of Sample. Dilute the dihydrostreptomycin sample to be tested to a concentration of 0.5 mg./ml. (estimated). Transfer a 3.0 ml. aliquot to a test tube fitted with a ground glass joint.

Blank. Use 3.0 ml. of distilled water.

Procedure. To each tube containing 3.0 ml. of standard, sample, and blank, add 3.0 ml. of 0.5 N sulfuric acid. Fit an air condenser (7 mm. tubing, 300 mm. long, fitted with a ground glass joint) into each tube and heat in a boiling water bath for two hours. Cool the tubes to room temperature and dilute the contents to 25 ml. with distilled water. Determine the absorbance of each of the solutions at 265 mμ and at 380 mμ using a suitable ultraviolet spectrophotometer. The blank is used to set the instrument to zero absorbance at the two respective wave lengths. Prepare a standard curve on coordinate graph paper, plotting the difference in the absorbance obtained at the two wave lengths on the ordinate scale and the concentration of dihydrostreptomycin base on the abscissa. The concentration of dihydrostreptomycin in the sample is obtained by reading the difference in the absorbance at the two wave lengths from the standard curve. To calculate the potency of the sample, multiply the concentration of dihydrostreptomycin found by appropriate factors in accordance with the dilutions made.

METHOD 3: Oxidized Nitroprusside Method for Streptomycin or Dihydrostreptomycin.[8,9]

Reagents. The reagents are sodium nitroprusside solution, 10 per cent w/v; potassium ferricyanide solution, 10 per cent w/v; sodium hydroxide solution, 10 per cent w/v; and oxidized nitroprusside solution. The latter is prepared by mixing equal volumes of the 10 per cent sodium nitroprusside, 10 per cent potassium ferricyanide, and 10 per cent sodium hydroxide solutions in the order named. A deep red color is formed which changes to a yellow-green after standing at room temperature for approximately 15 minutes. Dilute 1.0 ml. of this yellow-green solution with water to 100 ml. and shake. This is the oxidized nitroprusside solution to be used in the test. It should be prepared fresh daily. (Each of the 10 per cent solutions described is stable for at least two months when stored in an amber bottle.)

Preparation of Standard. Prepare an aqueous solution of the working standards of streptomycin or dihydrostreptomycin containing 0.2 mg./ml. Transfer 1.0, 2.0, 3.0, 4.0, 5.0, 6.0, and 7.0 ml. aliquots to small flasks. Add 9.0, 8.0, 7.0, 6.0, 5.0, 4.0, and 3.0 ml. of water to give each a 10 ml. volume.

Preparation of Sample. Dilute the sample to be tested to a streptomycin or dihydrostreptomycin concentration of 0.1 mg./ml. (estimated). Use 10 ml. of this solution in the test.

Blank. Use 10 ml. of distilled water.

Procedure. To each flask containing 10 ml. of the standards, sample, and blank, add 10 ml. of the oxidized nitroprusside solution and allow the color to develop at room temperature for three minutes. Determine the absorbance of each of the solutions at 490 mμ using a suitable spectrophotometer. The blank is used to set the instrument to zero absorbance. (The orange-red color produced is stable for 30 minutes.) Prepare a standard curve on coordinate graph paper, plotting the absorbance on the ordinate scale and the concentration of streptomycin base or dihydrostreptomycin base on the abscissa. For the sample the absorbance found is used to obtain the concentration of streptomycin or dihydrostreptomycin directly from the standard curve. To obtain the potency of the sample, multiply the concentration found by the appropriate factors in accordance with the dilutions made.

Section C: Assay of Streptomycin and Dihydrostreptomycin Salts and Pharmaceutical Dosage Forms

Streptomycin Sulfate, Streptomycin Hydrochloride, Streptomycin Trihydrochloride Calcium Chloride, Dihydrostreptomycin Sulfate, and Dihydrostreptomycin Hydrochloride. The structural formula for streptomycin base or dihydrostreptomycin base is as follows:

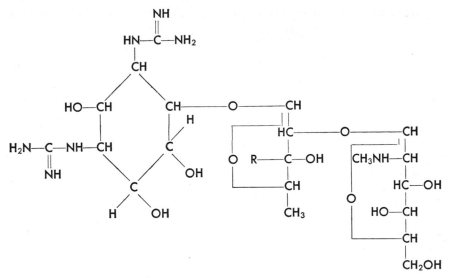

R=CHO = streptomycin base
R—CH$_2$O = dihydrostreptomycin base
Streptomycin base: C$_{21}$H$_{39}$N$_7$O$_{12}$. M.W. = 581.58. Theoretical potency = 1000 μg./mg.
Streptomycin sulfate: (C$_{21}$H$_{39}$N$_7$O$_{12}$)$_2$ (H$_2$SO$_4$)$_3$. M.W. = 1457.40. Theoretical potency = 798 μg./mg.
Streptomycin hydrochloride: (C$_{21}$H$_{39}$N$_7$O$_{12}$)·3HCl. M.W. = 690.99. Theoretical potency = 842 μg./mg.
Streptomycin trihydrochloride calcium chloride: (C$_{21}$H$_{39}$N$_7$O$_{12}$·3HCl)CaCl$_2$. M.W. = 1492.97. Theoretical potency = 779 μg./mg.
Dihydrostreptomycin base: C$_{21}$H$_{41}$N$_7$O$_{12}$. M.W. = 583.60. Theoretical potency = 1000 μg./mg.
Dihydrostreptomycin sulfate: (C$_{21}$H$_{41}$N$_7$O$_{12}$)$_2$ (H$_2$SO$_4$)$_3$. M.W. = 1461.43. Theoretical potency = 799 μg./mg.
Dihydrostreptomycin hydrochloride: (C$_{21}$H$_{41}$N$_7$O$_{12}$)·3HCl. M.W. = 693.01. Theoretical potency = 842 μg./mg.

Streptomycin and dihydrostreptomycin salts are extremely soluble in water. To assay, dissolve an accurately weighed sample or the contents of a vial in sterile distilled water to make a stock solution containing 1 mg./ml. (estimated), and assay by the microbiologic assay procedures or chemical assay procedures described in Sections A and B of this Chapter.

Streptomycin or Dihydrostreptomycin Ointments. Accurately weigh the tube and contents and squeeze approximately 1 Gm. into a blending jar containing 50 ml. of phosphate buffer no. 3, *pH* 8. Reweigh the tube to obtain weight of ointment used in the test. Using a high-speed blender, blend the mixture for three minutes. Dilute an aliquot of the mixture to contain 100 μg./ml. of streptomycin or dihydrostreptomycin base (estimated). Transfer 1.0 ml. of this solution to a 100 ml. volumetric flask and make up to volume with phosphate buffer no. 3, *pH* 8. Assay this last dilution by microbiologic assay in Method 1, Section A of this Chapter.

It has been found in the assay of ointments, or any preparation in which a slightly turbid extract may be obtained, that it is better to use the cylinder-plate method than the turbidimetric procedure where interference may be encountered due to the turbidity of the solution.

Streptomycin or Dihydrostreptomycin Tablets. Place 12 tablets in a mortar and add approximately 20 ml. of phosphate buffer no. 3, *p*H 8. Disintegrate the tablets by grinding with a pestle. Transfer with the aid of small portions of the buffer solution to a 500 ml. volumetric flask and make to volume with phosphate buffer no. 3, *p*H 8. Make the proper estimated dilutions in phosphate buffer no. 3, *p*H 8 and assay by the microbiologic assay in Method 1, Section A of this Chapter.

The sample may also be prepared as follows: Place 12 tablets in a blending jar and add approximately 200 ml. of a 500 ml. quantity of phosphate buffer no. 3, *p*H 8. After blending for one minute with a high-speed blender, add the remainder of the 500 ml. of buffer. Blend again for one minute, make the proper estimated dilutions in phosphate buffer no. 3, *p*H 8, and assay by the microbiologic assay in Method 1, Section A of this Chapter.

Streptomycin Sulfate Solution or Dihydrostreptomycin Sulfate Solution. These solutions usually contain buffers, stabilizing agents, and preservatives in addition to the antibiotic. None of these ingredients interfere with the microbiologic assays. Dilute the solution with distilled water to a concentration of 1.0 mg./ml. (estimated), make the proper estimated dilutions in phosphate buffer no. 3, *p*H 8, and assay this solution by the microbiologic assay in Method 1, Section A of this Chapter. If the microbiologic assay in Method 2 is used, dilute the sample with water instead of buffer. For streptomycin solutions, chemical assay in Method 1 may be used and for dihydrostreptomycin solution chemical assay in Method 2 may be used, Section B of this Chapter.

Streptomycin or Dihydrostreptomycin Syrup. Dilute with distilled water to a concentration of 1.0 mg./ml. (estimated) make the proper estimated dilution in phosphate buffer no. 3, *p*H 8, and assay by the microbiologic assay in Method 1, Section A of this Chapter. If the microbiologic assay in Method 2 is used, dilute with water instead of buffer.

Streptomycin, Pectin, and Kaolin in Aluminum Hydroxide Gel. Dilute with distilled water to a concentration of 1.0 mg./ml. (estimated), make proper estimated dilutions in phosphate buffer no. 3, *p*H 8, and assay by the microbiologic assay in Method 1, Section A of this Chapter.

Streptomycin or Dihydrostreptomycin Otic (Ear Drops). Dilute with distilled water to a concentration of 1.0 mg./ml. (estimated) and assay as described for streptomycin or dihydrostreptomycin syrup.

Streptomycin or dihydrostreptomycin otic preparations may also contain antifungal agents in addition to the antibiotic. These antifungal agents do not interfere in the microbiologic assay.

Streptomycin, or Dihydrostreptomycin, Kaolin, Pectin, and Aluminum Hydrox-

ide Gel Powder (*Veterinary*). Use 3 Gm. of powder as a sample and proceed as directed for streptomycin or dihydrostreptomycin tablets.

Streptomycin or Dihydrostreptomycin for Inhalation Therapy. This preparation contains nothing but finely powdered streptomycin sulfate or dihydrostreptomycin sulfate and is assayed as directed under streptomycin sulfate.

Streptomycin-dihydrostreptomycin Sulfate. This preparation is a mixture of equal portions of both antibiotics.

TOTAL POTENCY. Dilute the sample with distilled water to a concentration of 1.0 mg./ml. (estimated) and assay by the microbiologic assay in Method 1 or 2, Section A of this Chapter, using equal portions of the streptomycin and dihydrostreptomycin standards in preparing the standard curve, or by chemical assay in Method 3, Section B of this Chapter.

STREPTOMYCIN CONTENT. Assay an aliquot of this 1.0 mg./ml. solution by the chemical assay in Method 1, Section B of this Chapter.

DIHYDROSTREPTOMYCIN CONTENT. The difference between the total potency and the streptomycin content is the dihydrostreptomycin content.

Solution of Streptomycin-dihydrostreptomycin Sulfate. This preparation is an aqueous solution of a mixture of equal portions of streptomycin and dihydrostreptomycin. Assay by the same procedure described under streptomycin-dihydrostreptomycin sulfates.

Streptomycylidene Isonicotinyl Hydrazine Sulfate. $(C_{21}H_{44}N_{10}O_{12})_2$ $(H_2SO_4)_3$. M.W. = 1695.66. Theoretical potency = 686 μg./mg.
Isonicotinic acid hydrazide reacts with the aldehyde group of streptomycin to form a Schiff base, streptomycylidene isonicotinyl hydrazide. The compound itself is not believed to possess any streptomycin activity. However, in aqueous solution it hydrolyzes to form streptomycin and isonicotinic acid hydrazide. An equilibrium usually exists and the percentage of free streptomycin present depends upon the dilution, temperature, pH, and time of standing. In order to insure complete hydrolysis so that the streptomycin content of the compound may be determined, the following procedure is used. Dilute the sample with hydrochloric acid solution pH 1.5 to 1,000 μg./ml. (estimated streptomycin activity). Heat at 50 C. for 30 minutes, cool rapidly, and assay by the microbiologic assay in Method 1 or 2, Section A of this Chapter.

Streptomycin-dihydrostreptomycin Sulfate and Isonicotinic Acid Hydrazide for Aqueous Injection. This preparation is usually marketed in two sizes. One size contains 0.25 Gm. streptomycin, 0.25 Gm. dihydrostreptomycin, and 0.1 Gm. isonicotinic acid hydrazide; the other size contains 0.5 Gm. streptomycin, 0.5 Gm. dihydrostreptomycin, and 0.25 Gm. isonicotinic acid hydrazide.

TOTAL POTENCY. Prepare the sample as follows: Accurately weigh sufficient sample to give approximately 500 mg. of antibiotic activity and transfer to a medium porosity sintered-glass filter funnel that has been fitted with a ground glass stopper. Add 15 ml. of benzaldehyde, stopper the funnel, and shake occasionally for three minutes. Filter off the benzaldehyde through the sintered plate with vacuum. Repeat the shaking with two more 15 ml. portions of benzaldehyde, discarding all benzaldehyde filtrates. Wash the residue in the funnel with about 10 ml. of acetone, discarding the acetone filtrate. This process removes the isonicotinic acid hydrazide. Dissolve the streptomycin and dihydrostreptomycin remaining in the funnel with about 25 ml. of water and transfer the solution to a 500 ml. volumetric flask. Wash the funnel with water and transfer the washings to the volumetric flask. Finally, wash the funnel with water by filtering through the sintered plate with vacuum, add the filtrate to the flask, and make to 500 ml. with water. This solution, containing about 1 mg./ml. of activity, is assayed for total potency by the microbiologic assay in Methods 1 or 2, Section A of this Chapter, or by chemical assay in Method 3, Section B of this Chapter.

STREPTOMYCIN CONTENT. Determine the streptomycin content by using chemical assay in Method 1, Section B of this Chapter.

DIHYDROSTREPTOMYCIN CONTENT. The dihydrostreptomycin content is the difference between the total potency and the streptomycin content.

Section D: Determination of Streptomycin or Dihydrostreptomycin in Body Fluids and Other Substances

Blood Serum. Use microbiologic assay in Method 3, Section A of this Chapter. The working stock standard containing 100 µg./ml. is further diluted in phosphate buffer no. 3, pH 8, to 40 µg./ml. From this, the standard curve is prepared using normal human serum or 7.0 per cent bovine albumin solution (see Chapter 21) as the diluent.

The blood sample is prepared as in "blood serum," Chapter 2. The serum is placed in the cups undiluted unless a concentration greater than 4.0 µg./ml. is expected in which case the sample should be diluted to an estimated 1.0 µg./ml. with the bovine albumin diluent. One or more plates are used, depending on the quantity of serum available.

Urine. Urine is diluted according to its estimated streptomycin or dihydrostreptomycin content with phosphate buffer no. 3, pH 8, to an estimated 1.0 µg./ml. and assayed by microbiologic assay in Method 3, Section A of this Chapter.

Tissue. Tissue is prepared in the same manner as described in "tissue," Chapter 2, except that phosphate buffer no. 3, pH 8, is used in the extraction. The extract is assayed by the microbiologic assay in Method 3, Section A of this Chapter.

Milk. The working stock standard of streptomycin or dihydrostreptomycin containing 100 μg./ml. is further diluted in phosphate buffer no. 3, pH 8, to 40 μg./ml. From this, the standard curve is prepared using the same concentrations as described in the microbiologic assay in Method 3, Section A of this Chapter, except the diluent is milk diluted 1:2 in phosphate buffer no. 3, pH 8. As noted in the assay for penicillin in milk, the milk used as the diluent should have been previously tested for absence of inhibitory substances by placing cups on the assay plates, and noting that no zone of inhibition occurs. The sample under test is diluted 1:2 in phosphate buffer no. 3, pH 8, and assayed as described under the microbiologic assay in Method 3, Section A of this Chapter. If concentrations of drug greater than 4.0 μg./ml. are anticipated, the sample is diluted to an estimated 1.0 μg./ml. in milk diluted 1:2 in phosphate buffer no. 3, pH 8.

4 THE TETRACYCLINES
(Chlortetracycline, Oxytetracycline, and Tetracycline)

Section A: Microbiologic Assay Methods for the Tetracyclines

Two methods are described, a turbidimetric method using *M. pyogenes* var. *aureus* and a cylinder-plate method using *Bacillus cereus* var. *mycoides* as test organisms. As has been previously mentioned, turbidimetric methods are not generally adaptable for the measurement of blood, body fluids, etc., due to interference by coloring matter or turbidity of the substance being tested. In such instances the cylinder-plate method is used. The *M. pyogenes* var. *aureus* turbidimetric method for the tetracyclines is, however, satisfactory to use for the various pharmaceutical dosage forms because the organism is so sensitive to the drugs that the large dilution required eliminates interfering substances. The reference point on the standard curve for chlortetracycline is 0.06 μg. and for oxytetracycline and tetracycline is 0.24 μg., the test organism being about one fourth as sensitive to the latter two drugs.

METHOD 1: Turbidimetric Assay Using *Micrococcus pyogenes* var. *aureus* as the Test Organism. (ATCC 6538-P.)

Chlortetracycline. TEST CULTURE AND MEDIA. Use medium no. 1 for maintaining the test organism. Transfer the organism to fresh agar slants and incubate at 32 to 35 C. overnight. For use in the assay suspend the growth from a fresh slant in a small amount of nutrient broth no. 3. Add sufficient of this dense suspension to about 150 ml. of nutrient broth no. 3, which has been warmed to 37 C. to give a light transmission reading of 85 per cent using a filter at 6,500 Å. units in a Lumetron 400-A photoelectric colorimeter. To prepare the daily inoculum for the tests, add 40 ml. of this suspension to each liter of nutrient broth no. 3 needed for the day's work.

WORKING STANDARD AND STANDARD CURVE. Weigh out carefully an appropriate amount of the chlortetracycline hydrochloride working standard, which is kept at room temperature in a tightly stoppered vial, and dilute to 1,000 μg./ml. in water. This solution, when refrigerated, will keep for seven days. This standard solution may be preserved for at least two months by freezing in small aliquots at −20 C. Each aliquot should be sufficient for one day's use only and should *not* be refrozen after thawing.

To prepare solutions for the standard curve, make a further dilution of the stock solution in phosphate buffer no. 4, *p*H 4.5, to contain 0.1 μg./ml. To a triplicate series of 16 by 125 mm. test tubes add 0.1, 0.2, 0.3, 0.4, 0.5, 0.6, 0.7, 0.8, 0.9, and 1.0 ml., respectively, of the 0.1 μg./ml. solution. Adjust volume of all the tubes to 1.0 ml. with phosphate buffer no. 4, *p*H 4.5.

To prepare solutions for use in adjusting the photoelectric colorimeter, add 1.0 ml. of standard containing 1.0 μg./ml. to each of 10 tubes. To another set of 10 tubes add 1.0 ml. of phosphate buffer no. 4, *p*H 4.5. The former set of 10 tubes contains enough drug to prevent multiplication of the test organism while the latter set permits normal growth.

PREPARATION OF THE SAMPLE. Dilute the sample under test with phosphate buffer no. 4, *p*H 4.5, to contain 0.06 μg./ml. (estimated). If the sample contains a large amount of chlortetracycline, preliminary dilutions may be prepared in distilled water to about 1 mg./ml. and the final dilutions made in the buffer. Add 1.0 ml. of the final dilution to each of three, 16 by 125 mm., test tubes.

To each of all of these tubes prepared as described, add 9.0 ml. of inoculated broth prepared as described under "test culture and medium." Place all tubes immediately in a water bath at 37 C. for three to four hours. Then add 0.5 ml. of formalin diluted 1:3 to each tube and read the light transmission in a Lumetron 402-E photoelectric colorimeter using a broad-band filter having a wave length of 5,800 Å. units. Other suitable photoelectric colorimeters may be used.

ESTIMATION OF POTENCY. Set the slide wire scale of the Lumetron photoelectric colorimeter at 80. Adjust the instrument so that the galvanometer scale reads about zero, using the pooled contents of the tubes with normal growth (buffer only), and to read about 100 with the pooled contents of the tubes in which no growth has occurred (1.0 μg. chlortetracycline). The other points of the curve will fall in between these two, thus completing the full standard curve.

Average the galvanometer readings for each concentration of the standard. Plot these values on cross section paper using average galvanometer readings as the ordinate and chlortetracycline concentrations as the abscissa. Prepare the standard curve by connecting successive points with a straightedge. Since the final concentration of chlortetracycline per ml. of broth is equivalent to the concentration per ml. of the standard solution used, the latter concentrations for each concentration level of the standard may be expressed as per cent and substituted on the abscissa of the standard curve. Thus the 0.06 μg. concentration is 100 per cent, the 0.05 μg. concentration is 83.3 per cent, etc. If this is done, the per cent potency of the sample under test may be read directly from the standard curve. Determine the galvanometer reading of each of the three tubes of the sample under test, average the three figures, and determine the potency on the standard curve just described.

Tetracycline. The turbidimetric assay for tetracycline is carried out as described for chlortetracycline with the exceptions to be noted.

WORKING STANDARD. The working standard is tetracycline hydrochloride, which is weighed out and kept in the same manner as chlortetracycline, except that it is dissolved in 0.01 N hydrochloric acid instead of water to make the 1.0 mg./ml. stock solution. This stock solution may be kept in a refrigerator for one week. *Do not freeze.*

STANDARD CURVE. To prepare solutions for the standard curve make a dilution of the stock standard in phosphate buffer no. 4, pH 4.5, to contain 0.4 μg./ml. To a triplicate series of tubes add 0.1, 0.2, 0.3, 0.4, 0.5, 0.6, 0.7, 0.8, 0.9, and 1.0 ml. of this 0.4 μg./ml. buffer solution of tetracycline hydrochloride. Adjust the volume of all of the tubes to 1.0 ml. with phosphate buffer no. 4, pH 4.5. To prepare solutions for use in adjusting the photoelectric colorimeter, follow the procedure as described under chlortetracycline, except the 10 tubes for the galvanometer reading of 100 contain 1.0 ml. of standard containing 4.0 μg./ml. of tetracycline hydrochloride. The reference point for the tetracycline standard curve is 0.24 μg./ml. (This is four times the concentration used for chlortetracycline.)

PREPARATION OF SAMPLE. Dilute the sample to be tested in sufficient 0.01 N hydrochloric acid to give an appropriate stock solution. Further dilute in phosphate buffer no. 4, pH 4.5, to contain an estimated concentration of 0.24 μg./ml. of tetracycline hydrochloride.

Oxytetracycline. This assay is performed in exactly the same way as for tetracycline except that the standard is oxytetracycline hydrochloride. (Note that the chlortetracycline and tetracycline standards are the hydrochloride salts and 1,000 μg. of the hydrochloride equals 1,000 μg. of activity. However, oxytetracycline is evaluated in terms of oxytetracycline base and 1,000 μg. of the base equals 1,000 μg. of activity. One mg. of pure oxytetracycline hydrochloride equals 927 μg. of activity.)

METHOD 2: Cylinder-plate Method Using *Bacillus cereus* var. *mycoides* as the Test Organism. (ATCC 9634.)

Chlortetracycline. CYLINDERS (CUPS). Use stainless steel cylinders with an outside diameter of 8 mm. ($\pm$0.1 mm.), an inside diameter of 6 mm. ($\pm$0.1 mm.), and a length of 10 mm. ($\pm$0.1 mm.).

CULTURE MEDIA. Use agar medium no. 1 for carrying the test organism. Use agar medium no. 8 for both the base and seed layers.

WORKING STANDARD. The working standard is prepared as described under the turbidimetric assay.

PREPARATION OF SAMPLE. The method of preparing samples is described under Section D of this Chapter.

PREPARATION OF TEST ORGANISM. The organism is grown at a temperature of 30 C., kept under refrigeration, and transferred about once a month. A suspension of the organism is prepared as follows: Streak several agar slants (medium no. 1) heavily with the test organism and incubate for 24 hours at 30 C. Wash oif the growth with approximately 5 ml. of sterile distilled water onto the surface of a Roux bottle containing 300 ml. of agar medium no. 1. Spread the suspension over the entire surface with the aid of sterile glass beads. Incubate one week at 30 C. Wash off the growth from the agar surface with 30 ml. of sterile distilled water into a glass stoppered flask. Heat shock this suspension for 30 minutes at 65 C. Wash three times with sterile distilled water, centrifuging between each washing, and heat shock as before. Maintain the suspension under refrigeration. Determine the per cent of spore suspension (usually 0.1 per cent) to be added to the seed layer to give a sensitivity to chlortetracycline of about 0.005 μg./ml.

PREPARATION OF PLATES. Add 6.0 ml. of melted agar medium no. 8 to each Petri dish (20 by 100 mm.) or special flat bottom Petri dishes (100 by 22 mm.). (The surface upon which the Petri dishes are placed must be perfectly level. The regular 100 by 20 mm. Petri dishes are usually satisfactory, except that an occasional dish may have too high a convex center and the 6.0 ml. of agar for the base layer is not sufficient to cover the bottom. For this reason some prefer the flat bottom Petri dish.) Distribute the agar evenly in the dish, cover with porcelain tops glazed only on the outside or other suitable covers, and allow to harden. Melt agar medium no. 8 for the secondary (seed) layer, cool to 55 to 60 C., and add the proper amount of spore suspension. Mix well and add 4 ml. of this seeded medium to the hardened base layer. Tilt the plates back and forth to spread the inoculated medium evenly over the surface. After this seed layer has hardened place six cylinders on the inoculated agar surface so that they are at approximately 60 degree intervals on a 2.8 cm. radius.

STANDARD CURVE AND ASSAY PROCEDURE. *Standard curve.* Dilute the working standard with phosphate buffer no. 4, pH 4.5, to concentrations of 0.08, 0.06, 0.04, 0.02, 0.01, and 0.005 μg./ml. The reference point is 0.04 μg./ml. A total of 15 plates is used for the standard curve (three plates for each concentration of the curve except the 0.04 μg./ml. reference point, which is included on each plate). Fill three cylinders on each plate with the 0.04 μg./ml. concentration of chlortetracycline and the other three cylinders with the concentration under test. Thus there will be 45 of the 0.04 μg./ml. determinations and nine determinations for each of the other concentrations on the curve. Incubate the plates for 16 to 18 hours at 30 C. and measure the diameter of each zone of inhibition. Average the readings of the 0.04 μg./ml. concentration and the readings of the concentration tested for each set of three plates and average also all 45 readings of the 0.04 μg./ml. concentration. The average of the 45 readings of the 0.04 μg./ml. concentration is the correction point for the curve. Correct the average value obtained for each concentration to the figure it would be if the 0.04 μg./ml. reading for that set of three plates were the same as the correction point. Thus, if in correcting the 0.02 μg./ml. concentration the average of the 45 readings of the 0.04 μg./ml. concentration is 18 mm. and the average of the 0.04 μg./ml. concentration of this set of three plates is 17.8 mm., the correction is $+0.2$ mm. If the average reading of the 0.02 μg./ml. concentration of these same three plates is 15 mm., the corrected value is then 15.2 mm. Plot these corrected values including the average of the 45 readings of the 0.04 μg./ml. concentration on two-cycle semilogarithmic paper, using the concentrations in μg./ml. as the ordinate (the logarithmic scale) and the diameter of the zone of inhibition as the abscissa. Draw the standard curve through these points.

Assay of sample. Use one or more (usually three) plates for each sample. Fill three cylinders on each plate with the 0.04 μg./ml. standard and three cylinders with the 0.04 μg./ml. (estimated) sample, alternating standard and sample. Incubate the plates for 16 to 18 hours at 30 C. and measure the diameter of each circle of inhibition. Average the zone readings of the standard and average the zone readings of the sample on the plates used. If the sample gives a larger average zone size than the average of the standard, add the difference between them to the 0.04 μg./ml. zone size of the standard curve. If the average sample zone size is smaller than the standard value, subtract the difference between them from the 0.04 μg./ml. zone size of the standard curve. From the curve read the concentration corresponding to these corrected values of zone sizes.

Tetracycline and Oxytetracycline. These two antibiotics are assayed in the same manner as chlortetracycline. The only difference is in the concentrations used in the preparation of the standard curve. Both tetracycline and oxytetracycline are only about one fifth as active as chlortetracycline against the test organism. Thus if the spore suspension is adjusted so that the test plate is sensitive to 0.005 μg./ml. of chlortetracycline, the same plate will show a zone of inhibition with 0.025 μg./ml. of the other two antibiotics. The concentrations used in preparing the standard curve are five times those used for chlortetracycline, namely: 0.025, 0.05, 0.10, 0.20 (reference point), 0.40, and 0.80 μg./ml. The unknown sample is diluted in phosphate buffer no. 4, pH 4.5, to an estimated concentration of 0.20 μg./ml. The remainder of the procedure is the same as for chlortetracycline.

Section B: Chemical Methods for Chlortetracycline, Oxytetracycline, and Tetracycline

Chlortetracycline, oxytetracycline, and tetracycline all contain the same phenolic hydroxyl groups and they all react with ferric chloride in acidic solution to give an orange-brown color. Method 1 therefore is a general method applicable to all three tetracyclines. The method may be used to determine the tetracyclines in such products as capsules, ointments, tablets, and troches, after suitable filtration or extraction to eliminate any insoluble or immiscible material. In the ferric chloride method it is important that the standard and unknown solutions have the same acidity. The color developed with ferric chloride is stable for at least two hours.

Chlortetracycline and tetracycline when heated with hydrochloric acid develop a stable yellow color. Oxytetracycline does not give this reaction, its solutions remain colorless. Therefore Method 2 measures only chlortetracycline and tetracycline and can be used to determine the quantity of either of these antibiotics in the presence of oxytetracycline. The concentration of acid used is not too critical over the range from 1 to 4 N hydrochloric acid. While a five minute heating period has been chosen, the maximum color develops in three minutes and is the same after 10 minutes heating. The method has been used successfully to determine chlortetracycline or tetracycline in capsules, troches, tablets, and powders.

The addition of alkali to solutions of oxytetracycline or tetracycline produces a yellow color having an absorption maximum at 380 mμ, whereas chlortetracycline gives a yellow color that rapidly disappears and gives practically no absorption at 380 mμ. Method 3 can therefore be used to measure oxytetracycline or tetracycline in the presence of chlortetracycline. In the method strict adherence to reading the absorption exactly six minutes after the addition of the alkali must be observed, since there is a slow but definite decrease in absorbance with time.

Chlortetracycline in alkaline solution develops a blue fluorescence in ultraviolet light. Since both the rate of development of this fluorescence and the intensity are dependent upon pH, it is necessary that the alkaline solution used to develope the fluorescence be highly buffered and that it be at a pH at which the rate of conversion is sufficiently slow, at room temperature, to permit measurement of any initial, or blank, fluorescence. In Method 4 the optimum conditions for the quantitative measurement of chlortetracycline by its fluorescence are given. While five minutes heating at 100 C. was chosen, the maximum fluorescence develops in three minutes and heating for 30 minutes has no further effect. The fluorescence that develops after heating is quite stable for several hours.

Method 4 is fairly specific for chlortetracycline. Under the same conditions tetracycline does not give any fluorescence even in quantities up to 500 μg./10 ml. Tetracycline will, however, if present in large quantities, quench some of the chlortetracycline fluorescence. For example, 25.0 μg. of chlortetracycline plus 250.0 μg. of tetracycline gives only about half of the anticipated chlortetracycline fluorescence. Oxytetracycline does give some fluorescence under the conditions of the method but only to the extent of about 10 per cent of that given by chlortetracycline. Oxytetracycline, like tetracycline, if present in large quantities, will quench some of the chlortetracycline fluorescence. The magnitude of this quenching effect is about the same as with tetracycline. From this discussion one can see that chlortetracycline may be quantitatively determined in mixtures of oxytetracycline and tetracycline if it is present in the largest proportion. The method cannot be used, however, to determine very small amounts of chlortetracycline in the presence of large quantities of oxytetracycline or tetracycline.

METHOD 1: Ferric Chloride Colorimetric Method for Chlortetracycline, Oxytetracycline, and Tetracycline.

This method, adapted from Monastero et al,[10] may be used to determine any of these three antibiotics. It is described in detail for the assay of oxytetracycline. If chlortetracycline or tetracycline are to be determined, use the same procedure only substitute chlortetracycline or tetracycline standards for that of oxytetracycline.

Reagents. Ten per cent ferric chloride stock solution. Dissolve 5 Gm. of ferric chloride in 50 ml. 0.1 N hydrochloric acid.

A 0.05 per cent ferric chloride solution. Dilute 1.0 ml. of the 10 per cent ferric chloride solution to 200 ml. with 0.01 N hydrochloric acid. Prepare the solution fresh daily.

A 0.01 N hydrochloric acid solution.

Preparation of Standard. Prepare a solution of the oxytetracycline hydrochloride standard by dissolving enough standard in 0.01 N hydrochloric acid to give a solution containing 0.25 mg./ml. oxytetracycline base. Transfer 2.0, 4.0, and 6.0 ml. of the standard solution to 50 ml. flasks. Add 8.0, 6.0, and 4.0 ml. of 0.01 N hydrochloric acid to the flasks, respectively, to give each a total volume of 10.0 ml.

Preparation of Sample. Dilute the sample to be tested with 0.01 N hydrochloric acid to a concentration of 0.1 mg./ml. of oxytetracycline base (estimated). Transfer 10.0 ml. of this solution to a 50 ml. flask.

Blank. Transfer 10.0 ml. of the 0.01 N hydrochloric acid solution to a 50 ml. flask.

Procedure. To each of the flasks containing standard, sample, and blank, add 10.0 ml. of the 0.05 per cent ferric chloride solution, mix, and allow to stand at room temperature for 10 minutes. Transfer the solution to a 2 cm. absorption cell. Use a suitable photoelectric colorimeter and set the instrument to read 100 per cent transmittance at 490 mμ with the blank solution. Obtain the transmittance of the standards and sample at 490 mμ. Prepare a standard curve of the transmittances obtained on the standard solutions on semilogarithmic paper, plotting the transmittance on the logarithmic ordinate scale and the concentration of oxytetracycline base on the abscissa. Calculate the oxytetracycline content of the sample under test from the standard curve.

METHOD 2: Acid Colorimetric Method for Chlortetracycline or Tetracycline.[11]

Reagents. A 2 N hydrochloric acid solution.

Preparation of Standard. Prepare an aqueous solution of the chlortetracycline hydrochloride or tetracycline hydrochloride working standard to contain 1.0 mg./ml. Transfer 0.5, 1.0, and 1.5 ml. aliquots to 50 ml. volumetric flasks. Add 1.5, 1.0, and 0.5 ml. of distilled water to give each a 2.0 ml. volume.

Preparation of Sample. Dilute the sample to be tested to a concentration of 0.5 mg./ml. of chlortetracycline hydrochloride or tetracycline hydrochloride (estimated). Transfer a 2.0 ml. aliquot to a 50 ml. volumetric flask.

Preparation of Blanks. Prepare blanks for the standard by transferring 0.5, 1.0, and 1.5 ml. aliquots of the standard chlortetracycline or tetracycline hydrochloric acid solution to 50 ml. volumetric flasks. Add 1.5, 1.0, and 0.5 ml. of distilled water to give each a 2.0 ml. volume. Prepare a blank for the sample by transferring a 2.0 ml. aliquot of the sample solution to a 50 ml. volumetric flask.

Procedure. To each flask containing the standard and sample solutions add 5.0 ml. of 2 *N* hydrochloric acid. To each of the flasks containing the blank solutions add 5.0 ml. water. (No acid is added to the blank solutions at this point.) Heat all flasks in a boiling water bath for five minutes, then cool the flasks under tap water, add 5.0 ml. of 2 *N* hydrochloric acid to the blank solutions, and make all flasks to 50 ml. with distilled water. Using a suitable spectrophotometer and 1 cm. cells determine the transmittance of the standard and sample solutions at 440 mμ after first setting the instrument at 100 per cent transmittance with the corresponding blank solution. Prepare a standard curve on semilogarithmic paper, plotting the transmittance of the standard solutions on the logarithmic ordinate scale and the concentration of chlortetracycline hydrochloride or tetracycline hydrochloride on the abscissa. Calculate the chlortetracycline hydrochloride or tetracycline hydrochloride content of the sample from their respective standard curves.

METHOD 3: Ultraviolet Spectrophotometric Method for Oxytetracycline or Tetracycline.

Reagents. A 5 *N* sodium hydroxide solution.

Preparation of Standard. Prepare a solution of the oxytetracycline hydrochloride or tetracycline hydrochloride standard by dissolving enough standard in water to give a solution containing 0.1 mg./ml. of oxytetracycline base or tetracycline hydrochloride. Transfer 10.0, 15.0, 20.0, and 25.0 ml. aliquots of the standard solution to 100 ml. volumetric flasks.

Preparation of Sample. If the drug is the hydrochloride salt, dissolve in water to give a concentration of 0.1 mg./ml. (estimated). If the drug is the free base, dissolve in 0.1 *N* hydrochloric acid using 5 ml. for each 100 mg. of drug and dilute with water to give a concentration of 0.1 mg./ml. (estimated). Transfer 15 ml. to a 100 ml. volumetric flask.

Blank. Transfer 15 ml. of distilled water to a 100 ml. volumetric flask.

Procedure. To each of the flasks containing standard, sample, and blank, add 70 ml. of water and 5.0 ml. 5 *N* sodium hydroxide, make to volume with water, and mix well. Transfer the solutions to a 1 cm. absorption cell. Use a suitable spectrophotometer and set the instrument to read zero absorbance at 380 mμ with the blank solution. Determine the absorbance of the standard solutions and the sample at 380 mμ exactly six minutes after the addition of the sodium hydroxide. Prepare a standard curve of the absorbances obtained on the standard solutions on coordinate graph paper, plotting the absorbance on the ordinate scale and concentration on the abscissa. Calculate the oxytetracycline or tetracycline content of the sample from their respective standard curves.

METHOD 4: Fluorometric Method for Chlortetracycline.

This method was adapted from Levine et al.[11]

Reagents. QUININE SULFATE SOLUTION. Dissolve 20.0 mg. of U.S.P. quinine sulfate in 1,000 ml. of 0.1 N sulfuric acid. Dilute 5 ml. of this solution to 200 ml. with 0.1 N sulfuric acid.

PHOSPHATE BUFFER, pH 7.6. Mix eight volumes of 20 per cent (w/v) dibasic potassium phosphate solution with one volume of 20 per cent (w/v) monobasic potassium phosphate solution.

Preparation of Standard. Prepare an aqueous solution of the chlortetracycline hydrochloride standard to contain 3.5 µg./ml. This solution should be freshly prepared. Transfer 2.0, 4.0, 6.0, 8.0, and 10.0 ml. aliquots to matched 18 by 150 mm. Pyrex test tubes (these tubes are used as cells in the instrument). Add 8.0, 6.0, 4.0, 2.0, and 0 ml. of water to give each a volume of 10.0 ml.

Preparation of Sample. Dilute the sample to be tested to contain 20 µg./10 ml. chlortetracycline hydrochloride (estimated). Transfer 10.0 ml. to one of the matched 18 by 150 mm. Pyrex test tubes.

Procedure. Set the fluorometer (Coleman Electronic Photofluorometer Model 12, with filter B1 for the incident light and filter B2 for the emitted fluorescence) to give a scale reading of 35 with the quinine sulfate solution. To each test tube containing the standards and sample add 2.0 ml. of phosphate buffer, pH 7.6. Mix and read the fluorescence immediately. This is the blank reading. Next heat the tubes in a boiling water bath for five minutes. Cool and read the fluorescence in from 15 minutes to 1 hour. Prepare a standard curve on coordinate graph paper plotting the difference in the scale readings before (blank) and after heating of the standard solutions as the ordinate and the concentration of chlortetracycline hydrochloride per 10 ml. as the abscissa. Subtract the blank reading from the reading obtained after heating of the sample and calculate its potency from the standard curve.

Section C: Assay of the Tetracyclines and Their Pharmaceutical Dosage Forms

Chlortetracycline, Chlortetracycline Hydrochloride, Oxytetracycline, Oxytetracycline Hydrochloride, Tetracycline, and Tetracycline Hydrochloride. The chemical structures of the three tetracyclines are shown in the following diagrams.

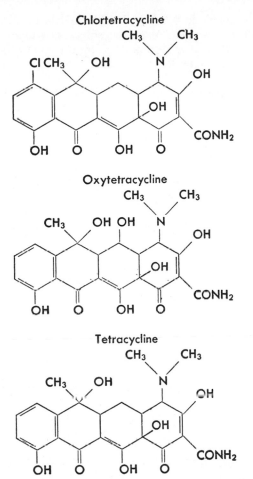

CHLORTETRACYCLINE BASE: $C_{22}H_{23}N_2O_8Cl$. M.W. = 478.88. Theoretical potency = 1,076 µg./mg.

CHLORTETRACYCLINE HYDROCHLORIDE: M.W. = 515.34. Theoretical potency = 1,000 µg./mg.

Chlortetracycline hydrochloride has a solubility in water of approximately 13 mg./ml. To assay, dissolve an accurately weighed sample in distilled water to make a solution containing 1 mg./ml. (estimated). Assay this solution by microbiologic assay for chlortetracycline in Method 1, Section A, or by chemical assay in Method 1, 2, or 4, Section B, of this Chapter.

OXYTETRACYCLINE BASE: $C_{22}H_{24}N_2O_9$. M.W. = 460.43. Theoretical potency = 1,000 µg./mg.
Oxytetracycline base · 2H₂O: M.W. = 496.45. Theoretical potency = 927 µg./mg.

Oxytetracycline base and its hydrate are insoluble in water; however, they are easily dissolved in 0.1 N hydrochloric acid. To assay, dissolve an accurately weighed sample in 0.1 N hydrochloric acid to make a solution containing 1 mg./ml. (estimated). Assay this solution by microbiologic assay for oxytetracycline in Method 1, Section A, or by chemical assay in Method 1 or 3, Section B of this Chapter.

OXYTETRACYCLINE HYDROCHLORIDE: M.W. = 496.90. Theoretical potency = 927 μg./mg.

Oxytetracycline hydrochloride has a solubility in water of approximately 500 mg./ml. However, concentrated solutions precipitate on standing. To assay, dissolve an accurately weighed sample in 0.01 N hydrochloric acid to make a solution containing 1 mg./ml. (estimated). Assay this solution by microbiologic assay for oxytetracycline in Method 1, Section A, or by chemical assay in Method 1 or 3, Section B of this Chapter.

TETRACYCLINE BASE: $C_{22}H_{24}N_2O_8$. M.W. = 444.43. Theoretical potency = 1,082 μg./mg.

Tetracycline base · 3H₂O: M.W. = 498.48. Theoretical potency = 965 μg./mg.
Tetracycline base · 6H₂O: M.W. = 552.53. Theoretical potency = 870 μg./mg.

Tetracycline base and its hydrates are insoluble in water; however, they are easily dissolved in 0.01 N hydrochloric acid. To assay, dissolve an accurately weighed sample in 0.01 N hydrochloric acid to make a solution containing 1 mg./ml. (estimated). Assay this solution by microbiologic assay for tetracycline in Method 1, Section A, or by chemical assay in Method 1, 2, or 3, Section B of this Chapter.

TETRACYCLINE HYDROCHLORIDE: M.W. = 480.90. Theoretical potency = 1,000 μg./mg.

Tetracycline hydrochloride has a solubility in water of about 160 mg./ml.; however, such solutions precipitate on standing. To assay, dissolve an accurately weighed sample in 0.01 N hydrochloric acid to make a solution containing 1 mg./ml. (estimated). Assay this solution by microbiologic assay for tetracycline in Method 1, Section A, or by chemical assay in Method 1, 2, or 3, Section B of this Chapter.

Chlortetracycline Hydrochloride, Oxytetracycline Hydrochloride, or Tetracycline Hydrochloride for Intravenous Injection. The commercial preparation of chlortetracycline hydrochloride or oxytetracycline hydrochloride for intravenous injection contains a mixture of the dry hydrochloride and dry sodium glycinate. When water is added to prepare the injection, it will have a pH of about 8.5 to 9.0. Since both of these drugs are not too stable in an alkaline medium, they should be assayed promptly after the diluent has been added. Dissolve the contents of a vial in distilled water to a concentration of 1 mg./ml. (estimated) and within five minutes make the further estimated dilutions in phosphate buffer no. 4, pH 4.5. Assay this solution by microbiologic assay for chlortetracycline or oxytetracycline Method 1, Section A, or by the appropriate chemical assay method in Section B of this Chapter.

The tetracycline hydrochloride preparation for intravenous injection contains tetracycline hydrochloride and ascorbic acid and when diluted with water has a pH of about 2. This solution is more stable than the alkaline solutions of the chlortetracycline and oxytetracycline preparations. However, it is still wise to assay promptly after the diluent has been added. Dissolve the contents of a vial in distilled water, dilute with 0.01 N hydrochloric acid to 1 mg./ml. (estimated) and assay by microbiologic assay for tetracycline in Method 1, Section A, or by the appropriate chemical assay method in Section B of this Chapter.

Oxytetracycline Hydrochloride or Tetracycline Hydrochloride for Intramuscular Injection. These preparations are dry powders containing the antibiotic salt, procaine hydrochloride, magnesium chloride, and ascorbic acid. Aqueous diluent is added prior to use. To assay, add the amount of diluent recommended in the labeling, withdraw one dose of the solution with a hypodermic syringe and needle and dilute with 0.01 N hydrochloric acid to a concentration of 1 mg./ml. (estimated). Assay this solution by microbiologic assay for tetracycline or oxytetracycline in Method 1, Section A, or by the appropriate chemical assay method in Section B of this Chapter.

Chlortetracycline Hydrochloride, Oxytetracycline Hydrochloride, or Tetracycline Hydrochloride Ointment. Accurately weigh approximately 1 Gm. into a separatory funnel containing approximately 50 ml. of peroxide-free ether. Shake ointment and ether until homogeneous. Shake with a 25 ml. portion of phosphate buffer no. 4, pH 4.5. Remove the buffer layer and repeat the extraction with three 25 ml. quantities of buffer. Combine the extracts and make the proper estimated dilutions in the buffer solution.

The sample may also be prepared by placing an accurately weighed sample consisting of 0.5 to 1 Gm. into a glass blending jar containing 200 ml. of the buffer solution. Using a high-speed blender, blend the mixture for approximately three minutes and make proper estimated dilutions in the buffer solution.

Assay by microbiologic assays in Method 1, Section A, or by a chemical assay method in Section B of this Chapter.

Chlortetracycline Hydrochloride, Oxytetracycline Hydrochloride, or Tetracycline Hydrochloride Capsules. Place three capsules, if 250 mg. per capsule, or five capsules, if 100 mg. or 50 mg. per capsule, in a glass blending jar containing 500 ml. of 0.01 N hydrochloric acid. Using a high-speed blender, blend for 3 to 5 minutes. Assay the solution (may be turbid due to excipients present in capsule) by microbiologic assays in Method 1, Section A, or by appropriate chemical method in Section B of this Chapter. In the case of the chemical assay methods it may be necessary to filter or centrifuge to obtain a clear solution.

Chlortetracycline Hydrochloride, Oxytetracycline Hydrochloride, or Tetracycline Hydrochloride Tablets. The tablets may be soluble tablets or coated tablets. They may also contain sulfonamides in addition to the tetracyclines. Prepare the solution for analysis in the same manner as described under capsules, Section C of this Chapter. Assay by microbiologic assays in Method 1, Section A, or by the appropriate chemical assay method in Section B of this Chapter. In the case of coated tablets, if calcium carbonate has been used in the coating, it may be necessary to use stronger acid to neutralize it and dissolve the drug.

Chlortetracycline Hydrochloride, Oxytetracycline Hydrochloride, or Tetracycline Hydrochloride Troches. Follow the same procedure used for capsules, Section C of this Chapter, using 12 troches for the sample.

Chlortetracycline Hydrochloride, Oxytetracycline Hydrochloride, or Tetracycline Hydrochloride Powder (for Oral Use). These preparations may be sold as a flavored powder, which is administered by adding a teaspoonful of this powder to milk or other liquid, or as a powder to which water or flavored diluent (elixir) is added at the time of dispensing and the resultant solution or suspension taken by the teaspoonful or drops. If it is the first type of powder, use 3 Gm. as sample and follow the same blender procedure used for capsules, Section C of this Chapter. If it is the second type, add the amount of water or diluent recommended in the labeling to the contents of the bottle, shake thoroughly, remove a 5 ml. or other suitable aliquot, and dilute with 0.01 N hydrochloric acid to give a concentration of 1 mg./ml. (estimated). Make the proper estimated dilutions in phosphate buffer no. 4, *p*H 4.5, and assay by microbiologic assays in Method 1, Section A, or by the appropriate chemical assay method in Section B of this Chapter. For the chemical methods filter or centrifuge the final dilutions if necessary.

Oxytetracycline or Tetracycline Powder. These preparations are similar to the second type of oral powders mentioned in the last paragraph. They differ in that they contain the free base or amphoteric form of the drug instead of the hydrochloride. They are assayed using the same method as described in the last paragraph.

Chlortetracycline Hydrochloride, Oxytetracycline Hydrochloride, or Tetracycline Hydrochloride Ophthalmic (Eye Drops). These preparations are dry powders containing the hydrochloride of the drug, sodium chloride, and sodium borate. Water is added at the time of dispensing and the resulting solution is used as an eye drop. Dilute the contents of a vial with distilled water as directed in the labeling. Dilute an aliquot with 0.01 N hydrochloric acid to give a concentration of 1 mg./ml. (estimated). Make the proper estimated dilution in phosphate buffer no. 4, *p*H 4.5, and assay by microbiologic assays in Method 1, Section A, or by the appropriate chemical assay method in Section B of this Chapter.

Chlortetracycline Hydrochloride, Oxytetracycline Hydrochloride, or Tetracycline Hydrochloride Otic (Ear Drops). These preparations are sold in two bottles, one containing only the hydrochloride of the drug and the other bottle a diluent to be mixed with the drug. Dilute the contents of the vial containing the drug with the diluent as directed in the labeling. Dilute a suitable aliquot of the prepared preparation with 0.01 N hydrochloric acid to a concentration of 1 mg./ml. (estimated). Make proper estimated dilutions in phosphate buffer no. 4, *p*H 4.5, and assay by microbiologic assays in Method 1, Section A, or by the appropriate chemical assay method in Section B of this Chapter.

Chlortetracycline Hydrochloride, Oxytetracycline Hydrochloride, or Tetracycline Hydrochloride Dental Cones. Follow the same procedure used for capsules, Section C of this Chapter, using 12 cones for the sample.

Chlortetracycline Hydrochloride, Oxytetracycline Hydrochloride, or Tetracycline Hydrochloride Dental Paste. This preparation is similar to an ointment. Use an accurately weighed sample of about 2 Gm. of the paste and place in a glass blending jar containing 200 ml. of distilled water. Using a high-speed blender, blend for three to five minutes. Make the proper estimated dilutions in phosphate buffer no. 4, *p*H 4.5, and assay by microbiologic assays in Method 1, Section A, or by the appropriate chemical assay method in Section B of this Chapter.

Chlortetracycline Hydrochloride, Oxytetracycline Hydrochloride, or Tetracycline Hydrochloride Surgical Powder. This preparation is sold as a powder in vials with a shaker top and contains the hydrochloride of the drug mixed with a soluble starch or beta lactose diluent. Dissolve an accurately weighed sample of the powder of approximately 1 Gm. in enough 0.01 *N* hydrochloric acid to give a concentration of 1 mg./ml. of the drug (estimated). Make the proper estimated dilution in phosphate buffer no. 4, *p*H 4.5, and assay by microbiologic assays in Method 1, Section A, or by the appropriate chemical assay method in Section B of this Chapter.

Chlortetracycline Hydrochloride, Oxytetracycline Hydrochloride, or Tetracycline Hydrochloride Suppositories. Place three suppositories into a separatory funnel containing approximately 50 ml. of peroxide-free ether. Shake the suppositories and ether until homogeneous. Shake with a 50 ml. portion of phosphate buffer no. 4, *p*H 4.5. Remove the buffer layer and repeat the extraction with three 50 ml. quantities of buffer. Combine the extracts and centrifuge an aliquot at 2,000 r.p.m. for five minutes. Remove an aliquot of the supernatant liquid and assay by microbiologic assays in Method 1, Section A, or by the appropriate chemical assay method in Section B of this Chapter.

Chlortetracycline Hydrochloride Gauze Packing. This product is absorbent gauze that has been impregnated with the hydrochloride of the drug. The gauze usually contains 4 mg. of the hydrochloride per gram or from 1 to 4 mg. per linear foot of gauze depending on the width. Use three gauze packings to obtain the average weight and average linear length per packing. Assay each gauze packing by placing the entire packing in 500 ml. of 0.1 *N* hydrochloric acid and allow to soak with frequent agitation for not less than two hours. Assay the solution by microbiologic assay for chlortetracycline in Method 1, Section A, or by chemical assay procedure in Method 4, Section B of this Chapter.

Oxytetracycline Hydrochloride Gauze Pads. These are gauze pads usually 3 by 3 inches impregnated with oxytetracycline hydrochloride and contain 2 mg. per square inch of pad. Use an entire pad and assay as described under chlortetracycline gauze packing, Section C of this Chapter, using microbiologic assay for oxytetracycline in Method 1, Section A of this Chapter.

Chlortetracycline Hydrochloride Dressing. These are gauze pads impregnated with a chlortetracycline ointment. Each pad, 4 by 4 inches, contains about 240 mg. of chlortetracycline hydrochloride. The pads are enclosed in sealed foil envelopes. Remove the foil envelope and place the entire pad, rolled in a cylindrical shape, in a separatory funnel containing 200 ml. of ether. Shake to dissolve the ointment from the gauze pads. Shake the mixture with 50 ml. of phosphate buffer no. 4, *p*H 4.5. Remove the buffer layer and repeat the extraction with three 50 ml. portions of buffer. Combine the extracts and make the proper estimated dilutions in the buffer solution. Assay by microbiologic assay for chlortetracycline in Method 1, Section A, or by the appropriate chemical assay method in Section B of this Chapter.

Chlortetracycline Hydrochloride, Oxytetracycline Hydrochloride, or Tetracycline Hydrochloride with Vasoconstrictor (Nose Drops). These preparations are usually sold in two bottles, one containing the hydrochloride of the drug and the other the diluent containing the vasoconstrictor. Dilute the contents of the bottle containing the drug with the vasoconstrictor diluent as directed in the labeling. Dilute a suitable aliquot with 0.01 *N* hydrochloric acid to a concentration of 1 mg./ml. (estimated). Make the proper estimated dilutions in phosphate buffer no. 4, *p*H 4.5 and assay by microbiologic assays in Method 1, Section A, or by the appropriate chemical assay method in Section B of this Chapter.

Calcium Chlortetracycline Oral Drops. When chlortetracycline is made alkaline and treated with a calcium salt, an insoluble calcium compound of chlortetracycline is formed. Calcium chlortetracycline consists of one atom of calcium for each molecule of chlortetracycline. It is sold as a flavored aqueous suspension containing enough calcium chlortetracycline to be equivalent to 100 mg./ml. of chlortetracycline hydrochloride. Dilute a one ml. aliquot of the suspension with 0.01 *N* hydrochloric acid to give a concentration of 1 mg./ml. (chlortetracycline hydrochloride equivalent) (estimated). Make the proper estimated dilutions in phosphate buffer no. 4, *p*H 4.5, and assay by microbiologic assay for chlortetracycline in Method 1, Section A, or by the appropriate chemical assay method in Section B of this Chapter.

Calcium Chlortetracycline Syrup. This preparation is a suspension of calcium chlortetracycline in a flavored syrup vehicle, containing the equivalent of 125 mg. of chlortetracycline hydrochloride per 4 ml. Use a 4 ml. aliquot of the syrup and assay as under calcium chlortetracycline oral drops, Section C of this Chapter.

Calcium Chlortetracycline Oral Suspension with Sulfonamides. This preparation is a flavored aqueous suspension containing enough calcium chlortetracycline to be equivalent to 125 mg. of chlortetracycline hydrochloride per 4 ml. Use a 4 ml. aliquot and assay as under calcium chlortetracycline oral drops, Section C of this Chapter. The sulfonamides do not interfere in the assay.

Calcium Chlortetracycline Cream. This is a cream or ointment for topical use and contains a suspension of calcium chlortetracycline in an emulsified water base. Place approximately 1 Gm. of the cream, accurately weighed, in a blending jar containing 200 ml. of 0.01 *N* hydrochloric acid. Using a high-speed blender, blend for two to three minutes. Make proper estimated dilutions in phosphate buffer no. 4, *p*H 4.5, and assay by microbiologic assay for chlortetracycline in Method 1, Section A, or by the appropriate chemical assay method in Section B of this Chapter.

Oxytetracycline Hydrochloride in Oil. This is a suspension of oxytetracycline hydrochloride in oil for injection into poultry. Use 1.0 ml. of the suspension and assay as under ointments, Section C of this Chapter.

Tetracycline Oral Suspension. Transfer 1 ml. of the well-shaken suspension to a suitable high-speed blender containing 500 ml. of 0.01 *N* hydrochloric acid. Blend for five minutes, make the proper estimated dilutions in phosphate buffer no. 4, *p*H 4.5, and assay by microbiologic assay for tetracycline in Method 1, Section A of this Chapter.

Section D: Determination of the Tetracyclines in Body Fluids and Other Substances

Blood Serum. The cylinder-plate assay, Method 2, Section A of this Chapter, is used for the assay of the tetracyclines in blood serum, except for the following modifications. Solutions of the working standards are diluted to 8.0 μg./ml. for tetracycline and oxytetracycline, and to 1.6 μg./ml. for chlortetracycline in phosphate buffer no. 4, *p*H 4.5. All three antibiotics are further diluted with a diluent containing one part of 3.5 per cent bovine albumin solution (Chapter 21) plus two parts of phosphate buffer no. 4, *p*H 4.5.

It will be noted that this bovine albumin diluent differs from that described in Chapter 2, Section D, for penicillin. This is because the protein binding power is different for the tetracyclines, and the albumin solution has been adjusted to equal the binding power of normal serum. If normal serum (free of inhibitory substances) is used, it is also diluted one part to two parts of phosphate buffer no. 4, *p*H 4.5, in making diluent for the standard curve. In the assay of the tetracyclines in the presence of protein material, we encounter the same phenomenon as that described in Chapter 1 in which dilution of the antibiotic containing protein solution reveals activity as demonstrated by zones of inhibition which, without dilution, would remain undetected, i.e., no zones of inhibition would be obtained.

Using either the phosphate buffer-bovine albumin solution (1 + 2) or phosphate buffer-diluted normal serum (1 + 2) prepare the standard curve for chlortetracycline by diluting the 1.6 μg./ml. concentration 1:10. Further dilute in the phosphate buffer serum or phosphate buffer albumin solution (1 + 2) this 0.16 μg./ml. concentration by halves to obtain concentrations for the standard curve of 0.16, 0.08, 0.04, 0.02, 0.01, and 0.005 μg./ml. The concentrations of tetracycline and oxytetracycline for the standard curve are obtained in the same manner by diluting the 8.0 μg./ml. concentration in either of these diluents to obtain concentrations of 0.80, 0.40, 0.20, 0.10, 0.05, and 0.025 μg./ml. The reference point for all three drugs is the same as previously described: 0.04 μg./ml. for chlortetracycline and 0.20 μg./ml. for tetracycline and oxytetracycline.

The samples under test are diluted 1:3 (one part plus two) in phosphate buffer no. 4, *p*H 4.5. If concentrations of chlortetracycline greater than 0.16 μg./ml. are expected, the 1:3 dilution of serum is appropriately diluted further in the albumin or normal serum diluted 1:3 with phosphate buffer no. 4, *p*H 4.5. The same is done with tetracycline and oxytetracycline if the anticipated concentration is greater than 0.8 μg./ml.

Urine. The urine is diluted in phosphate buffer no. 4, *p*H 4.5, to an estimated 0.04 μg./ml. for chlortetracycline and 0.20 μg./ml. for tetracycline or oxytetracycline and assayed by the cylinder-plate assay in Method 2, Section A of this Chapter. Urine should not be assayed undiluted for small quantities of the antibiotic but should be diluted at least 1:3 because of the occasional presence of normal inhibitory substances.

Tissue. Tissue is prepared as described in Chapter 2, Section D, except that phosphate buffer no. 4, *p*H 4.5, is used as the extractive and assayed by microbiologic assay in Method 2, Section A of this Chapter.

Milk. Milk samples containing the tetracyclines are diluted 1:3 in phosphate buffer no. 4, *p*H 4.5, and assayed by microbiologic assay in Method 2, Section A of this Chapter. In this case the appropriate standard is diluted in normal milk (free of inhibitory substances), which has been diluted 1:3 in phosphate buffer no. 4, *p*H 4.5. If the concentration of the antibiotic in the milk is higher than the highest concentration on the curve, the 1:3 dilution of the milk is further diluted with normal milk which has been diluted 1:3 in phosphate buffer no. 4, *p*H 4.5.

Animal Feed Supplements and Mixed Feeds. CHLORTETRACYCLINE. *Preparation of sample for feed supplement.* Grind 2 Gm. of the feed supplement in a mortar with 50 ml. of acid-acetone (1 volume 4 *N* hydrochloric acid, 13 volumes acetone, 6 volumes distilled water). Transfer to a centrifuge tube. Wash the mortar and pestle with 50 ml. of the acid-acetone and add to the centrifuge tube. Shake the tube for five minutes and centrifuge for approximately 15 minutes at 2,000 r.p.m. Remove 10 ml. of the supernatant and adjust to *p*H 4.5 with 1 *N* sodium hydroxide. Dilute 1 ml. of this to an estimated chlortetracycline concentration of 0.04 μg./ml. with phosphate buffer no. 4, *p*H 4.5, taking into consideration the dilution factor introduced by the added sodium hydroxide. Assay by microbiologic assay for chlortetracycline in Method 2, Section A of this Chapter.

Preparation of sample for final feed. Grind 10 Gm. of feed with 50 ml. of acid-acetone in a mortar. Transfer to a centrifuge tube. Wash the mortar and pestle with 50 ml. of acid-acetone and add to the centrifuge tube. Shake well for five minutes and centrifuge for approximately 15 minutes at 2,000 r.p.m. Remove 10 ml. of the supernatant and adjust to *p*H 4.5 with 1 *N* sodium hydroxide. Dilute 1 ml. of this to an estimated chlortetracycline concentration of 0.04 μg./ml. with phosphate buffer no. 4, pH 4.5, taking into consideration the dilution factor introduced by the added sodium hydroxide. Assay by the microbiologic assay for chlortetracycline in Method 2, Section A of this Chapter.

OXYTETRACYCLINE. *Preparation of sample for feed supplement.* Grind 2 Gm. of the feed supplement in a mortar with 50 ml. of acid-methanol (20 ml. concentrated hydrochloric acid per liter methanol). Transfer to a centrifuge tube. Wash the mortar and pestle with 50 ml. of acid-methanol and add to the centrifuge tube. Shake well for five minutes and centrifuge for approximately 15 minutes at 2,000 r.p.m. Remove 10 ml. of the supernatant and adjust to pH 4.5 with 1 N sodium hydroxide. Dilute 1 ml. of this to an estimated oxytetracycline concentration of 0.2 μg./ml. with phosphate buffer no. 4, pH 4.5, taking into consideration the dilution factor introduced by the added sodium hydroxide. Assay by microbiologic assay for tetracycline in Method 2, Section A of this Chapter.

Preparation of sample for final feed. Grind 10 Gm. of feed with 50 ml. of acid-methanol in a mortar. Transfer to a centrifuge tube. Wash the mortar and pestle with 50 ml. of acid-methanol and add to the centrifuge tube. Shake well for five minutes and centrifuge for approximately 15 minutes at 2,000 r.p.m. Remove 10 ml. of the supernatant and adjust to pH 4.5 with 1 N sodium hydroxide. Dilute 1 ml. of this to an estimated oxytetracycline concentration of 0.2 μg./ml. with phosphate buffer no. 4, pH 4.5, taking into consideration the dilution factor introduced by the added sodium hydroxide. Assay by microbiologic assay for tetracycline in Method 2, Section A of this Chapter.

5 CHLORAMPHENICOL

Section A: Microbiologic Assay Methods for Chloramphenicol

Method 1, to be described, is a cylinder-plate method using *S. lutea* as the test organism. It may be used to assay chloramphenicol and its various pharmaceutical dosage forms. However, it is not sensitive enough for the assay of chloramphenicol in blood, body fluids, and similar substances. The sensitivity of this method may be increased by using a lighter inoculum and a base layer containing agar without nutrients. This has been done in Method 2. Even with these modifications in Method 2, it is only possible to measure concentrations of chloramphenicol of about 3 μg./ml. Usually microbiologic assays are so sensitive that chemical methods cannot approach them in this respect and are not used in the assay of body fluids, tissue, or milk. However, chloramphenicol is an exception and the chemical assay Method 2 described in Section B of this Chapter is capable of measuring as little as 0.1 μg./ml.

METHOD 1: Cylinder-plate Method Using *Sarcina lutea* as the Test Organism. (ATCC 9341.)

Cylinders (Cups). Use stainless steel cylinders with an outside diameter of 8 mm. ($\pm$0.1 mm.), an inside diameter of 6 mm. ($\pm$0.1 mm.), and a length of 10 mm. ($\pm$0.1 mm.).

Culture Media. Use agar medium no. 1 for both the seed and base layers and for maintaining the test organism. Use broth medium no. 3 for preparing a suspension of the test organism.

Working Standard. Carefully weigh out an appropriate amount of the chloramphenicol working standard, which is kept at room temperature in a tightly stoppered vial, dissolve in a small amount of ethanol to facilitate solution, and then dilute in phosphate buffer no. 1, *p*H 6, to give a solution containing 1,000 μg./ml. This stock solution may be kept at 15 C. or less for one month.

Preparation of Sample. The method of preparing the sample of the various chloramphenicol preparations is described under the individual dosage forms in Section C of this Chapter. The final dilution tested should be prepared in phosphate buffer no. 1, *pH* 6, and have an estimated concentration of 50 µg./ml.

Preparation of Test Organism. The test organism is maintained by transferring once a week on agar medium no. 1. The incubation temperature is 26 C. Streak an agar slant heavily with the test organism and incubate overnight at 26 C. Wash the growth off in about 3 ml. of nutrient broth medium no. 3. Use the suspension so obtained to inoculate a series of agar plates or the surface of a Roux bottle containing 300 ml. of nutrient agar medium no. 1. Spread the suspension over the entire surface with the aid of sterile glass beads. Incubate for 24 hours at 26 C. Wash the growth from the agar surface with about 20 ml. of nutrient broth medium no. 3. If an aliquot of this bulk suspension when diluted 1:10 in nutrient broth gives a 10 per cent light transmission in a Lumetron 400-A photoelectric colorimeter equipped with a filter having a wave length of 6,500 Å. units, it is satisfactory for use. It may be necessary to adjust the bulk suspension so that an aliquot diluted 1:10 gives 10 per cent light transmission. (The adjusted bulk suspension only and not the 1:10 dilution is used in preparing the seed layer.) Usually the addition of 1.0 to 1.5 ml. of the adjusted bulk suspension to each 100 ml. of nutrient agar, which has been melted and cooled to 48 C., will give plates of proper density. It is always wise to run test plates to determine the exact amount of the suspension to add to each 100 ml. of agar to give appropriate, clear, sharp zones.

Preparation of Plates. Add 21 ml. of melted nutrient agar medium no. 1 to each Petri dish (20 by 100 mm.). Distribute the agar evenly in the plates, cover with porcelain covers, glazed only on the outside or other suitable covers, and allow to harden. Use the plates the same day they are prepared. Add 4 ml. of seeded agar (prepared as previously) to each plate, tilting the plates back and forth to spread the inoculated agar evenly over the surface. After this seed layer has hardened, place six cylinders on the inoculated agar surface so that they are at approximately 60 degree intervals on a 2.8 cm. radius.

Standard Curve and Assay Procedure. STANDARD CURVE. Use concentrations of chloramphenicol standard of 30.0, 35.0, 40.0, 45.0, 50.0, 55.0, 60.0, 65.0, and 70.0 µg./ml. prepared from the stock standard (1,000 µg./ml.) by diluting in phosphate buffer no. 1, *pH* 6. A total of 24 plates is used in the preparation of the standard curve, three plates for each concentration except the 50 µg./ml. concentration. The latter concentration is the reference point and is included on each plate. On each of three plates fill three cylinders with the 50 µg./ml. standard and the other three cylinders with the concentration of the standard under test. Thus there will be 72 of the 50 µg. determinations and nine determinations for each of the other concentrations on the curve. Incubate the plates for 16 to 18 hours at 32 to 35 C. and measure the diameter of the zones of inhibition. Average the readings of the 50 µg./ml. concentration and the readings of the concentrations tested for each set of three plates, and average also all 72 readings of the 50 µg./ml. concentration. The average of the 72 readings of the 50 µg./ml. concentration is the correction point for the curve.

Correct the average value obtained for each concentration to the figure it would be if the 50 μg./ml. readings for that set of three plates were the same as the correction point. Thus, if in correcting the 40 μg./ml. concentration, the average of the 72 readings of the 50 μg./ml. concentration is 18 mm. and the average of the 50 μg./ml. concentration of this set of three plates is 17.8 mm., the correction is plus 0.2 mm. If the average reading of the 40 μg./ml. concentration of these same three plates is 15 mm., the corrected value is then 15.2 mm. Plot these corrected values, including the average of the 72 of the 50 μg./ml. concentration on two-cycle semilogarithmic paper, using the concentrations in μg./ml. as the ordinate (logarithmic scale) and the diameter of the zone of inhibition as the abscissa. Draw the standard curve through these points.

ASSAY OF SAMPLE. Use one or more plates for each sample (usually three) and fill three cylinders on each plate with the 50 μg./ml. standard and three cylinders with the sample diluted to an estimated 50 μg./ml. with phosphate buffer no. 1, pH 6, alternating standard and sample. Incubate the plates for 16 to 18 hours at 32 to 35 C. and measure the diameter of each circle of inhibition. Average the zone readings of the standard and average the zone readings of the sample on the plates used. If the sample gives a larger average zone size than the average of the standard, add the difference between them to the 50 μg./ml. zone size of the standard curve. If the average sample zone size is smaller than the standard value, subtract the difference between them from the 50 μg./ml. zone size of the standard curve. From the curve read the concentration corresponding to these corrected values of zone sizes.

METHOD 2: Modification of Method 1 for the Assay of Chloramphenicol in Blood Serum and Other Substances.

Culture Media. Use 1.5 per cent agar, plain without any nutrients for the base layer. Use agar medium no. 4 for the seed layer.

Test Organism. The test organism suspension is prepared as described for Method 1, Section A of this Chapter. The amount of this suspension used in preparing the seed layer is 0.1 ml. for every 100 ml. of agar medium no. 4 which has been melted and cooled to 48 C.

Preparation of Plates. Care must be taken to make sure that the surface on which the Petri dishes are placed is perfectly flat. Ordinary 100 by 20 mm. dishes like those used in other plate assays are usually satisfactory, except that an occasional plate may have an unusually high convex center and the base agar layer is not sufficient to cover the bottom. For this reason some prefer to use a special Petri dish with a flat bottom, 100 by 22 mm. Add 6 ml. of melted non-nutrient agar to each dish and allow to harden. Add 4 ml. of seeded nutrient agar to each plate and spread evenly over the surface of the dish.

Standard Curve and Assay Procedure. The chloramphenicol standard curve is prepared by diluting the chloramphenicol stock solution in phosphate buffer no. 1, pH 6, to make concentrations of 3, 5, 10, 20, 30, and 40 μg./ml. The 10 μg./ml. concentration is the reference point of the curve.

Section B: *Chemical Methods for Chloramphenicol*

Method 1 is simply a physical measurement of the absorption of an aqueous solution of chloramphenicol at 278 mμ. The method is satisfactory for pure samples of chloramphenicol and some of the pharmaceutical dosage forms. The method would obviously not be satisfactory in the presence of substances giving strong absorption at this same wave length.

Another way of using the spectrophotometric method for determining chloramphenicol is to calculate the $E_{1\,cm.}^{1\%}$ value for the pure drug at 278 mμ and use this value to calculate the potency of unknowns. Using a solution containing 20 μg./ml. of pure chloramphenicol, the $E_{1\,cm.}^{1\%}$ value has been found to be 298. If one determines the 1 cm. absorbance of an unknown sample of chloramphenicol at 278 mμ and calculates the $E_{1\,cm.}^{1\%}$ value, this value divided by 298 and multiplied by 100 will give the per cent potency of the unknown. This procedure is satisfactory to use if one has run a standard curve on the spectrophotometer with pure chloramphenicol and checked this $E_{1\,cm.}^{1\%}$ value (298) with different concentrations.

The nitro group of chloramphenicol may be reduced to an amino group, which can be diazotized and coupled with reagents, such as N-(1-naphthyl) ethylenediamine, to form colored compounds. This is the basis of Method 2. Titanous chloride, zinc-hydrochloric acid, and stannous chloride have been used to reduce the nitro group. The use of titanous chloride is inconvenient because the reagent must be protected from atmospheric oxidation and requires another step to remove the excess reagent. Zinc-hydrochloric acid and stannous chloride reductions require heating under hydrolytic conditions. Sodium hydrosulfite has been found to be the most desirable reducing agent. It brings about the reduction at room temperature and the excess reagent is removed by the nitrous acid which concurrently diazotizes the amine. The color after the two hour development is stable for at least 30 minutes.

It has been reported that the major portion of chloramphenicol is converted in the animal organism into two biologically inactive products: the amine which results from hydrolytic removal of the dichloroacetyl group and the glucuronide of chloramphenicol. In determining the chloramphenicol content of body fluids, tissues, and milk, it is necessary to separate the intact chloramphenicol from these products. This is accomplished by using chloroform-ethyl acetate extraction as described in Method 3.

Since chloramphenicol is prepared synthetically as well as by fermentation and since it is optically active, the optical rotation should always be determined. The specific rotation values for chloramphenicol are given in Section C of this Chapter.

METHOD 1: Ultraviolet Spectrophotometric Method.

Preparation of Standard. Dissolve 25.0 mg. of the chloramphenicol working standard in about 100 ml. of distilled water, warming to hasten solution. Cool to room temperature, dilute to exactly 1,000 ml. with distilled water, and mix thoroughly. Use this solution which contains 25.0 μg./ml. and also from this solution prepare dilutions containing 5.0, 10.0, 15.0, and 20.0 μg./ml.

Preparation of Sample. Dilute the sample to be tested in distilled water to contain 20.0 μg./ml. (estimated).

Preparation of Blank. Use distilled water.

Procedure. Transfer the standard, blank, and sample solutions to 1 cm. absorption cells and determine the absorbance at 278 mμ in a suitable spectrophotometer after setting the instrument to read zero absorbance at 278 mμ with the blank. Prepare a standard curve of the absorbances obtained on the standard solutions on coordinate graph paper, plotting the absorbance on the ordinate scale and concentration of chloramphenicol on the abscissa. Determine the chloramphenicol content of the sample from the standard curve.

METHOD 2: Colorimetric Method.

This method was adapted from Levine and Fischbach.[12]

Reagents. The reagents are: sodium hydrosulfite, 0.3 N sodium hydroxide, 5 per cent sodium nitrite solution, 5 per cent sulfamic acid solution, 0.5 per cent N-(1-naphthyl) ethylenediamine dihydrochloride solution, and concentrated hydrochloric acid (36 to 37 per cent).

Preparation of Standard. Use the same standard solution described for chemical procedure Method 1, Section B of this Chapter (25.0 μg./ml. of chloramphenicol) to prepare dilutions containing 5.0, 10.0, 15.0, 20.0, and 25.0 μg./ml.

Preparation of Sample. Dilute the sample to be tested in distilled water to contain 15.0 μg./ml. (estimated).

Preparation of Blank. Use 2.0 ml. of distilled water and run it through the procedure, adding the reagents to it just as though it were a sample.

Procedure. To 2.0 ml. portions of the standard, sample, and blank in 10 ml. volumetric flasks, add 1.0 ml. of 0.3 N sodium hydroxide and 25 mg. of sodium hydrosulfite. Let stand at room temperature for 15 minutes. Add 0.5 ml. of 5 per cent sodium nitrite solution and 5 to 10 drops of hydrochloric acid. After one to three minutes add 1.0 ml. of 5 per cent sulfamic acid solution. Nitrous fumes remaining in the flask above the liquid will react with the coupling reagent to give a high blank; remove them by brief aspiration, e.g., under water-pump vacuum for several seconds. Add 0.5 ml. of 0.5 per cent N-(1-naphthyl) ethylenediamine dihydrochloride solution. Make up to 10 ml. volume with distilled water. At the end of two hours transfer the solutions to 1 cm. absorption cells. Use a suitable photoelectric colorimeter and set the instrument to read 100 per cent transmittance at 558 mμ with the blank solution. Obtain the transmittance of the standards and sample at 558 mμ. Prepare a standard curve of the transmittances obtained on the standard solutions on semilogarithmic paper, plotting the transmittance on the logarithmic ordinate scale and the concentration of the chloramphenicol on the abscissa. Calculate the concentration of the sample under test from the standard curve.

METHOD 3: Modified Method 2 for Body Fluids, Tissue, and Other Substances.

Follow the same procedure as described under Method 2 except for the following.

Extract the sample, prepared as described in Section D of this Chapter, with two 25 ml. portions of chloroform-ethyl acetate (2:1 by volume). Filter the solvent through a dry filter paper and evaporate to dryness on a steam bath, with an air current impinging on the surface of the solvent to facilitate evaporation and to prevent creeping. Dissolve the residue in 3 ml. of 0.1 N sodium hydroxide, add 25 mg. of sodium hydrosulfite, and continue as previously.

The final solution after addition of the N-(1-naphthyl) ethylenediamine dihydrochloride solution will usually be turbid. Clarify by shaking a portion of the solution in a glass stoppered tube with a small amount of chloroform followed by centrifugation. Read the transmittance of the aqueous phase after two hours.

If the color of the final solution is so dark that the readings do not fall within the limits chosen for the standard curve, dilute with distilled water until the color is within the desired range.

Section C: Assay of Chloramphenicol and its Pharmaceutical Dosage Forms

Chloramphenicol. D-(-)-threo-2-dichloroacetamido-1-p-nitrophenyl-1,3-proanediol. The structural formula for chloramphenicol is as follows:

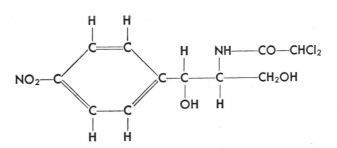

$C_{11}H_{12}O_5N_2Cl_2$. M.W. = 323.14. Theoretical potency = 1,000 μg./mg. Specific rotation $[\alpha]_D^{20°}$ = + 20° (absolute ethanol, C = 5 Gm./100 ml.); $[\alpha]_D^{25°}$ = + 18.5° (absolute ethanol, C = 5 Gm./100 ml.). Melting point 149 to 153 C. Extinction coefficient $E_{1\ cm.}^{1\%}$ = 298 at 278 mμ.

Chloramphenicol is an extremely bitter tasting, neutral substance and has a solubility in water of approximately 2.5 mg./ml. To assay, dissolve an accurately weighed sample in a small amount of ethanol, further dilute with water to 1.0 mg./ml. (estimated) and assay by the microbiologic assay in Method 1, Section A, or by chemical assay in Method 1 or 2, Section B of this Chapter.

Chloramphenicol Palmitate. The structural formula for chloramphenicol palmitate is as follows:

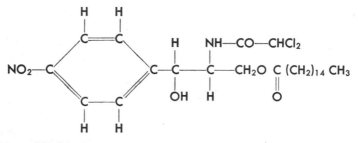

M.W. = 561.54. Theoretical potency = 575 μg./mg. The melting point ranges from 86 to 92 C. Extinction coefficient E $\vert_{cm.}^{1\%}$ = 178 in absolute ethanol at 271 mμ.

Chloramphenicol palmitate is insoluble in water, soluble in alcohol. The ester has no biologic activity and cannot be assayed by microbiologic assays. It is assayed by the following spectrophotometric method. Dissolve 50 mg. of the sample in absolute ethanol and make to 100 ml. in a volumetric flask with absolute ethanol. Transfer a 5 ml. aliquot to another 100 ml. volumetric flask and make to volume with absolute ethanol. With a suitable spectrophotometer determine the absorbance of the solution in a 1 cm. cell at 271 mμ compared with absolute ethanol as a blank. Multiply the absorbance figure obtained by the appropriate factor to obtain the absorbance value of a 1 per cent solution. The $E_{1\,cm.}^{1\%}$ value of the sample multiplied by 575, divided by 178, represents the μg. of chloramphenicol per mg. of chloramphenicol palmitate.

Chloramphenicol Capsules. Place the contents of 10 capsules and the empty capsules in 100 ml. of ethyl alcohol and using a high-speed blender, blend for approximately two minutes. Add to the blender 400 ml. of phosphate buffer no. 1, *p*H 6, and blend for approximately two minutes. Withdraw a 1.0 ml. aliquot, make the proper estimated dilutions in phosphate buffer no. 1, *p*H 6, and assay by microbiologic assay in Method 1, Section A of this Chapter. The spectrophotometric Method 1, Section B of this Chapter, may also be used, in which case proceed as follows: Place the contents of 10 capsules in a 250 ml. volumetric flask. Add 20 ml. of ethanol to the flask and shake for at least one minute. Make to volume with distilled water and mix thoroughly. Dilute a suitable aliquot of the solution with distilled water to contain 20 μg./ml. and proceed as directed in spectrophotometric Method 1, Section B of this Chapter.

Chloramphenicol Ointment. Accurately weigh approximately 1 Gm. of the ointment and place in a blending jar containing 100 ml. of phosphate buffer no. 1, pH 6. Using a high-speed blender, blend the mixture for two minutes, make the proper estimated dilutions in the buffer solution and assay by the microbiologic assay in Method 1, Section A of this Chapter.

Chloramphenicol Ophthalmic. Dissolve (or suspend) the contents of the bottle in the amount of diluent recommended in the labeling, further dilute with phosphate buffer no. 1, pH 6, and assay by microbiologic assay in Method 1, Section A of this Chapter.

Chloramphenicol Otic (Ear Drops). Assay by the same procedure described for chloramphenicol ophthalmic, Section C of this Chapter.

Chloramphenicol Solution. This product is sold as a combination package intended primarily for intravenous injection. One bottle contains chloramphenicol and the other bottle, a solvent, which is a 50 per cent solution of dimethylacetamide. Assay the bottle containing the chloramphenicol by dissolving in distilled water and assay using microbiologic assay in Method 1, Section A, or chemical assay in Method 1 or 2, Section B of this Chapter.

Chloramphenicol for Aqueous Injection (Suspension). This preparation is sold as a dry powder to which diluent is added just prior to use. Add the amount of water indicated in the labeling of the drug to the vial and shake well. Remove an aliquot of the suspension equivalent to 0.4 Gm. of chloramphenicol, transfer to a 50 ml. volumetric flask, and make to volume with absolute alcohol. Quickly remove 1.0 ml. and make to the proper estimated dilution in phosphate buffer no. 1, pH 6. Assay by microbiologic assay in Method 1, Section A of this Chapter.

The spectrophotometric Method 1 may also be used, in which case proceed as follows: Add to the vial the amount of water indicated in the labeling and shake vigorously until a uniform suspension is obtained. Transfer an aliquot of this suspension, equivalent to 0.4 Gm. of chloramphenicol, to a 1,000 ml. volumetric flask, add about 20 ml. of ethanol, shake to effect solution, and dilute to 1,000 ml. with distilled water. Dilute a suitable aliquot of this solution to contain 20 μg./ml. and determine the absorbance as directed in spectrophotometric Method 1, Section B of this Chapter.

Chloramphenicol Palmitate Oral Suspension. This preparation is a flavored aqueous suspension of chloramphenicol palmitate and contains the equivalent of 125 mg. of chloramphenicol per 4 ml. dose or 31.25 mg./ml.

Using a hypodermic syringe, transfer 1.0 ml. of the suspension to a separatory funnel containing 10 ml. of water and 25 ml. of chloroform. Shake for one minute, allow the layers to separate, and filter the lower chloroform layer through a pledget of cotton. Transfer a 1.0 ml. portion of the clear chloroform filtrate to a 100 ml. volumetric flask, make to volume with absolute ethanol, and mix. With a suitable spectrophotometer, determine the absorbance of this solution at 271 mμ, using as a blank 1.0 ml. of chloroform U.S.P. diluted to 100 ml. with absolute ethanol. The number of mg. of chloramphenicol contained in each ml. of chloramphenicol palmitate oral suspension is obtained by the following calculation:

$$C = \frac{A \times 25{,}000 \times 0.575}{178}$$

Where C = the number of mg. of chloramphenicol in 1.0 ml. of the chloramphenicol palmitate suspension;

  A = the absorbance of the solution at 271 mμ;

  25,000 = dilution factor;

  0.575 = the factor for converting chloramphenicol palmitate to chloramphenicol;

  178 = extinction coefficient of chloramphenicol palmitate at 271 mμ.

Section D: Determination of Chloramphenicol in Body Fluids and Other Substances

Blood Serum. The concentration of chloramphenicol in blood serum may be assayed by a microbiologic or chemical method. Efforts to develop a microbiologic assay for chloramphenicol with a sensitivity of 1.0 μg./ml. or less have not been successful. The chemical method has a sensitivity of about 0.1 μg./ml. Microbiologic assay in Method 2 is sensitive to about 3 μg./ml. of chloramphenicol and is presented as a tentative method. It should be pointed out that in increasing the sensitivity of the plate method for chloramphenicol the sensitivity may also be increased to certain nonspecific substances that may be present in blood serum and other substances, and normal controls should be included. This is not only true of chloramphenicol, but, as previously emphasized, of other antibiotic assays as well.

MICROBIOLOGIC ASSAY. The blood sample is prepared as in Section D, Chapter 2. Use the microbiologic assay in Method 2, Section A of this Chapter. The chloramphenicol standard is diluted to a concentration of 400 μg./ml. in phosphate buffer no. 1, pH 6, and from this working dilutions for the standard curve and tests are made using normal serum. The concentrations of chloramphenicol in normal serum for the standard curve are 3, 5, 10, 20, and 40 μg./ml. If the concentration of chloramphenicol in the sample under test is expected to be greater than 16 μg./ml., the serum is diluted with normal serum to an estimated 10 μg./ml. concentration and assayed.

CHEMICAL METHOD. Use the chemical assay in Method 3, Section B of this Chapter. To 5 ml. of serum (5 ml. is optimum but less can be used) add 5 ml. of 0.2 M phosphate buffer, pH 6. (To prepare, add the proper portions of 0.2 M dibasic potassium phosphate plus 0.2 M monobasic potassium phosphate to give pH 6.) Extract with two 25 ml. portions of chloroform-acetate (2:1 by volume) as directed.

Urine. Urine may be assayed by either the microbiologic assay in Method 2, Section A, or by chemical assay in Method 3, Section B of this Chapter.

If the microbiologic method is used, the chloramphenicol standard is diluted in phosphate buffer no. 1, *pH* 6. The urine is also diluted in phosphate buffer no. 1, *pH* 6, to an estimated 10 μg./ml. of chloramphenicol. For the chemical assay use 2 ml. of urine and 5 ml. of 0.2 *M* phosphate buffer, *pH* 6.

Tissues and Other Substances. Tissues are homogenized as described in Section D, Chapter 2, and the microbiologic or chemical assays carried out as described for urine Section D of this Chapter.

6 BACITRACIN

Section A: Microbiologic Assay Methods for Bacitracin

A cylinder-plate method using *Micrococcus flavus* is described in Method 1. Method 2 is a modification of Method 1 in which the sensitivity of the method is increased about fivefold so that measurement of the small concentrations encountered in blood, body fluids, and tissues can be accomplished. The increase in the lower range in Method 2 is achieved by using less medium in the base layer and a lighter inoculum of the test organism in the seed layer.

No chemical assay methods for bacitracin are available.

METHOD 1: Cylinder-Plate Method Using *Micrococcus flavus* as the Test Organism. (ATCC 10240.)

Cylinders (Cups). Use stainless steel cylinders with an outside diameter of 8 mm. (±0.1 mm.), an inside diameter of 6 mm. (±0.1 mm.), and a length of 10 mm. (±0.1 mm.).

Culture Media. Use agar medium no. 1 for carrying the test organism and for the seed layer and agar medium no. 2 for the base layer.

Working Standard. The working standard is kept under refrigeration in tightly stoppered vials which in turn are kept in larger stoppered tubes containing a suitable desiccant. The standard is hygroscopic and a convenient quantity should be dried in a vacuum oven at a temperature of 60 C. and a vacuum of 5 mm. of mercury or less for three hours. Using this dried standard, dilute to an appropriate concentration (100 units) with phosphate buffer no. 1, *p*H 6. This stock solution is stable for at least two weeks under refrigeration, and for several months if held at −20 C.

Preparation of Sample. Methods for preparing samples of various preparations are described in Section B of this Chapter.

Preparation of Test Organism. Inoculate a Roux bottle containing 300 ml. of nutrient agar medium no. 1 from a fresh agar slant of *M. flavus*, and incubate 18 hours at 32 to 35 C. Wash off the growth in 25 ml. of sterile 0.9 per cent sodium chloride (normal saline) solution. If an aliquot of this bulk suspension, when diluted 1:50 in normal saline solution gives 75 per cent light transmission in a Lumetron 400-A photoelectric colorimeter with a 6,500 Å. unit filter, the bulk suspension is satisfactory for use. It may be necessary to adjust the bulk suspension so that an aliquot does give 75 per cent light transmission when diluted 1:50. (The adjusted bulk suspension only and not the 1:50 dilution of it is used in preparing the seed layer.) Run test plates to determine the quantity of this suspension to be added to each 100 ml. of agar medium no. 1 to give clear, sharp, inhibitory zones of appropriate size. Usually 0.3 to 0.5 ml. of the adjusted bulk suspension to each 100 ml. of agar medium no. 1, which has been melted and cooled to 48 C., is sufficient.

Preparation of Plates. Add 21 ml. of melted agar medium no. 2 to each Petri dish (20 by 100 mm.), distribute evenly, cover with porcelain covers glazed only on the outside or other suitable covers, and allow to harden. Add 4.0 ml. of agar medium no. 1 which has been seeded with the suspension of *M. flavus* as already described. Spread evenly over the hardened base layer. After this seed layer has hardened, place six cylinders on the inoculated agar surface so that they are at approximately 60 degree intervals on a 2.8 cm. radius.

Standard Curve and Assay Procedure. STANDARD CURVE. Dilute the standard bacitracin solution to contain 0.6, 0.7, 0.8, 0.9, 1.0 (reference point), 1.1, 1.2, 1.3, 1.4, and 1.5 units/ml. in phosphate buffer no. 1, *p*H 6. A total of 27 plates is used in the preparation of the standard curve, three plates for each concentration except the 1.0 unit/ml. solution. The latter concentration is used as the reference point and is included on each plate. On each of three plates fill three cylinders with the 1.0 unit/ml. concentration of standard and the other three cylinders with the concentration under test. Thus there will be 81 of the 1 unit determinations and nine determinations for each of the other concentrations of the curve. Incubate 16 to 18 hours at 32 to 35 C. After incubation read the diameters of the circles of inhibition. Average the readings of the 1.0 unit/ml. concentration and the readings of the point tested for each set of three plates and average also all 81 readings of the 1.0 unit/ml. concentration. The average of the 81 readings of the 1.0 unit/ml. concentration is the correction point for the curve. Correct the average value obtained for each concentration to the figure it would be if the 1.0 unit/ml. reading for that set of three plates were the same as the correction point. Thus, if in correcting the 0.8 unit/ml. concentration, the average of the 81 readings of the 1.0 unit/ml. concentration is 18 mm. and the average of the 1.0 unit/ml. concentration of this set of three plates is 17.8 mm., the correction is plus 0.2 mm. If the average reading of the 0.8 unit/ml. concentration of these same three plates is 15 mm. the corrected value is then 15.2 mm. Plot these corrected values, including the average of the 81 of the 1 unit concentration, on two-cycle semilogarithmic paper, using the concentrations in units/ml. as the ordinate (logarithmic scale) and the diameter of the zone of inhibition as the abscissa. Draw the standard curve through these points.

ASSAY OF SAMPLE. Use one or more plates (usually three) for each sample. Fill three cylinders on each plate with the 1.0 unit standard and three with an estimated 1.0 unit/ml. of the sample under test in phosphate buffer no. 1, *p*H 6, alternating sample and standard. Incubate the plates for 16 to 18 hours at 32 to 35 C. and measure the diameter of each circle of inhibition. Average the zone readings of the standard and average the zone readings of the sample on the plates used. If the sample gives a larger average zone size than the average of the standard, add the difference between them to the 1.0 unit/ml. zone size of the standard curve. If the average sample zone size is smaller than the standard zone size, subtract the difference between them from the 1.0 unit/ml. zone size of the standard curve. From the curve read the concentration corresponding to these corrected values of zone sizes.

METHOD 2: Modified Cylinder-plate Method for the Determination of Bacitracin in Body Fluids, Tissues, and Other Substances.

Proceed as directed in the microbiologic assay in Method 1, Section A of this Chapter with the following exceptions.

Use 10 ml. of nutrient agar medium no. 2 for the base layer.

Use 0.2 ml. of the adjusted bulk suspension for adding to each 100 ml. of seed agar medium no. 1 which has been melted and cooled to 48 C.

Use concentrations of bacitracin standard for preparing the standard curve of 0.02, 0.03, 0.06, 0.10, 0.20, 0.40, and 0.80 unit/ml. in phosphate buffer no. 1, *p*H 6. Thus 18 plates are used for preparing the standard curve and the reference point is the 0.20 unit/ml. concentration.

Incubate the plates for 16 to 18 hours at 26 C.

Section B: **Assay of Bacitracin and its Pharmaceutical Dosage Forms**

Bacitracin. Bacitracin is a polypeptide. The commercial preparation is probably a mixture of three different bacitracins, A, B, and C, but chiefly A type. Bacitracin A has been reported to have a molecular weight of about 1,500 and consists of the following proportions and kinds of amino acids: cysteine, 1; ornithine, 1; lysine, 1; histidine, 1; aspartic acid, 2; glutamic acid, 1; phenylalanine, 1; isoleucine, 2; and leucine, 1. No chemical assay method is available for bacitracin. It is believed that the potency of pure bacitracin A is around 72 units/mg. Bacitracin is very soluble in water. To assay bacitracin powder dissolve an accurately weighed sample or the contents of a vial in buffer no. 1, *p*H 6, to give a solution containing 1 unit/ml. (estimated) and assay by the microbiologic assay in Method 1, Section A of this Chapter.

Bacitracin Methylene Disalicylate. When an aqueous solution of bacitracin is treated with a salt of methylene disalicylic acid, a precipitate results that is believed to be the bacitracin salt of methylene disalicylic acid. This salt is insoluble in water and the usual organic solvents. It is soluble in sodium bicarbonate solution or alkalies between *p*H 7.0 to 8.5.

To assay, place an accurately weighed sample of approximately 1 Gm. in a blending jar, add 99 ml. of a 2 per cent aqueous solution of sodium bicarbonate and 1 ml. of a 10 per cent aqueous solution of polysorbate 80 and blend for three minutes in a high-speed blender. Allow the foam to subside, remove an aliquot of the solution, dilute to 1.0 unit/ml. (estimated) with phosphate buffer no. 1, *p*H 6, and assay by the microbiologic assay in Method 1, Section A of this Chapter.

Zinc Bacitracin. When aqueous solutions of bacitracin are treated with zinc salts, a precipitate forms that is zinc bacitracin. It is fairly insoluble in water, having a solubility of about 40 to 50 units/ml. It dissolves in acid solution.

To assay, suspend an accurately weighed sample of approximately 100 mg. in 5 ml. of distilled water. Add 0.5 ml. of 3 *N* hydrochloric acid, stir until dissolved, transfer to a 100 ml. volumetric flask, and make to volume with distilled water. Dilute an aliquot of this solution to 1.0 unit/ml. (estimated) with phosphate buffer no. 1, *p*H 6, and assay by the microbiologic assay in Method 1, Section A of this Chapter.

Bacitracin Ointment. Place a convenient sized representative sample (usually about 1 Gm.) into a separatory funnel containing 50 ml. of peroxide-free ether. Shake ointment and ether until homogeneous. Shake with a 25 ml. portion of phosphate buffer no. 1, *p*H 6. Remove the buffer layer and repeat the extraction with at least three 25 ml. quantities of buffer. Usually four extractions are sufficient, but enough extractions should be made to insure complete extraction. Combine the extracts and dilute to 1 unit/ml. (estimated) in phosphate buffer no. 1, *p*H 6.

The sample may also be prepared by placing an accurately weighed sample (1 Gm.) of the ointment into a blending jar containing 1 ml. of a 10 per cent aqueous solution of polysorbate 80 and sufficient phosphate buffer no. 1, *p*H 6, to give a volume of 100 ml. Using a high-speed blender, blend the mixture for two minutes and dilute an aliquot of the aqueous extract in buffer no. 1, *p*H 6, to 1 unit/ml. (estimated).

In either of these procedures assay the final dilution by the microbiologic assay in Method 1, Section A of this Chapter.

Bacitracin Tablets. Place five tablets in a mortar and add approximately 20 ml. of phosphate buffer no. 1, *p*H 6. Disintegrate the tablets by grinding with a pestle. Transfer with the aid of small portions of the buffer solution to a 250 ml. volumetric flask and make to a volume of 250 ml. with the buffer solution. Dilute an aliquot to 1 unit/ml. (estimated) with phosphate buffer no. 1, *p*H 6.

The sample may also be prepared as follows: Place five tablets in a blending jar and add approximately 125 ml. of phosphate buffer no. 1, *p*H 6. After blending for one minute with a high-speed blender, add an additional 125 ml. of buffer. Blend again for one minute and dilute an aliquot to 1 unit/ml. (estimated) with phosphate buffer no. 1, *p*H 6.

In either of these procedures assay the final dilution by the microbiologic assay in Method 1, Section A of this Chapter.

Bacitracin Troches. Assay by the same procedure used for bacitracin tablets, Section B of this Chapter.

Bacitracin with Vasoconstrictor. Dissolve the contents of a bottle with the amount of diluent recommended in the labeling. Further dilute with phosphate buffer no. 1, *p*H 6, to 1 unit/ml. (estimated) and assay by the microbiologic assay in Method 1, Section A of this Chapter.

Bacitracin Ophthalmic. Assay by the same procedure used for bacitracin with vasoconstrictor, Section B of this Chapter.

Section C: Determination of Bacitracin in Body Fluids and Other Substances

Blood Serum. Use microbiologic assay Method 2, Section A of this Chapter. Dilute the working stock standard bacitracin to 10.0 units/ml. in phosphate buffer no. 1, *p*H 6. From this, the standard curve is prepared using normal human serum or 7 per cent bovine albumin solution (Chapter 21). The blood serum sample under test prepared as directed in Section D, Chapter 2, is added to the cups undiluted unless a concentration greater than 0.80 unit/ml. is expected, in which case, the sample should be diluted to an estimated 0.20 unit/ml. with the bovine albumin diluent. One or more plates are used.

Urine. Dilute the urine to give an estimated bacitracin content of 1.0 unit/ml. with phosphate buffer no. 1, *p*H 6, and assay by the microbiologic assay in Method 1, Section A of this Chapter.

Note that most normal urines will give a nonspecific zone of inhibition if added to the cups undiluted in Method 2. This does not occur when the less sensitive Method 1 is employed. Since bacitracin is readily excreted by the kidneys, the concentration in the urine is usually high and the dilution for assay is sufficient to eliminate nonspecific zones of inhibition and Method 2 is satisfactory. If, however, one is interested in detecting small amounts of bacitracin in undiluted urine, Method 1 should be employed to avoid false positive results.

Tissue. Prepare tissue samples in the same manner as described under Penicillin, Section D, Chapter 2, and assay by the microbiologic assay in Method 2, Section A of this Chapter.

Milk. Use microbiologic Method 2. Dilute the bacitracin stock standard to 10.0 units/ml. in phosphate buffer no. 1, *p*H 6, and from this make dilutions for the standard curve in normal milk, i.e., milk containing no inhibitory substance. Add the milk to the cups undiluted unless a concentration greater than 0.80 unit/ml. is anticipated in which case dilute the sample with milk to an estimated 0.20 unit/ml.

Animal Feed Supplements and Mixed Feeds. FEED SUPPLEMENTS. Grind 3 Gm. of sample with 50 ml. of 20 per cent pyridine in phosphate buffer no. 1, *p*H 6. Pour into a centrifuge tube. Wash the mortar and pestle with 50 ml. of phosphate buffer no. 1, *p*H 6, and add to the first washing in the centrifuge tube. Shake the centrifuge tube for five minutes. Centrifuge for approximately 15 minutes at 2,000 r.p.m. Remove 1 ml. and dilute to an estimated bacitracin concentration of 0.2 unit/ml. with phosphate buffer no. 1, *p*H 6. Assay by the microbiologic assay in Method 2, Section A of this Chapter.

FINAL FEED. Grind 10 Gm. of feed in a mortar with 50 ml. of 20 per cent pyridine in phosphate buffer no. 1, *p*H 6. Transfer to a centrifuge tube. Wash the mortar and pestle with a second 50 ml. of 20 per cent pyridine in phosphate buffer no. 1, *p*H 6. Add to centrifuge tube. Shake well for five minutes and centrifuge for approximately 15 minutes at 2,000 r.p.m. Dilute 1 ml. of supernatant to an estimated bacitracin concentration of 0.2 unit/ml. with phosphate buffer no. 1, *p*H 6. Assay by the microbiologic assay in Method 2, Section A of this Chapter.

7 TYROTHRICIN

Section A: Microbiologic Assay Method for Tyrothricin

Tyrothricin consists of two active components, gramicidin and tyrocidine. The tyrocidine fraction is inactivated to a considerable degree by serum, exudates, and body fluids and hence plays a minor role in the action of tyrothricin. The active portion is the gramicidin, which is not appreciably affected by serum. Since gramicidin is the active ingredient of tyrothricin, microbiologic tests are designed to detect this substance, and they do not test for the amount of tyrocidine present. In some broth dilution tests the test organism is sensitive to tyrocidine, which interferes with the assay of gramicidin. In this case bovine serum albumin is added to the culture medium to inhibit the action of tyrocidine. This is the basis of the present U.S.P. XIV test for tyrothricin. In the test to be described the strain of *Streptococcus faecalis* used is so highly sensitive to gramicidin and insensitive to tyrocidine that the addition of bovine serum albumin is not necessary. The M 19 strain used in this test is sensitive to 0.0004 μg./ml. of gramicidin, but to only 3.0 μg. of tyrocidine. This high sensitivity also has the advantage of eliminating possible interfering antibacterial substances used in compounding the various tyrothricin formulations.

METHOD 1: Turbidimetric Assay Method Using *Streptococcus faecalis* (Group D) Strain M 19 as the Test Organism. (ATCC 10541.)

Test Culture and Media. Use agar medium no. 2 for maintaining the test organism and broth medium no. 3 for preparing the inoculum and for conducting the test. Inoculate broth medium no. 3 from a fresh agar slant of the test organism and incubate at 25 C. for 18 to 24 hours. Add 1 ml. of this broth culture to every 100 ml. of broth medium no. 3 needed for the test.

Stock Standard and Working Standard. The reference standard is a mixture consisting of 20 per cent crystalline gramicidin and 80 per cent crystalline tyrocidine hydrochloride. Accurately weigh 25 to 50 mg. of each and dilute each with absolute ethyl alcohol to make 1 mg./ml. of solution. Mix 1.0 ml. of the gramicidin solution and 4.0 ml. of the tyrocidine solution to obtain 5 ml. containing 1 mg./ml. of tyrothricin. If the U.S.P. reference standard is used, prepare a solution in absolute alcohol containing 1.0 mg./ml. Maintain under refrigeration and take precautions to prevent evaporation. Dilute this stock solution in absolute ethyl alcohol to make 1.0 μg./ml. tyrothricin (0.2 μg./ml. of gramicidin). This is the working standard.

Standard Curve and Assay Procedure. Dilute the working standard in absolute ethyl alcohol to make concentrations of 0.08, 0.12, 0.16, 0.20, 0.24, 0.28, and 0.32, μg./ml. Further dilute 1.0 ml. of each of these dilutions with 9.0 ml. of sterile distilled water to make concentrations of 0.008, 0.012, 0.016, 0.020, 0.023, 0.028, and 0.032 μg.‖ml. Add 1 ml. of each concentration to each of six tubes (16 by 125 mm.). Add 9 ml. of inoculated broth (already described) to each tube of the standard series and to each tube containing the sample under test. Place immediately in a water bath at 37 C. and incubate for three hours. Then add 0.5 ml. of formalin diluted 1 to 3 to each tube.

Preparation of Sample. Prepare the sample as described in Section B of this Chapter and dilute with absolute ethyl alcohol to an estimated 0.20 μg./ml. if the product is tyrothricin or to 0.040 μg./ml. if the product is gramicidin. Further dilute in sterile distilled water to 0.020 μg./ml. for tyrothricin or 0.0040 μg./ml. for gramicidin. Add 1 ml. of this final dilution to each of six tubes (16 by 125 mm.) and add 9 ml. of inoculated broth and incubate as previously.

Estimation of Potency. Read the light transmission in a Lumetron 402-E photoelectric colorimeter using a broad-band filter having a wave length of 5,800 Å. units or other suitable photoelectric colorimeter. If the Lumetron instrument is used, set the slide wire scale at 80. Adjust the instrument so that the galvanometer scale reads about zero using the pooled contents of the tubes with the least amount of antibiotic and reads about 100 with the pooled contents of the tubes containing the largest amount. The other points of the curve will fall in between these two, thus completing the standard curve. Average the galvanometer readings for each concentration of the standard. Plot these values on cross section paper using average galvanometer readings as the abscissa and tyrothricin concentrations in μg. per tube as the ordinate. Prepare the standard curve by connecting successive points with a straightedge. Since the final concentration of tyrothricin per ml. of broth is equivalent to the concentration per ml. of the standard solution used, the latter concentration for each concentration level of the standard may be expressed as per cent and substituted on the ordinate of the standard curve. Thus the 0.020 μg. concentration is 100 per cent, the 0.016 μg. concentration 80.0 per cent, and so on. If this is done, the per cent potency of the sample under test may be read directly from the standard curve.

Section B: **Assay of Tyrothricin and its Pharmaceutical Dosage Forms**

Tyrothricin is a mixture of polypeptides. It may be separated into a crystalline neutral fraction called gramicidin and a crystalline basic fraction called tyrocidine. In spite of the fact that gramicidin is crystalline, it is a mixture of polypeptides. Gramicidins A and B have been isolated and two other types are also believed to exist. The following amino acids have been found to be present in gramicidins A and B: glycine, alanine, valine, leucine, and tryptophane. Gramicidin B contains only about 85 per cent of the tryptophane contained in gramicidin A. The gramicidins are insoluble in water, soluble in alcohol and propylene glycol. The gramicidin sold in commerce is a mixture of the different types of gramicidins.

Tyrocidine also, even though crystalline, has been found to be a mixture. Tyrocidines A, B, and C have been isolated. Tyrocidine A has been thoroughly studied and it is a cyclic decapeptide that may be represented as follows:

```
┌────L-tyrosine-L-valine-L-ornithine-L-leucine-D-phenylalanine────────┐
└─L-glutamine-L-asparagine-D-phenylalanine-L-phenylalanine-L-proline──┘
```

It has an empirical formula $C_{66}H_{86}O_{13}N_{13}$ and a molecular weight of 1,270. Tyrocidine A has only two functional groups, the hydroxyl group of the tyrosine and the amino group of the ornithine portion of the molecule. It forms a crystalline hydrochloride. The salt is insoluble or only sparingly soluble in chloroform, water, acetone, or ether. It is fairly soluble in methanol or ethanol and readily soluble in aqueous methanol or ethanol.

Occasionally preparations are labeled in terms of their gramicidin content or gramicidin is actually used in the product instead of tyrothricin. In such cases the product is assayed in the same manner as for tyrothricin only it is diluted in absolute ethyl alcohol to give a stock solution of 0.040 μg./ml. of gramicidin (estimated) and further diluted with water to 0.0040 μg./ml. for comparison with the 0.020 μg./ml. standard tyrothricin which contains 20 per cent gramicidin.

Tyrothricin Powder. Because of the insolubility of tyrothricin in water, absolute ethyl alcohol is used to dissolve it for assay purposes. Dissolve an accurately weighed sample in alcohol, dilute in this same solvent to a concentration of 0.20 μg./ml. (estimated), further dilute tenfold with water and assay by the microbiologic assay method, Section A of this Chapter.

Alcohol or Propylene Glycol Solutions of Tyrothricin. Dilute an accurately measured aliquot of the solution with absolute ethyl alcohol to a concentration of 0.20 μg./ml. of tyrothricin (estimated), further dilute tenfold with water and assay by the microbiologic method, Section A of this Chapter.

Tyrothricin Troches. Grind about five troches in 10 to 20 ml. of water in a mortar and transfer to a 100 ml. volumetric flask by washing with successive portions of absolute ethyl alcohol, and make up to volume. Filter, dilute an aliquot of the filtrate with absolute ethyl alcohol to a concentration of 0.20 μg./ml. of tyrothricin (estimated), further dilute tenfold with water, and assay by the microbiologic method, Section A of this Chapter.

Tyrothricin Ointments or Creams. Because of the variety of ointment bases used in tyrothricin formulations, it is not possible to recommend one extraction procedure suitable for all products. They may, however, be divided into two types, water-soluble and water-insoluble.

WATER-INSOLUBLE BASES. Place 1 to 3 Gm. of ointment in a 250 ml. separatory funnel and add 100 ml. of petroleum ether. Shake well until solution occurs, add 20 ml. of 80 per cent ethyl alcohol, and shake vigorously. Allow this mixture to stand until two layers are formed. Draw off the bottom alcohol layer into a 100 ml. volumetric flask. Repeat this procedure until approximately 90 ml. of the bottom alcohol layer is collected into the flask. Care should be taken to prevent any residual petroleum ether from entering the flask from the separatory funnel. Dilute to 100 ml. with absolute ethyl alcohol. Further dilute an aliquot with absolute ethyl alcohol to a concentration of 0.20 µg./ml. of tyrothricin (estimated), further dilute tenfold with water and assay by the microbiologic method, Section A of this Chapter.

WATER-SOLUBLE BASES. Thoroughly mix 2 to 5 Gm. of ointment with 25 to 40 ml. of distilled water and make up to 100 ml. with absolute ethyl alcohol. Further dilute an aliquot of this with absolute ethyl alcohol to a concentration of 0.20 µg./ml. of tyrothricin (estimated), then dilute tenfold with water and assay by the microbiologic assay method, Section A of this Chapter.

Tyrothricin in Mineral Oil Emulsions. Assay by the same procedure described under tyrothricin ointments with water-insoluble bases, Section B of this Chapter.

Tyrothricin Nose Drops. Dilute an accurately measured aliquot with absolute alcohol to a concentration of 0.20 µg./ml. of tyrothricin (estimated), further dilute tenfold with water and assay by the microbiologic assay method, Section A of this Chapter.

Tyrothricin Otic (Ear Drops). Assay by the same procedure described under tyrothricin nose drops, Section B of this Chapter.

Tyrothricin Mouth Wash. Assay by the same procedure described under tyrothricin nose drops, Section B of this Chapter.

Tryothricin Adhesive Gauze Pads. Soak the adhesive gauze pad in white gasoline until the adhesive can be easily removed. Allow the gasoline to drain from the gauze pad and then place in a Petri dish and dry for one hour at 37 C. with the lid of the dish partially removed. Place the pad in a test tube containing 10 ml. of absolute ethyl alcohol. Agitate thoroughly. Withdraw a 1.0 ml. aliquot, dilute with absolute ethyl alcohol to a concentration of 0.20 µg./ml. of tyrothricin (estimated) further dilute tenfold with water and assay by the microbiologic assay method, Section A of this Chapter.

8 POLYMYXIN

Section A: Microbiologic Assay Methods for Polymyxin

Method 1 described later is a cylinder-plate assay method using *Brucella bronchiseptica* as the test organism. This method is useful in measuring the potency of polymyxin and most of its pharmaceutical dosage forms. The reference point on the standard curve, however, is 100 units/ml. Therefore, if, for example, polymyxin ointment containing 1,000 units/Gm. is to be assayed, it can be diluted only 1 to 10 and not much leeway is available for extraction and dilution. The zone size obtained in this cylinder-plate assay is markedly affected by the concentration of the phosphate buffer used. It has been found that the sensitivity of the assay can be increased tenfold merely by changing the concentration of the phosphate buffer from 1 to 10 per cent. This is the basis for the modification of Method 1 and is described as Method 2.

The *Brucella bronchiseptica* method has also been modified to make it sensitive enough to use for blood, tissue, and other substances. Method 3 describes these modifications.

No reliable chemical methods for the assay of polymyxin are available at this time.

METHOD 1: Cylinder-plate Assay Using *Brucella bronchiseptica* as the Test Organism. (ATCC 4617.)

Cylinders (Cups). Use stainless steel cylinders with an outside diameter of 8 mm. (±0.1 mm.), an inside diameter of 6 mm. (±0.1 mm.), and a length of 10 mm. (±0.1 mm.).

Culture Media. Use medium no. 9 for the base layer and for maintaining the test organism. Use medium no. 10 for the seed layer.

Working Standard. Weigh out a sufficient quantity of the polymyxin B sulfate working standard and make a 10,000 units/ml. stock solution by diluting with phosphate buffer no. 1, *p*H 6. This solution may be used for at least two weeks if kept in a refrigerator.

Preparation of Sample. The method of preparing the sample of the various polymyxin preparations is described under the individual dosage forms in Section B of this Chapter.

Preparation of Test Organism. The test organism is maintained by transferring once a week on agar medium no. 9. Inoculate a Roux bottle containing agar medium no. 9 from a stock slant and incubate 24 hours at 32 to 35 C. Wash the growth into sterile distilled water and standardize the resulting organism suspension to 50 per cent light transmission in a Lumetron 400-A photoelectric colorimeter using a filter having a wave length of 6,500 Å. units. Run test plates and use in the assay the amount of inoculum (usually about 0.25 ml.) per 100 ml. of seed agar medium no. 10 melted and cooled to 48 C., which gives about a 15 mm. zone of inhibition against the test organism with the 100 units/ml. solution of polymyxin. Make a new suspension when satisfactory zones are no longer obtained.

Preparation of Plates. Add 21 ml. of melted medium no. 9 to each Petri dish (20 by 100 mm.). Distribute the agar evenly in the plates, cover with porcelain covers glazed only on the outside or other suitable covers, and allow to harden. Use the plates the same day they are prepared. Add 4 ml. of seeded agar (prepared as previously) to each plate, tilting the plates back and forth to spread the inoculated agar evenly over the surface. After the seed layer has hardened, place six cylinders on the inoculated agar surface so that they are at approximately 60 degree intervals on a 2.8 cm. radius.

Standard Curve and Assay Procedure. STANDARD CURVE. Use concentrations of polymyxin standard of 60, 70, 80, 90, 100, 110, 120, 130, 140, and 150 units/ml. prepared from the stock standard solution (10,000 units/ml.) by diluting in phosphate buffer no. 1, pH 6. A total of 27 plates is used in the preparation of the standard curve, three plates for each concentration except the 100 units/ml. concentration. The latter concentration is the reference point and is included on each plate. On each of three plates fill three cylinders with the 100 units/ml. standard and the other three cylinders with the concentration of the standard under test. Thus there will be 81 of the 100 unit determinations and nine determinations for each of the other concentrations on the curve. Incubate the plates for 16 to 18 hours at 37 C. and measure the diameter of the zones of inhibition. Average the readings of the 100 units/ml. concentration and the readings of the concentration tested for each set of three plates and average also all 81 readings of the 100 units/ml. concentration. The average of the 81 readings of the 100 units/ml. concentration is the correction point for the curve. Correct the average value obtained for each concentration to the figure it would be if the 100 units/ml. reading for that set of three plates were the same as the correction point. Thus, if in correcting the 90 units/ml. concentration the average of the 81 readings of the 100 units/ml. concentration is 15 mm. and the average of 100 units/ml. concentration of this set of three plates is 14.8 mm., the correction is plus 0.2 mm. If the average reading of the 90 units/ml. concentration of these same three plates is 13 mm., the corrected value is then 13.2 mm. Plot these corrected values, including the average of the 81 of the 100 units/ml. concentration on two-cycle semilogarithmic paper, using the concentrations in units/ml. as the ordinate (logarithmic scale) and the diameter of the zone of inhibition as the abscissa. Draw the standard curve through these points.

ASSAY PROCEDURE. Use one or more plates for each sample (usually three) and fill three cylinders on each plate with the 100 units/ml. standard and three cylinders with the sample diluted to an estimated 100 units/ml. with phosphate buffer no. 1, *p*H 6, alternating standard and sample. Incubate the plates for 16 to 18 hours at 37 C. and measure the diameter of each circle of inhibition. Average the zone readings of the standard and average the zone readings of the sample on the plates used. If the sample gives a larger average zone size than the average of the standard, add the difference between them to the 100 units/ml. zone size of the standard curve. If the average sample zone size is smaller than the standard value, subtract the difference between them from the 100 units/ml. zone size of the standard curve. From the curve read the concentration corresponding to these corrected values of zone sizes.

Some laboratories prefer to use glycine buffer no. 5, *p*H 2, for preparing the working standard, standard curve, and samples. In our hands this buffer is satisfactory but has no significant advantage over the phosphate buffer no. 1.

METHOD 2: Modification of Method 1.

The use of a 10 per cent phosphate buffer no. 6, *p*H 6, in place of the 1 per cent phosphate buffer no. 1, *p*H 6, increases the sensitivity of the assay method about tenfold. This is useful in the assay of ointments or other preparations containing 10,000 units/Gm., or less. The more sensitive assay permits more leeway for the extraction and dilution of the sample under test and lessens the possibility of interference from other antibacterial agents that may be present in preparations. The modification is as follows: Make a 1,000 units/ml. stock solution of the standard polymyxin by diluting a weighed sample in phosphate buffer no. 6, *p*H 6. From this stock solution prepare polymyxin concentrations of 6.0, 7.0, 8.0, 9.0, 10.0, 11.0, 12.0, 13.0, 14.0, and 15.0 units/ml. for making the standard curve. The 10.0 units/ml. concentration is the reference point. The sample is prepared using phosphate buffer no. 6, *p*H 6, and finally diluted in the same buffer to a final concentration of 10.0 units/ml. (estimated).

METHOD 3: Modification of Method 2 for the Assay of Polymyxin in Blood Serum and Other Substances.

The conduct of this test is the same as described under Method 2 with these exceptions: Dilute the polymyxin standard in 4 per cent phosphate buffer no. 7, *p*H 6, to contain concentrations of 0.50, 1.0, 2.0, 5.0, 10.0, 20.0, 30.0, and 40.0 units/ml. The 10.0 units/ml. concentration is the reference point. Special diluents will be mentioned under Section C of this Chapter. In the preparation of plates, add 10 ml. of agar medium no. 9 to each 20 by 100 mm. Petri dish for the base layer. The organism suspension is prepared as described in Method 1 and approximately 0.20 ml. of this suspension is added to each 100 ml. of agar medium no. 10 for the seed layer. Four ml. of this inoculated agar is added to the hardened base layer on each plate, tilting the plates back and forth to spread the inoculated agar evenly over the surface.

Section B: Assay of Polymyxin and its Pharmaceutical Dosage Forms

Polymyxin Sulfate. Five polymyxins have been isolated and identified. They are all polypeptides and have been designated as A, B, C, D, and E types. The polymyxin sold commercially in the United States is chiefly polymyxin B. The following table shows the composition of the polymyxins.

	A	B	C	D	E
D—Leucine	+	+	0	+	+
L—Phenylalanine	0	+	+	0	0
D—Serine	0	0	0	+	0
L—Threonine	+	+	+	+	+
L—α, γ-diaminobutyric acid	+	+	+	+	+
D—6-Methyloctan-1-oic acid	+	+	+	+	+

Recently Hausmann and Craig [13] have fractionated a sample of polymyxin B into two compounds designated as polymyxins B_1 and B_2. These two polymyxins contain threonine, leucine and phenylalanine, and α, γ-diaminobutyric acid. They differ in that B_1 contains isopelargonic acid, while B_2 contains 6-methyloctan-1-oic acid.

The polymyxins are believed to have a cyclic structure and a molecular weight around 1,100 to 1,200. They are basic and form salts, such as hydrochlorides and sulfates. The salts are soluble in water and methanol. Polymyxin B sulfate has been assigned a theoretical potency of 10,000 units/mg. There are no reliable chemical assay methods for the polymyxins.

To assay polymyxin sulfate, dilute an accurately weighed sample or the contents of a vial with phosphate buffer no. 1, *p*H 6, to a concentration of 100 units/ml. (estimated) and follow the microbiologic assay in Method 1, Section A of this Chapter.

Polymyxin Sulfate Ointment. Accurately weigh approximately 1 Gm. of the ointment and place it in a separatory funnel containing approximately 50 ml. of peroxide-free ether. Shake ointment and ether until homogeneous. Shake with a 25 ml. portion of phosphate buffer no. 6, *p*H 6. Remove the buffer layer and repeat the extraction with three 25 ml. quantities of buffer. Combine the extracts and dilute to 10.0 units/ml. (estimated) with phosphate buffer no. 6, *p*H 6.

The sample may also be prepared by placing an accurately weighed sample of approximately 1 Gm. of the ointment into a blending jar containing 100 ml. of phosphate buffer no. 6, *p*H 6. Using a high-speed blender, blend the mixture for two minutes, and dilute an aliquot of the aqueous extract to 10.0 units/ml. (estimated) with phosphate buffer no. 6, *p*H 6.

In either of these procedures assay the final dilution by microbiologic assay Method 2, Section A of this Chapter.

Polymyxin Sulfate Tablets Soluble. Place five tablets in a mortar and add approximately 20 ml. of phosphate buffer no. 1, *p*H 6. Disintegrate the tablets by grinding with a pestle and add sufficient phosphate buffer no. 1, *p*H 6, to give a concentration of 100 units/ml. (estimated). Assay by the microbiologic assay in Method 1, Section A of this Chapter.

Polymyxin Sulfate Otic Solution. Dilute an accurately measured aliquot of the solution with phosphate buffer no. 1, *p*H 6, to a concentration of 100 units/ml. (estimated) and assay by the microbiologic assay in Method 1, Section A of this Chapter.

Section C: Determination of Polymyxin in Body Fluids and Other Substances

Blood Serum. Use microbiologic assay in Method 3, Section A of this Chapter. The diluent for preparing the standard curve is made by mixing equal parts of 7 per cent bovine albumin (Chapter 21) and 8 per cent phosphate buffer no. 8, *p*H 6. The polymyxin working standard is diluted to a concentration of 400 units/ml. in phosphate buffer no. 7, *p*H 6. From this further dilutions are made in the buffer no. 8-bovine albumin solution already described to obtain concentrations for the standard curve as described in Method 3, Section A of this Chapter.

The blood serum prepared as directed in Section D, Chapter 2, is diluted with an equal part of phosphate buffer no. 8, *p*H 6, and added to the cups on the plates. If the concentration of polymyxin is expected to be greater than 80 units/ml. (40 units/ml. when diluted 1:2) the serum is diluted in the buffer no. 8-bovine albumin solution already described to an estimated 10.0 units/ml. In determining the final potency the 1:2 or greater dilution must be taken into account.

Urine. Dilute the urine to an estimated 10.0 units/ml. in phosphate buffer no. 7, *p*H 6, and assay using the microbiologic assay in Method 3, Section A of this Chapter.

Tissue. Tissue is treated as described in Section D, Chapter 2, except phosphate buffer no. 7, *p*H 6, is used as the extractive and assayed by the microbiologic assay in Method 3, Section A of this Chapter.

Milk. Milk is assayed in a manner similar to that used in the assay for blood serum. The diluent for the standard curve is made by mixing equal parts of normal milk and phosphate buffer no. 8, *p*H 6. The sample is diluted with an equal part of the same buffer. If concentrations greater than 80 units/ml. are anticipated, the milk sample is diluted in the buffer-milk solution just described.

Animal Feed Supplements and Mixed Feeds. Polymyxin has little or no growth promoting properties and hence is not currently added to feeds for animal use.

9 NEOMYCIN

Section A: **Microbiologic Assay Methods for Neomycin**

A cylinder-plate assay method is described under Method 1 using *M. pyogenes* var. *aureus* as the test organism. A modification of this method is given under Method 2 for the assay of neomycin in body fluids, tissues, and other substances.

Two other microbiologic assay methods are also in general use. One method is a turbidimetric procedure using *K. pneumoniae* as the test organism and is similar to that described under streptomycin, Method 2, Section A, Chapter 3. The other is a cylinder-plate method using *B. subtilis*, which is similar to that under streptomycin, Method 1, Section A, Chapter 3. However, there are three different types of neomycin: A, B, and C, each of which gives a different potency value depending upon the organism used to test it. Neomycin A has been reported to give a value of 1,700 units (Waksman) when tested against *B. subtilis* and 20 units against *K. pneumoniae*. In our laboratory when a sample of neomycin C sulfate was assayed against a pure neomycin B sulfate standard (730 µg./mg.) using the *M pyogenes* var. *aureus* cylinder-plate method, a value of 565 µg./mg. was obtained. Using the *B. subtilis* plate method, a value of 394 µg./mg. was obtained. As the commercial neomycin seems to contain only neomycins B and C, the A type need not be considered. The commercial drug varies from practically pure B to 50 per cent B and C. Because the *M. pyogenes* var. *aureus* cylinder-plate method gives more nearly the same potency value for both neomycin B or C, it is the method of choice and is the only one given in detail.

When neomycin was discovered, it was evaluated in terms of Waksman units. Later, when it became desirable to use the drug in terms of the metric system, pure neomycin B base was assigned a value of 1,000 µg./mg. One Waksman unit is equivalent to 3.3 µg. of pure neomycin base.

METHOD 1: Cylinder-plate Assay Using *Micrococcus pyogenes* var. *aureus* as the Test Organism. (ATCC 6538P.)

Cylinders (Cups). Use stainless steel cylinders with an outside diameter of 8 mm. (±0.1 mm.), an inside diameter of 6 mm. (±0.1 mm.), and a length of 10 mm. (±0.1 mm.).

Culture Media. Use agar medium no. 11 for both the base and seed layers and agar medium no. 1 for carrying the test organism.

Working Standard. Keep the working standard at room temperature in tightly stoppered vials which in turn are kept in larger stoppered vials containing a suitable desiccant. Dry a portion of the working standard for three hours at 60 C. and a pressure of 5 mm. or less and use this dried portion to make a convenient stock solution by diluting with phosphate buffer no. 3, *p*H 8. This stock solution will keep for at least one month when stored under refrigeration (15 C. or less). If kept at −20 C., it will keep indefinitely.

Preparation of Sample. The methods of preparing the sample for the various neomycin preparations are described under the individual dosage forms in Section B of this Chapter.

Preparation of Test Organism. Maintain the test organism on agar medium no. 1 and transfer to a fresh slant once a week. Inoculate a fresh slant of agar medium no. 1 with the test organism and incubate at 32 to 35 C. for 16 to 24 hours. Wash the culture from the slant with sterile saline onto the surface of a Roux bottle containing 300 ml. of medium no. 1. Incubate at 32 to 35 C. for 16 to 24 hours. Wash the resulting growth from the agar surface with about 50 ml. of sterile saline. Standardize this suspension by dilution until it will give 80 per cent light transmission through a filter having a wave length of 6,500 Å. units in a Lumetron 400-A photoelectric colorimeter. Run test plates to determine the quantity of suspension to be added to each 100 ml. of agar melted and cooled to 48 C., for the seed layer which will give sharp, clear zones of inhibition. This quantity is usually about 0.5 per cent of the adjusted suspension. The suspension may be used until it fails to give clear, sharp zones.

Preparation of Plates. Add 21 ml. of melted nutrient agar medium no. 11 to each Petri dish (20 by 100 mm.). Distribute the agar evenly in the plates, cover with porcelain covers glazed only on the outside or other suitable covers, and allow to harden. Use the plates the same day they are prepared. Add 4 ml. of seeded agar (prepared as previously) to each plate, tilting the plates back and forth to spread the inoculated agar evenly over the surface. After the seed layer has hardened, place six cylinders on the inoculated agar surface so that they are at approximately 60 degree intervals on a 2.8 cm. radius.

Standard Curve and Assay Procedure. STANDARD CURVE. Use concentrations of neomycin standard of 4.0, 6.0, 8.0, 10.0, 12.0, 15.0, and 20.0 µg./ml. prepared from the stock standard by diluting in phosphate buffer no. 3, *p*H 8. A total of 18 plates is used in the preparation of the standard curve, three plates for each concentration except the 10.0 µg./ml. concentration. The latter concentration is the reference point and is included on each plate. On each of three plates, fill three cylinders with the 10.0 µg./ml. standard and the other three cylinders with the concentration of the standard under test. Thus there will be 54 of the 10.0 µg./ml. determinations and nine determinations for each of the other concentrations on the curve. Incubate the plates for 16 to 18 hours at 32 to 35 C. and measure the diameter of zones of inhibition. Average the readings of the 10.0 μg./ml. concentration and the readings of the concentration tested for each set of three plates, and average also all 54 readings of the 10.0 μg./ml. concentration. The average of the 54 readings of the 10.0 μg./ml. concentration is the correction point for the curve. Correct the average value obtained for each concentration to the figure it would be if the 10.0 μg./ml. reading for that set of three plates were the same as the correction point. Thus, if in correcting the 8.0 μg./ml. concentration, the average of the 54 readings of the 10.0 μg./ml. concentration is 18 mm. and the average of the 10.0 μg./ml. concentration of this set of three plates is 17.8 mm., the correction is plus 0.2 mm. If the average reading of the 8.0 μg./ml. concentration of these same three plates is 15 mm., the corrected value is then 15.2 mm. Plot these corrected values, including the average of 54 of the 10.0 μg./ml. concentration on two-cycle semilogarithmic paper, using the concentrations in μg./ml. as the ordinate (logarithmic scale) and the diameter of the zone of inhibition as the abscissa. Draw the standard curve through these points.

ASSAY PROCEDURE. Use one or more plates for each sample (usually three) and fill three cylinders on each plate with the 10.0 μg./ml. standard and three cylinders with the sample diluted to an estimated 10.0 μg./ml. with phosphate buffer no. 3, pH 8, alternating standard and sample. Incubate the plates for 16 to 18 hours at 32 to 35 C. and measure the diameter of each circle of inhibition. Average the zone readings of the standard and average the zone readings of the sample on the plates used. If the sample gives a larger average zone size than the average of the standard, add the difference between them to the 10.0 μg./ml. zone size of the standard curve. If the average sample zone size is smaller than the standard value, subtract the difference between them from the 10.0 μg./ml. zone size of the standard curve. From the curve read the concentration corresponding to these corrected values of zone sizes.

METHOD 2: Modification of Method 1 for the Assay of Neomycin in Blood Serum and Other Substances.

Proceed as directed in the microbiologic assay in Method 1, Section A of this Chapter, except that only 10 ml. of medium no. 11 is used as the base layer. The standard curve and assay procedure are the same as described in Method 1, except as otherwise directed in Section D of this Chapter.

Section B: Assay of Neomycin and its Pharmaceutical Dosage Forms

Neomycin Sulfate. Three different types of neomycin have been reported and designated as neomycins A, B, and C. It has recently been shown that neomycin A is actually one of the degradation products of either neomycin B or C and may be obtained by methanolysis of B or C. Neomycin A, also called neamine, can also be isolated from fermentation broths of *Streptomyces fradiae*. Hydrolysis of neomycin A gives the *meso* form of 1,3-diamino-4,5,6-trihydroxycyclohexane ($C_6H_{14}N_2O_3$). The empirical formula of neomycin A is believed to be $C_{12}H_{26}N_4O_6$. Neomycin A possesses biologic activity. Neomycins B and C are believed to be isomeric. The specific rotation of neomycin B is $+54$ degrees and neomycin C is $+80$ degrees. The structures of neomycins B and C have not yet been worked out. The methanolysis of neomycins B and C yields two basic fractions, one of these fractions is neomycin A, just mentioned, and the other has been named methyl-neobiosaminide. Further hydrolysis of the methyl-biosaminides yields furfural, indicating carbohydrate moities. Neomycins B and C have eight nitrogens in the molecule and it has been reported that all eight are basic amino groups, although there is some controversy over this. One empirical formula that has been suggested for neomycins B and C is $C_{29}H_{58}O_{16}N_8$. The sulfate would have 4 sulfuric acids if there are eight basic nitrogens. On this basis, the molecular weight of neomycin base would be 774.84 and the molecular weight of the sulfate 1167.16. Pure neomycin base has been assigned a theoretical potency of 1,000 $\mu g/mg$. The sulfate would contain 66.4 per cent of neomycin base and would have a theoretical potency of 664 $\mu g./mg$. If only six basic nitrogens are present, the sulfate would have a molecular weight of 1,068.88 and a theoretical potency of 726 $\mu g./mg$.

The neomycin sulfate sold commercially varies in composition from practically pure neomycin B to about 50 per cent mixtures of neomycin B and C. The sulfate is very soluble in water. To assay neomycin sulfate, dissolve an accurately weighed sample in phosphate buffer no. 3, pH 8, to give a solution containing 10 $\mu g./ml$. of neomycin base (estimated) and assay by the microbiologic assay in Method 1, Section A of this Chapter.

Neomycin Sulfate Ointment. Accurately weigh approximately 1 Gm. of the ointment and place it in a separatory funnel containing approximately 50 ml. of peroxide-free ether. Shake ointment and ether until homogeneous. Shake with a 25 ml. portion of phosphate buffer no. 3, pH 8. Remove the buffer layer and repeat the extraction with three 25 ml. quantities of buffer and any additional quantities as may be necessary to insure complete extraction. Combine the extracts and dilute to 10 $\mu g./ml$. (estimated) with phosphate buffer no. 3, pH 8.

The sample may also be prepared by placing an accurately weighed sample of approximately 1 Gm. of the ointment in a blending jar containing 499 ml. of phosphate buffer no. 3, pH 8, and 1 ml. of a 10 per cent aqueous solution of polysorbate 80. Using a high-speed blender, blend the mixture for five minutes and dilute an aliquot of the aqueous extract to 10 $\mu g./ml$. (estimated) with phosphate buffer no. 3, pH 8.

In either of these procedures, assay the final dilution by the microbiologic assay in Method 1, Section A of this Chapter.

Neomycin Sulfate Tablets. Place five tablets in a mortar and add approximately 20 ml. of phosphate buffer no. 3, pH 8. Disintegrate the tablets by grinding with a pestle. Transfer with the aid of small portions of the buffer solution to a 500 ml. volumetric flask and make to a volume of 500 ml. with the buffer solution. Dilute an aliquot to 10 $\mu g./ml$. (estimated) with phosphate buffer no. 3, pH 8.

The sample may also be prepared as follows: Place five tablets in a blending jar and add approximately 200 ml. of a 500 ml. quantity of phosphate buffer no. 3, pH 8. After blending for one minute with a high-speed blender, add the remainder of the 500 ml. of buffer. Blend again for one minute and dilute an aliquot to 10 μg./ml. (estimated) with phosphate buffer no. 3, pH 8.

After either of these procedures, assay the final dilution by the microbiologic assay in Method 1, Section A of this Chapter.

Neomycin Sulfate Ophthalmic. Dilute an accurately measured aliquot of the solution with phosphate buffer no. 3, pH 8, to 10 μg./ml. (estimated) and assay by the microbiologic assay in Method 1, Section A of this Chapter.

Neomycin Sulfate Nasal Spray. Dilute an accurately measured aliquot of the solution with phosphate buffer no. 3, pH 8, to 10 μg./ml. (estimated) and assay by the microbiologic assay in Method 1, Section A of this Chapter.

Section C: Determination of Neomycin in Body Fluids and Other Substances

Blood Serum. Use microbiologic assay in Method 2, Section A of this Chapter. Dilute the stock solution of the working standard to 40 μg./ml. in phosphate buffer no. 3, pH 8. Further dilute this 40 μg./ml. solution with normal serum for the standard curve using concentrations of neomycin of 0.02, 0.05, 0.10, 0.50, 1.0 (reference point), 2.0, and 4.0 μg./ml. and proceed as described in Method 2, Section A of this Chapter. Bovine albumin solution binds neomycin to such an extent that it cannot be used as a diluent. Neomycin is the only antibiotic so far encountered that appears to have a higher activity in the diffusion-plate assay in the presence of serum than in its absence.

The blood serum sample under test, prepared as directed in Section D, Chapter 2, is added to the cups undiluted unless a concentration greater than 4 μg./ml. is expected, in which case, the sample should be diluted to an estimated 1.0 μg./ml. with normal serum.

Urine. Urine is diluted according to its estimated neomycin content to a concentration of 10 μg./ml. with phosphate buffer no. 3, pH 8, and assayed by Method 1, Section A of this Chapter.

Tissue. Tissue is treated in the same manner as described under penicillin, Section D, Chapter 2, except phosphate buffer no. 3, pH 8, is used in the extraction. Assay by the microbiologic assay in Method 1, Section A of this Chapter.

10 ERYTHROMYCIN

Section A: **Microbiologic Assay Methods for Erythromycin**

A cylinder-plate assay method using *S. lutea* as the test organism is described in Method 1. Method 2 is a modification of Method 1 for use in testing body fluids, tissue, or milk, where the concentration of erythromycin is small. In Method 2 the amount of medium used in the base layer is decreased and a lighter inoculum is used to increase the sensitivity of the method.

METHOD 1: Cylinder-plate Assay Using *Sarcina lutea* as the Test Organism. (ATCC 9341.)

Cylinders (Cups). Use stainless steel cylinders with an outside diameter of 8 mm. (±0.1 mm.), an inside diameter of 6 mm. (±0.1 mm.), and a length of 10 mm. (±0.1 mm.).

Culture Media. Use agar medium no. 11 for both base and seed layers and medium no. 1 for carrying the test organism.

Working Standard. Keep the working standard under refrigeration in tightly stoppered vials, which in turn are kept in larger stoppered vials containing a suitable desiccant. In an atmosphere of about 10 per cent relative humidity transfer 30 to 50 mg. of the standard to a tared weighing bottle. Weigh the bottle, remove the stopper, place in a vacuum oven, and dry at a temperature of 60 C. and a pressure of 5 mm. of mercury or less for three hours. At the end of the drying period fill the vacuum oven with air dried by passing it through silica gel. Replace the stopper as quickly as possible and place the weighing bottle in a desiccator over silica gel, allow to cool to room temperature, and reweigh. Dissolve the weight of dry working standard in sufficient methyl alcohol to give a concentration of 10,000 µg./ml. Further dilute with phosphate buffer no. 3, *p*H 8, to give a stock solution of 1,000 µg./ml. This stock solution may be kept under refrigeration for one week. If kept at −20 C. the standard will remain stable for a month or longer.

Preparation of Sample. The method for preparing the sample of the various erythromycin preparations is described under the individual dosage forms in Section C of this Chapter.

Preparation of Test Organism. Streak an agar slant heavily with the test organism and incubate 24 to 36 hours at 26 C. Wash the growth off in about 3 ml. of broth medium no. 3. Use the suspension so obtained to inoculate the surface of a Roux bottle containing 300 ml. of agar medium no. 1. Spread the suspension over the entire surface with the aid of sterile glass beads. Incubate for 24 hours at 26 C. Wash the growth from the agar surface with 20 ml. of broth medium no. 3. If an aliquot of this bulk suspension gives 10 per cent light transmission in a Lumetron 400-A photoelectric colorimeter with a 6,500 Å. unit filter, it is satisfactory for use. It may be necessary to adjust the bulk suspension so that when diluted 1:10 it gives 10 per cent light transmission. This adjusted bulk suspension and not the 1:10 dilution of it is used in preparing the seed layer. The bulk suspension is kept refrigerated and may be used until satisfactory zones are no longer obtained. Run test plates to determine the amount of the standardized suspension to add to each 100 ml. of agar medium no. 11 which has been melted and cooled to 48 C. to produce clear, sharp zones of inhibition of appropriate size. Usually 0.1 to 0.5 ml. is required.

Preparation of Plates. Add 21 ml. of agar medium no. 11 to each Petri dish (20 by 100 mm.). Distribute the agar evenly in the plates. Cover with porcelain covers glazed only on the outside or other suitable covers and allow to harden. Use the plates the same day they are prepared. Add 4.0 ml. of seeded agar prepared as previously to each plate, tilting the plates back and forth to spread the agar evenly over the surface. After this seed layer has hardened, place six cylinders on the inoculated agar surface so that they are at approximately 60 degree intervals on a 2.8 cm. radius.

Standard Curve and Assay Procedure. STANDARD CURVE. Prepare solutions for the standard curve by diluting the working standard in phosphate buffer no. 3, *p*H 8, to make concentrations of 0.6, 0.7, 0.8, 0.9, 1.0, 1.1, 1.2, 1.3, 1.4, and 1.5 µg./ml. Use three plates for the determination of each concentration on the curve except the 1.0 µg./ml. concentration, a total of 27 plates. The 1.0 µg./ml. concentration is the reference point of the curve. On each of three plates fill three cylinders with the 1.0 µg./ml. standard and the other three cylinders with the concentration of standard under test. Thus there will be 81 of the 1.0 µg. determinations and nine determinations for each of the other points on the curve. Incubate the plates for 16 to 18 hours at 32 to 35 C. and measure the diameters of the circles of inhibition. Average the readings of the 1.0 µg./ml. concentration and the readings of the concentration tested for each set of three plates and average also all 81 readings of the 1.0 µg./ml. concentration. The average of the 81 readings of the 1.0 µg./ml. concentration is the correction point for the curve. Correct the average value obtained for each concentration to the figure it would be if the average 1.0 µg./ml. reading for that set of three plates were the same as the correction point. Thus, if in correcting the 0.8 µg. concentration the average of the 81 readings of the 1.0 µg. concentration is 20.0 mm. and the average of the 1.0 µg. concentration of this set of three plates is 19.8 mm., the correction is plus 0.2 mm. If the average readings of the 0.8 µg. concentration of these same three plates is 19.0 mm., the corrected value is 19.2 mm. Plot these corrected values including the average of the 1.0 μg./ml. concentration on two-cycle semilogarithmic paper using the concentration in μg./ml. as the ordinate (the logarithmic scale) and the diameter of the zone of inhibition as the abscissa. Draw the standard curve through these points. As pointed out in the discussion of plate assays in the chapter on penicillin, when a sufficient number of satisfactory standard curves have been accumulated a master curve may be constructed thus obviating the necessity for setting up a curve each time samples are tested. In this case it is desirable to check the slope of the master curve at frequent intervals.

ASSAY OF SAMPLE. Use one or more plates for each sample (usually three) and fill three cylinders on each plate with the 1.0 μg./ml. standard and three cylinders with the sample diluted to an estimated 1.0 μg./ml. in phosphate buffer no. 3, *p*H 8, alternating standard and sample. Incubate the plates at 32 to 35 C. for 16 to 18 hours and measure the diameter of each circle of inhibition. Average the zone readings of the sample and average the zone readings of the standard. If the sample gives a larger average zone size than the average of the standard, add the difference between them to the 1.0 μg./ml. zone size of the standard curve. If the average sample zone size is smaller than the standard zone size, subtract the difference between them from the 1.0 μg./ml. zone size of the standard curve. From the curve read the potencies corresponding to these corrected values of zone sizes.

METHOD 2: Modification of Method 1 for the Assay of Erythromycin in Blood Serum and Other Substances.

The conduct of this test is essentially the same as described in Method 1 with these exceptions: In the preparation of plates add 10 ml. of agar medium no. 11 to each 20 by 100 mm. Petri dish for the base layer. Add 0.2 ml. of the adjusted bulk suspension to each 100 ml. of agar medium no. 11, which has been melted and cooled to 48 C. for the seed layer. In preparing the standard curve dilute the working standard to a concentration of 10.0 μg./ml. in phosphate buffer no. 3, *p*H 8. From this 10.0 μg./ml. concentration further dilute, using a suitable diluent as directed in Section D of this Chapter, to make concentrations of 0.02, 0.04, 0.06, 0.10, 0.20, 0.40, and 0.80 μg./ml. The 0.2 μg./ml. concentration is the reference point for the curve.

Section B: Physicochemical Method for Erythromycin

Direct spectrophotometric examination of erythromycin solutions does not provide adequate absorption suitable for the measurement of dilute solutions. After mild acid or alkaline hydrolysis, the absorption curves exhibit strong absorption in certain regions of the spectrum. It has been observed that solutions of erythromycin, when exposed to mild acid conditions do not, on subsequent alkaline hydrolysis, yield the characteristic increase in absorption at 236 mμ. In the method to be described, it has been found necessary to run an acid inactivated sample as a blank in order to obtain results that are comparable to those obtained by microbiologic assay.

The time of standing with acid, the concentration of acid, the time of heating with alkali, and the concentration of alkali have been carefully studied to give optimum conditions. Care should be taken that the same distilled water is used throughout the assay as well as in the reference cell for absorbance readings. Considerable variation in the absorbance of distilled water from different sources, when measured at 236 mμ, will cause appreciable errors in the method. Also all glassware used should be thoroughly cleaned in chromic acid cleaning solution.

It is advisable to run a point or two on the standard curve each day because, while the curve is a straight line, the slope may vary slightly from day to day.

Spectrophotometric Method. This method is adapted from Kuzel et al.[14]

REAGENTS. The reagents include: 0.05 N sulfuric acid, 0.05 N sodium hydroxide, and alkaline reagent prepared as follows: Dissolve 42 Gm. of trisodium phosphate, reagent grade, in 125 ml. of 0.5 N sodium hydroxide, and 100 ml. of distilled water. Warm on a steam bath to effect solution. Cool, dilute to 250 ml. with distilled water, and filter if necessary.

PREPARATION OF STANDARD. Accurately weigh approximately 50 mg. of the erythromycin standard, previously dried for three hours at 60 C. in vacuo, and transfer to a 250 ml. volumetric flask. Dissolve the standard completely in 50 ml. of methanol and dilute with distilled water to 250 ml. (This solution may be kept for one week in the refrigerator.) Transfer 2.5, 5.0, 7.5, and 10.0 aliquots to 25 ml. volumetric flasks. Add 7.5, 5.0, and 2.5 ml. of distilled water to the flasks to give each a total volume of 10.0 ml. Use four 25 ml. volumetric flasks for each concentration.

PREPARATION OF SAMPLE. Accurately weigh approximately 35 mg. of the erythromycin to be tested, dissolve it in 50 ml. of methanol and dilute to 250 ml. with distilled water. Place four 10.0 ml. aliquots into four 25 ml. volumetric flasks. The preparation of the sample for the various erythromycin products, such as tablets, will be described in Section C of this Chapter.

BLANK. Use distilled water.

PROCEDURE. To two flasks containing each concentration of the standard and two flasks of the sample add 1 ml. of 0.05 N sulfuric acid, mix thoroughly, and allow to stand for one hour (± 5 minutes). Meanwhile to the other two flasks of standard and two flasks of sample, add 2 ml. of the alkaline reagent and heat in a 60 C. ± 2 C. constant temperature water bath for 15 minutes. After heating, remove the flasks from the bath and cool in an ice bath until the contents are approximately at room temperature. Dilute to 25 ml. with distilled water and mix thoroughly. Transfer to 1 cm. absorption cells and determine the absorbance at 236 mμ in a suitable spectrophotometer against distilled water as a blank.

After the acid treated standards and sample have reacted for one hour, add 1 ml. of 0.05 N sodium hydroxide to each flask, 2 ml. of the alkaline reagent and heat in a 60 C. ± 2 C. water bath for 15 minutes. After heating, remove the flasks from the bath and cool in an ice bath until the contents are approximately at room temperature. Dilute to 25 ml. with distilled water and mix thoroughly. Transfer to 1 cm. absorption cells and determine the absorbance at 236 mμ against distilled water as a blank. Subtract these readings on the standard solutions from the corresponding absorbances obtained on the alkali treated (nonacid treated) standards and plot these differences as the ordinate against erythromycin concentration as the abscissa on graph paper. This is the standard curve.

The concentration of erythromycin in the sample is obtained by reading the difference between the absorbances of the acid treated and the alkali treated (nonacid treated) sample from the standard curve.

Section C: Assay of Erythromycin and its Pharmaceutical Dosage Forms

Erythromycin Base. The exact chemical structure of erythromycin has not yet been determined. It is believed to have an empirical formula of $C_{37}H_{67-69}NO_{13}$, which would give a molecular weight of 733.96 or 735.96. The base crystallizes as a dihydrate and may also contain solvent of crystallization. It is slightly soluble in water (about 1 mg./ml.) and soluble in alcohol, ether, and chloroform. It decomposes rapidly in acid solution. Erythromycin has only one nitrogen which is believed to be present as a dimethylamino group. One of the products of acid degradation of erythromycin that has been isolated is 3-dimethylamino-4-desoxy-5-methyl aldopentose, $C_8H_{17}NO_3$.

The anhydrous erythromycin base has been assigned a theoretical potency of 1,000 μg./mg.

A second type of erythromycin has been isolated and designated as erythromycin B. Erythromycin B is similar to erythromycin in most of its physical and chemical properties and probably differs from it only in some minor grouping. Microbiologically it is about 75 to 85 per cent as active.

Erythromycin Dihydrate. $C_{37}H_{67}NO_{13} \cdot 2H_2O$. M.W. = 770.0. Theoretical potency = 953 μg./mg.

To assay erythromycin base, dissolve about 100 mg. accurately weighed in 10 ml. methanol, dilute with phosphate buffer no. 3, pH 8, to give a concentration of 1.0 μg./ml. (estimated), and assay by the microbiologic assay in Method 1, Section A of this Chapter.

The physicochemical method, Section B of this Chapter, may also be used, in which case prepare the sample as follows: Accurately weigh approximately 35 mg., dissolve it in 50 ml. of methanol, and dilute to 250 ml. with distilled water.

Erythromycin Stearate. $C_{37}H_{67}NO_{13} \cdot HC_{18}H_{35}O_2$. M.W. = 1,018.13. Theoretical potency = 721 μg./mg.

Erythromycin sterate is a salt of erythromycin, not an ester, and is insoluble in water, soluble in methanol, ethanol, ether, and chloroform. To assay, dissolve about 200 mg., accurately weighed, in methanol and make to 100 ml.

with methanol. Immediately before putting in the cylinders, dilute an aliquot with phosphate buffer no. 3, pH 8, to give a concentration of 1.0 μg./ml. (estimated), and assay by the microbiologic assay in Method 1, Section A of this Chapter.

Erythromycin Ethylcarbonate (Ester). $C_{37}H_{66}NO_{13} \cdot COOC_2H_5$. M.W. = 806.06. Theoretical potency = 910 μg./mg.

Erythromycin ethylcarbonate is insoluble in water and soluble in methanol, ethanol, acetone, chloroform, ether, and dioxane. To assay dissolve about 100 mg., accurately weighed, in 40 ml. of methanol, dilute with water to 100 ml., and allow to stand for 48 hours at room temperature. (This allows the ester to hydrolyze completely to erythromycin.) At the end of this time dilute a suitable aliquot with phosphate buffer no. 3, pH 8, to give an erythromycin concentration of 1.0 μg./ml. (estimated) and assay by the microbiologic assay in Method 1, Section A of this Chapter.

The physicochemical method, Section B of this Chapter, may also be used, in which case prepare the sample as follows: Accurately weigh approximately 35 mg., dissolve in 50 ml. of methanol, and dilute to 250 ml. with distilled water.

Erythromycin Glucoheptonate. $C_{37}H_{67}NO_{13} \cdot C_7H_{14}O_8$. M.W. = 960.15. Theoretical potency = 764.3 μg./mg.

This salt is freely soluble in water, methanol, and ethanol and insoluble in ether. To assay, dissolve an accurately weighed sample in water to give an erythromycin concentration of 1.0 mg./ml. (estimated). Further dilute an aliquot of this solution with phosphate buffer no. 3, pH 8, to give an erythromycin concentration of 1.0 μg./ml. (estimated) and assay by the microbiologic assay in Method 1, Section A of this Chapter.

The physicochemical method, Section B of this Chapter, may also be used in which case prepare the sample as follows: Accurately weigh approximately 50 mg., dissolve in 50 ml. of methanol, and dilute to 250 ml. with distilled water.

Erythromycin Lactobionate. $C_{37}H_{67}NO_{13} \cdot C_{12}H_{22}O_{12}$. M.W. = 1,092.27. Theoretical potency = 672 μg./mg.

This salt is freely soluble in water. To assay, follow the same procedure that is described under erythromycin glucoheptonate, Section C of this Chapter.

Erythromycin Capsules. Transfer the contents of 10 capsules to a 500 ml. volumetric flask, add sufficient methanol to dissolve the erythromycin, and make to volume with methanol. Dilute a suitable aliquot with phosphate buffer no. 3, pH 8, to give an erythromycin concentration of 1.0 μg./ml. (estimated) and assay by the microbiologic assay in Method 1, Section A of this Chapter.

Erythromycin Tablets. These tablets are enteric coated and may contain erythromycin alone or erythromycin and sulfonamides. Either preparation may be assayed as follows: Place 10 tablets in a glass blending jar containing approximately 100 ml. of methanol. Blend for two minutes in a high-speed blender. Add 400 ml. of phosphate buffer no. 3, *p*H 8, and blend again for two minutes. Dilute a suitable aliquot with phosphate buffer no. 3, *p*H 8, to give an erythromycin concentration of 1.0 μg./ml. (estimated) and assay by the microbiologic assay in Method 1, Section A of this Chapter.

Sulfonamides and other substances in the tablets will interfere in the physicochemical method, Section B of this Chapter. However, this method may be used, if the erythromycin is separated from the interfering substances, by proceeding as follows: Finely grind 10 tablets by means of a mortar and pestle. Transfer an accurately weighed sample of the powdered tablets containing 35 mg. of erythromycin (estimated) to a 125 ml. separatory funnel. Add 25 ml. of chloroform and 25 ml. of water and shake for two minutes. Add 10 ml. of 10 per cent sodium hydroxide, shake for one minute, and collect the the chloroform layer in another separatory funnel. Repeat the extraction with three additional 20 ml. portions of chloroform and combine all the chloroform extracts. Shake the combined chloroform extracts with 10 ml. of water. Filter the chloroform layer through about 5 Gm. of anhydrous sodium sulfate, retained in a funnel by means of glass wool or cotton, into a 150 ml. beaker. Shake the aqueous wash with two 10 ml. portions of chloroform and rinse the filtering funnel and sodium sulfate with these washes, adding them to the combined chloroform extracts. Evaporate the chloroform gently on a steam bath with the aid of an air jet to a volume of 1 to 2 ml. and finish the evaporation to dryness with the air jet. Transfer the erythromycin residue quantitatively to a 250 ml. volumetric flask by dissolving in 10 ml. of methanol and washing the beaker with a further 40 ml. of methanol. Make to 250 ml. with water. This solution is then used as the sample solution and the method is followed as in Section B of this Chapter.

Erythromycin Ointment. Place an accurately weighed sample of approximately 1 Gm. of ointment in a glass blending jar containing 100 ml. of polyethylene glycol 400. Using a high-speed blender, blend the mixture for two minutes and filter the solution through a cotton plug or filter paper. Dilute the filtrate with phosphate buffer no. 3, *p*H 8, to give an erythromycin concentration of 1.0 μg./ml. (estimated) and assay by the microbiologic assay in Method 1, Section A of this Chapter.

Erythromycin Ethylcarbonate Oral Suspension. This preparation is sold both with and without sulfonamides. Both products are in the form of dry powders to which the pharmacist adds water just prior to dispensing. Both preparations are assayed as follows: Add the amount of water recommended in the labeling, shake well, and transfer a 5 ml. aliquot to a 100 ml. volumetric flask. Add 40 ml. of methanol to dissolve the erythromycin ethylcarbonate and make to 100 ml. with water. Allow to stand for 48 hours at room temperature to hydrolyze the ester, dilute a suitable aliquot with phosphate buffer no. 3, *p*H 8, to give an erythromycin concentration of 1.0 μg./ml. (estimated), and assay by the microbiologic assay in Method 1, Section A of this Chapter.

Erythromycin Coated Granules. Use the contents of 10 packets and follow the method described for erythromycin tablets, Section C of this Chapter, using the microbiologic assay procedure.

Erythromycin Stearate Oral Suspension. Transfer 5 ml. of the suspension to a 100 ml. volumetric flask and make to 100 ml. with methanol. Immediately before putting in the cylinders, dilute an aliquot with phosphate buffer no. 3, *p*H 8, to give a concentration of 1.0 μg./ml. (estimated) and assay by the microbiologic assay in Method 1, Section A of this Chapter.

Section D: Determination of Erythromycin in Body Fluids and Other Substances

Blood serum. Use the *S. lutea* cylinder-plate microbiologic assay, Method 2, Section A of this Chapter. The erythromycin working stock standard solution is diluted to a concentration of 10.0 μg./ml. in phosphate buffer no. 3, *p*H 8. From this further dilutions are made in 7 per cent bovine albumin (fraction V), prepared as described in Chapter 21, to make solutions for the standard curve of the same concentrations of erythromycin as described in Method 2 of this Chapter.

The blood sample is prepared as in Section D, Chapter 2, and the serum is placed in the cups undiluted unless a concentration greater than 0.80 μg./ml. is expected. In this case the sample should be diluted to an estimated 0.20 μg./ml. with bovine albumin solution.

Urine. Use the microbiologic assay in Method 2, Section A of this Chapter, for the assay of erythromycin in urine. Erythromycin is readily excreted in the urine and is found in concentrations varying from about 10 to 2,000 μg./ml. of urine, depending in part upon the dose and partly on the subject. Wide variations are found in different individuals on the same dose schedule. The urine is diluted to an estimated 0.20 μg./ml. for assay in phosphate buffer no. 3, *p*H 8.

Tissue. Tissue is prepared as described in Section D, Chapter 2, except phosphate buffer no. 3, *p*H 8, is used as the extractive, and the extract is then assayed using Method 2, Section A of this Chapter.

Milk. Use assay Method 2, Section A of this Chapter, and dilute the milk to an estimated 0.2 μg./ml. using normal milk. The standard curve is also made using milk free of inhibitory substances. If the dilution of the milk is expected to be 1:20 or greater, phosphate buffer no. 3, *p*H 8, is used as the diluent and the standard curve is set up in the same buffer. At this dilution the milk constituents do not interfere with the diffusion of erythromycin.

Animal Feed Supplements and Mixed Feeds. Erythromycin has the property of promoting animal growth but at the present time it is not used as a constituent of animal feeds.

11 CARBOMYCIN

Section A: *Microbiologic Assay Methods for Carbomycin*

A cylinder-plate method using *S. lutea* as the test organism is described for the assay of carbomycin and its dosage forms. For the assay of carbomycin in body fluids, this same method is modified to make it more sensitive. The increase in sensitivity is accomplished by using a lighter inoculum and less medium in the base layer. The modified procedure is described in Method 2.

METHOD 1: Cylinder-plate Assay Using *Sarcina lutea* as the Test Organism. (ATCC 9341.)

Cylinders (Cups). Use stainless steel cylinders with an outside diameter of 8 mm. (±0.1 mm.), an inside diameter of 6 mm. (±0.1 mm.), and a length of 10 mm. (±0.1 mm.).

Culture Media. Use agar medium no. 11 for both base and seed layers and agar medium no. 1 for carrying the test organism.

Working Standard. Keep the working standard under refrigeration in tightly stoppered vials, which in turn are kept in larger stoppered vials containing a suitable desiccant. The standard is hygroscopic and a convenient quantity should be dried in a vacuum oven at a temperature of 60 C. and a pressure of 5 mm. of mercury or less for three hours. Dissolve the weight of dry working standard in sufficient methyl alcohol to give a concentration of 1,000 μg./ml. Further dilute with phosphate buffer no. 3, *p*H 8, to give a stock solution of 100 μg./ml. The methyl alcohol solution and the proper amount of buffer should be added to each other rapidly to avoid precipitation. This stock solution may be kept under refrigeration for one week. If kept at −20 C., the standard will remain stable for a month or longer.

Preparation of Sample. The method for preparing the sample of the carbomycin preparations is described under the individual dosage forms in Section B of this Chapter.

Preparation of Test Organism. Streak an agar slant heavily with the test organism and incubate 24 to 36 hours at 26 C. Wash the growth off in about 3 ml. of broth medium no. 3. Use the suspension so obtained to inoculate the surface of a Roux bottle containing 300 ml. of agar medium no. 1. Spread the suspension over the entire surface with the aid of sterile glass beads. Incubate for 24 hours at 26 C. Wash the growth from the agar surface with 20 ml. of broth medium no. 3. If an aliquot of this bulk suspension, when diluted 1:10 with broth medium no. 3, gives 10 per cent light transmission in a Lumetron 400-A photoelectric colorimeter with a 6,500 Å. unit filter, it is satisfactory for use. It may be necessary to adjust the bulk suspension so that when diluted 1:10 it gives 10 per cent light transmission. This adjusted bulk suspension and not the 1:10 dilution of it is used in preparing the seed layer. The bulk suspension is kept refrigerated and may be used until satisfactory zones are no longer obtained. Run test plates to determine the quantity of this standardized suspension to be added to each 100 ml. of agar medium no. 11, melted and cooled to 48 C. to give clear, sharp inhibitory zones of appropriate size. This quantity is usually 0.1 to 0.5 ml.

Preparation of Plates. Add 21 ml. of agar medium no. 11 to each Petri dish (20 by 100 mm.). Distribute the agar evenly in the plates, cover with porcelain covers glazed only on the outside or other suitable covers, and allow to harden. Use the plates the same day they are prepared. Add 4.0 ml. of seeded agar prepared as previously to each plate, tilting the plates back and forth to spread the agar evenly over the surface. After the seed layer has hardened, place six cylinders on the inoculated agar surface so that they are at approximately 60 degree intervals on a 2.8 cm. radius.

Standard Curve and Assay Procedure. STANDARD CURVE. Prepare solutions for the standard curve by diluting the working standard in phosphate buffer no. 3, *p*H 8, to make concentrations of 0.6, 0.7, 0.8, 0.9, 1.0, 1.1, 1.2, 1.3, 1.4, and 1.5 μg./ml. Use three plates for the determination of each concentration on the curve except the 1.0 μg./ml. concentration, a total of 27 plates. The 1.0 μg./ml. concentration is the reference point of the curve. On each of three plates fill three cylinders with the 1.0 μg./ml. standard and the other three cylinders with the concentration of standard under test. Thus there will be 81 of the 1.0 μg. determinations and nine determinations for each of the other points on the curve. Incubate the plates for 16 to 18 hours at 32 to 35 C. and measure the diameters of the circles of inhibition. Average the readings of the 1.0 μg./ml. concentration and the readings of the concentration tested for each set of three plates and average also all 81 readings of the 1.0 μg./ml. concentration. The average of the 81 readings of the 1.0 μg./ml. concentration is the correction point for the curve. Correct the average value obtained for each concentration to the figure it would be if the average 1.0 μg./ml. reading for that set of three plates were the same as the correction point. Thus, if in correcting the 0.8 μg. concentration the average of the 81 readings of the 1.0 μg. concentration is 20.0 mm. and the average of the 1.0 μg. concentration of this set of three plates is 19.8 mm., the correction is +0.2 mm. If the average reading of the 0.8 μg. concentration of these same three plates is 19.0 mm., the corrected value is 19.2 mm. Plot these corrected values including the average of the 1.0 μg./ml. concentration on two-cycle semilogarithmic paper using the concentration in μg./ml. as the ordinate (the logarithmic scale) and the diameter of the zone of inhibition as the abscissa. Draw the standard curve through these points. As pointed out in the discussion of plate assays in the chapter on penicillin when a sufficient number of satisfactory standard curves have been accumulated a master curve may be constructed, thus obviating the necessity for setting up a curve each time samples are tested. In this case, it is desirable to check the slope of the master curve at frequent intervals.

ASSAY OF SAMPLE. Use one or more plates for each sample (usually three) and fill three cylinders on each plate with the 1.0 μg./ml. standard and three cylinders with the sample diluted to an estimated 1.0 μg./ml. in phosphate buffer no. 3, *p*H 8, alternating standard and sample. Incubate the plates at 32 to 35 C. for 16 to 18 hours and measure the diameter of each circle of inhibition. Average the zone readings of the sample and average the zone readings of the standard. If the sample gives a larger average zone size than the average of the standard, add the difference between them to the 1.0 μg./ml. zone size of the standard curve. If the average sample zone size is smaller than the standard zone size, subtract the difference between them from the 1.0 μg. zone size of the curve. From the curve read the potencies corresponding to these corrected values of zone sizes.

METHOD 2: Modification of Method 1 for the Assay of Carbomycin in Blood Serum and Other Substances.

Culture Medium. Use culture medium no. 11 for the base and seed layer.

Test Organism. The test organism suspension is prepared as described under Method 1. The amount of this suspension used in preparing the seed layer is 0.1 to 0.5 ml. of the adjusted bulk suspension for every 100 ml. of agar medium no. 11, which has been melted and cooled to 48 C.

Preparation of Plates. Add 6 ml. of nutrient agar no. 11 to each Petri dish (20 by 100 mm.), distribute evenly in the plates, and allow to harden. Use the plates the same day they are prepared. Add 4 ml. of seeded nutrient agar prepared as previously to each plate and spread evenly over the surface of the hardened base agar.

Standard Curve and Assay Procedure. Prepare a standard curve by diluting the carbomycin working standard stock solution to 20 μg./ml. in phosphate buffer no. 3, *p*H 8. From this, further dilutions are made in either normal serum or buffer as directed in Section C of this Chapter to make concentrations of 0.05, 0.08, 0.10, 0.20, 0.50, 1.0, and 2.0 μg./ml. The 0.5 μg./ml. concentration is the reference point of the curve.

Section B: Assay of Carbomycin and its Pharmaceutical Dosage Forms

Carbomycin. The exact chemical structure of carbomycin is not known. It has been reported to have an empirical formula of $C_{41}H_{67}NO_{16}$. On this basis, the molecular weight would be 830.0. It is monobasic and forms salts with mineral acids. The base is only partially soluble in water, but the salts, such as the hydrochloride, are freely soluble in water. Two types of carbomycin are known and have been designated as carbomycin A and carbomycin B. They are closely related in chemical structure and may be isomeric. They are reported to have the same antimicrobial activity.

Carbomycin base has been assigned a theoretical potency of 1,000 μg./mg. To assay carbomycin base, dissolve 100 mg. accurately weighed in 10 ml. methanol, dilute with phosphate buffer no. 3, pH 8, to give a concentration of 1.0 μg./ml. (estimated), and assay by the microbiologic assay in Method 1, Section A of this chapter.

Carbomycin Hydrochloride. $C_{41}H_{67}NO_{16}\cdot HCl.$ M.W. = 866.47. Theoretical potency = 958 μg./mg.

To assay, dissolve an accurately weighed sample in water to give a carbomycin concentration of 1.0 mg./ml. (estimated). Further dilute an aliquot of this solution with phosphate buffer no. 3, pH 8, to give a carbomycin concentration of 1.0 μg./ml. (estimated) and assay by the microbiologic assay in Method 1, Section A of this Chapter.

Carbomycin Tablets. Place 10 tablets in a glass blending jar containing approximately 100 ml. methanol. Blend for two minutes in a high-speed blender. Add 400 ml. of phosphate buffer no. 3, pH 8, and blend again for two minutes. Dilute a suitable aliquot with phosphate buffer no. 3, pH 8, to give a carbomycin concentration of 1.0 μg./ml. (estimated) and assay by the microbiologic assay in Method 1, Section A of this Chapter.

Section C: Determination of Carbomycin in Body Fluids and Other Substances

Blood Serum. Use the microbiologic assay in Method 2, Section A of this Chapter. The standard curve must be made in normal serum lacking inhibitory properties. Bovine albumin cannot be substituted for normal serum as it enhances the diffusion of carbomycin, even in low concentrations. The carbomycin working standard is diluted to 20 μg./ml. in phosphate buffer no. 3, pH 8, and from this dilutions are made in normal serum in the concentrations described in Method 2 for the standard curve. The blood sample is prepared as in Section D, Chapter 2, and the serum is placed in the cups undiluted. If concentrations greater than 2.0 μg./ml. are expected, dilute the serum under test to an estimated 0.50 μg./ml. in normal serum.

Urine. Use the microbiologic assay in Method 2, Section A of this Chapter. Carbomycin is not excreted in large amounts in the urine. Dilute the urine in phosphate buffer no. 3, pH 8, to an estimated 0.50 μg./ml.

Tissue. Tissue is treated as described in Section D, Chapter 2, except phosphate buffer no. 3, pH 8, is used as the extractive. Assay by Method 2, Section A of this Chapter.

Milk. Use the microbiologic assay in Method 2, Section A of this Chapter. Prepare the standard curve, using normal milk as the diluent. If a concentration of greater than 2.0 µg./ml. is anticipated, dilute the sample under test in normal milk to an estimated 0.50 µg./ml.

Animal Feed Supplements and Mixed Feeds. Carbomycin possesses growth promoting properties for some animals, but as yet is not used in commercial feeds.

12 VIOMYCIN

Section A: **Microbiologic Assay Methods for Viomycin**

Two types of methods are described, a cylinder-plate method using *B. subtilis* as the test organism and a turbidimetric method using *K. pneumoniae* as the test organism. In testing for viomycin in body fluids the *B. subtilis* cylinder-plate method can be made more sensitive by adding sodium sulfadiazine to the agar medium. This modification is described in Method 3.

METHOD 1: Cylinder-plate Method Using *Bacillus subtilis* as the Test Organism. (ATCC 6633.)

Cylinders (Cups). Use stainless steel cylinders with an outside diameter of 8 mm. (±0.1 mm.), an inside diameter of 6 mm. (±0.1 mm.), and a length of 10 mm. (±0.1 mm.).

Culture Media. Use agar medium no. 5 for both the seed and base layers. Maintain the test organism on agar medium no. 1.

Working Standard. The viomycin standard is the anhydrous viomycin base, which has been assigned a potency of 1,000 μg./ml. Dissolve a weighed sample of the anhydrous base in water to obtain a concentration of 1,000 μg./ml. Keep this stock solution at a temperature of 5 C. and do not use after one week.

Preparation of Sample. Dissolve the viomycin sulfate to be tested in phosphate buffer no. 3, pH 8, to give a viomycin concentration of 50 μg./ml. (estimated).

Preparation of Test Organism. Prepare a spore suspension by growing the organism in Roux bottles on agar medium no. 1, for one week at 37 C. Suspend the spores in sterile distilled water and heat for 30 minutes at 65 C. Wash the spore suspension three times with sterile distilled water, heat again for 30 minutes at 65 C., and resuspend in sterile distilled water. Maintain the spore suspension at approximately 15 C. Determine by appropriate tests the quantity of spore suspension to be added to each 100 ml. of agar medium no. 5 for the secondary layer that will give sharp, clear zones of inhibition. This quantity is usually 0.3 to 0.8 per cent. This spore suspension will keep for months at approximately 15 C.

An equally satisfactory suspension may be prepared by growing the organism in liquid medium no. 6 containing manganese, which induces spore formation. Inoculate medium no. 3 from a stock slant of *B. subtilis* and incubate at 26 C. for four to six days on a mechanical shaking apparatus (reciprocal shaker). Determine the degree of sporulation by direct smear and stain. If 80 per cent or more of the cells are in the spore state, centrifuge the culture, remove the supernatant, and reconstitute the cells to 30 per cent of the original broth volume with sterile saline. Heat shock the spore suspension by immersing in a water bath at 70 C. for 30 minutes and store under refrigeration. Determine by using trial plates the optimum percentage of inoculum, to be added as the secondary layer, to give clear, sharp zones, usually 0.3 to 0.8 per cent.

Preparation of Plates. Add 10 ml. of melted agar medium no. 5 to each Petri dish (20 by 100 mm.). Distribute the agar evenly in the plates, cover with porcelain covers glazed only on the outside or other suitable covers, and allow to harden. Use the plates the same day they are prepared. Melt the agar medium no. 5 to be used for the secondary (seed) layer, cool to 55 to 60 C., and add the spore suspension. Mix thoroughly and add 4 ml. of this seeded medium to each plate. Tilt the plates back and forth to spread the inoculated medium evenly over the surface. Place six cylinders on the inoculated agar surface so that they are at approximately 60 degree intervals on a 2.8 cm. radius.

Standard Curve and Assay Procedure. STANDARD CURVE. Prepare daily in phosphate buffer no. 3, *p*H 8, from the stock standard solution concentrations of 3, 10, 20, 30, 50, 100, 150, and 200 μg./ml. solutions. A total of 21 plates is used in the preparation of the standard curve, three plates for each solution except the 50 μg./ml. solution. This latter concentration is used as the reference point and is included on each plate. On each of three plates fill three cylinders with the 50 μg./ml. standard and the other three cylinders with the concentration under test. Thus there will be 63 of the 50 μg./ml. determinations and nine determinations for each of the other points on the curve. Incubate the plates for 16 to 18 hours at 37 C. and measure the diameter of each circle of inhibition. Average the readings of the 50 μg./ml. concentration and readings of the concentrations tested for each set of three plates and average also all 63 readings of the 50 μg./ml. concentrations. The average of the 63 readings of the 50 μg./ml. concentration is the correction point for the curve. Correct the average value obtained for each concentration to the figure it would be if the average 50 μg./ml. reading for that set of three plates were the same as the correction point. Thus, if in correcting the 30 μg./ml. concentration, the average of the 63 readings of the 50 μg./ml. concentration is 16.5 mm. and the average of the 50 μg./ml. concentration of this set of three plates is 16.3 mm., the correction is +0.2 mm. If the average readings of the 30 μg./ml. concentration of these same three plates is 15.9 mm., the corrected value is then 16.1 mm. Plot these corrected values including the average of the 50 μg./ml. concentration on two-cycle semilogarithmic paper using the concentration in μg./ml. as the ordinate (the logarithmic scale) and the diameter of the zone of inhibition as the abscissa. Draw the standard curve through these points. The eight points selected to determine the curve are arbitrary and should be so chosen that the limits of the curve will fill the needs of the laboratory. However, the potency of the sample under test should fall in the interval of from 60 to 150 per cent of the correction point of the standard curve.

ASSAY OF SAMPLE. Use three plates for each sample. Fill three cylinders on each plate with the 50 μg./ml. standard and three cylinders with the 50 μg./ml. (estimated) sample, alternating standard and sample. Incubate the plates for 16 to 18 hours at 37 C. and measure the diameter of each circle of inhibition. Average the zone readings of the standard and average the zone readings of the sample on the three plates used. If the sample gives a larger average zone size than the average of the standard, add the difference between them to the 50 μg./ml. zone size of the standard curve. If the average sample zone size is smaller than the standard zone size, subtract the difference between them from the 50 μg./ml. zone size of the curve. From the curve read the potencies corresponding to these corrected values of zone sizes.

METHOD 2: Turbidimetric Method Using *Klebsiella pneumoniae* as the Test Organism. (ATCC 10031.)

Test Culture and Media. Employ agar medium no. 7 for maintaining the test organism. Transfer stock cultures every two weeks for test purposes. Transfer the organism to fresh agar medium no. 7 slants and incubate overnight at 37 C. Suspend the growth from two to three of these slants in sterile distilled water and add approximately 5 ml. of culture suspension to each of two Roux bottles containing agar medium no. 7. Incubate the bottles overnight at 37 C., harvest the growth, and suspend in sufficient sterile distilled water to give a light transmission reading of 65 per cent, using a filter of 6,500 Å. units in a Lumetron 400-A photoelectric colorimeter. Keep the resulting suspension of organisms in the refrigerator and use for a period not to exceed two weeks. Prepare a daily inoculum by adding 1.0 ml. of this suspension to each 100 ml. of the broth medium no. 3 cooled to a temperature of approximately 15 C.

Working Standard and Standard Curve. To prepare solutions for the standard curve dilute the 1,000 μg./ml. working standard in distilled water to make concentrations of 20, 40, 60, 80, 100, 120, 140, 160, 180, and 200 μg./ml. The 100 μg./ml. concentration is the reference point of the curve. Add 1 ml. of each dilution to each of six test tubes (16 by 125 mm.).

Preparation of Sample. Dilute the sample under test in sterile distilled water to contain 100 μg./ml. (estimated). Add 1 ml. of this dilution to each of six test tubes (16 by 125 mm.). To each of all of these tubes prepared as just described, add 9 ml. of inoculated broth prepared as described under test culture and media. Place all tubes immediately in a water bath at 37 C. for 3 to 4 hours. After incubation add 0.5 ml. of formalin diluted 1:3 to each tube and read the light transmission in a Lumetron 402-E photoelectric colorimeter using a broad-band filter having a wave length of 5,300 Å. units. Other suitable instruments may be used.

Estimation of Potency. Set the slide wire scale of the Lumetron photoelectric colorimeter at 80. Adjust the instrument so that the galvanometer scale reads about 10 using the pooled contents of the six tubes containing the least amount of viomycin standard (20 μg./tube) and to about 90 using the pooled contents of the six tubes containing the highest concentration (200 μg./tube). Read and average the galvanometer readings for each six tubes of the intermediate concentrations. Plot these values on cross section paper employing average galvanometer readings as the ordinate, and viomycin concentrations as the abscissa. Prepare the standard curve by connecting successive points with a straightedge. Since the final concentration of viomycin per ml. of broth is equivalent to the concentration per ml. of the standard solutions used, the latter concentrations for each concentration level of the standard may be expressed as per cent and substituted on the abscissa of the standard curve. Thus the 100 μg./ml. concentration is 100 per cent, the 80 μg./ml. concentration is 80 per cent, etc. If this is done, the per cent potency of the sample under test may be read directly from the standard curve. Determine the galvanometer readings of each of the six tubes of the sample under test, average the six figures, and determine the potency from the standard curve already described. It is essential to run the standard curve simultaneously with the test samples.

METHOD 3: Modified Cylinder-plate Assay Method Using *Bacillus subtilis.*

Adapted from Method 1 and used for the determination of viomycin in body fluids, tissues, and similar substances.

Proceed as directed in the microbiologic assay in Method 1, Section A of this Chapter. For every 100 ml. of agar medium no. 5, add 1.4 ml. of a 1 per cent aqueous solution of sodium sulfadiazine. This makes a final concentration of 0.1 mg./ml. of sulfadiazine in the total 14 ml. of agar (base and seed layer). The standard curve and assay procedure are the same as described in Method 1, except the concentrations for the standard curve are made to contain 1.5, 3.0, 5.0, 10.0 (reference point), 20.0, 30.0, and 40.0 μg./ml. of viomycin. Special diluents for the standard curve which may be required are described under the individual test substances in Section C of this Chapter.

Section B: General Properties of Viomycin and Assay of its Pharmaceutical Dosage Form

Viomycin is a strongly basic polypeptide. It has been assigned a tentative empirical formula of $C_{18}H_{31-33}N_9O_8$. The molecular weight would be either 501.52 or 503.53. It forms water soluble crystalline salts, such as the hydrochloride and sulfate. The antibiotic possesses only one primary amino group and no free α-amino carboxy groups. On acid hydrolysis carbon dioxide, ammonia, urea, and amino acids are liberated. Some of the amino acids have been identified as L-serine, α, β-diaminopropionic acid and a basic amino acid isomeric with lysine. A guanidino compound has also been isolated.

Viomycin free base has been assigned a theoretical potency of 1,000 μg./

mg. If the formula for the sulfate is $(C_{18}H_{31}N_9O_8)_2 H_2SO_4$, the molecular weight would be 1,101.12 and the theoretical potency would be 911 μg./mg.

Only one dosage form of viomycin is used at this time, sterile vials of viomycin sulfate for injection. The viomycin sulfate is assayed as described in Section A of this Chapter.

Section C: Determination of Viomycin in Body Fluids

Blood serum. Use cylinder-plate assay Method 3, Section A of this Chapter, except for the following modifications. Dilute the 1,000 μg./ml. working standard in 7 per cent bovine albumin solution (prepared as described in Chapter 21 to make solutions for the standard curve. The concentrations of viomycin for the standard curve are the same as those described in Method 3. Normal serum, free of inhibitory substances and adjusted to a pH of 7.4, may also be used as a diluent for the standard curve.

The blood sample is prepared as in Section D, Chapter 2, and the serum is placed in the cups undiluted unless a concentration greater than 40 μg./ml. is expected, in which case the sample is diluted to an estimated 10 μg./ml. with the bovine albumin diluent.

Urine. Urine is diluted according to its estimated viomycin content with phosphate buffer no. 3, pH 8, to an estimated 10 μg./ml. and assayed by the microbiologic assay in Method 3, Section A of this Chapter.

13 FUMAGILLIN

Section *A:* **Assay Method for Fumagillin**

Fumagillin exhibits practically no antibacterial or antifungal activity. There-fore, the usual microbiologic assay methods are not applicable. The drug is an amebicide and it is active against *Endamoeba histolytica* at a dilution of 1:20,-000,000 or greater. *E. histolytica* may be used in tube dilution procedure to demonstrate the activity of fumagillin but the method is not refined enough for quantitative evaluation of potency.

Fumagillin is active against the specific bacteriophage of *M. pyogenes* var. *aureus* 209 P and a method depending upon this antibacteriophage activity has been reported. In this method plates are seeded with the *M. pyogenes* var. *aureus* and its specific bacteriophage. Upon incubation zones of *growth* appear around filter paper discs, which were saturated with solutions of fumagillin and placed on the plates before incubation. The remainder of the plate shows no growth due to the activity of the uninhibited bacteriophage. In our hands this method has not proved satisfactory for the quantitative estimation of fumagillin potency because the zones of growth are not sharp enough for accurate meas-urement.

In the absence of a suitable microbiologic method, the potency of fumagillin is measured by the ultraviolet spectrophotometric assay method to be de-scribed.

METHOD 1: Ultraviolet Spectrophotometric Assay Method for Fumagillin.

This method was adapted from Garrett and Eble.[15] (Note that fumagillin is light-sensitive and so nonactinic glassware should be used.) Transfer 100 mg. of the sample, accurately weighed, to a 100 ml. volumetric flask. Dissolve in 10 ml. of chloroform (reagent grade) and dilute to 100 ml. with 95 per cent ethyl alcohol. Transfer a 20 ml. aliquot to a 100 ml. volumetric flask and dilute to volume with 95 per cent ethyl alcohol. Transfer a 5 ml. aliquot of this second solution to a 250 ml. volumetric flask and dilute to volume with 95 per cent ethyl alcohol to obtain a solution containing 4.0 μg./ml. of fumagillin (0.0004 per cent). Determine the absorbance of this solution in a suitable spectro-photometer in a 1 cm. cell at 351 mμ against 95 per cent ethyl alcohol as the blank.

$$\mu g./mg. \text{ of fumagillin} = \frac{\text{absorbance at 351 } m\mu}{0.0004} \times \frac{1,000}{1,465}$$

where 1,465 is the specific absorbancy, $E_{1\,cm}^{1\%}$ of pure fumagillin at 351 $m\mu$.

Section B: Properties of Fumagillin and Assay of its Pharmaceutical Dosage Form

Fumagillin has been shown to be a monoester of decatetraenedioic acid $(C_{16-17}H_{25-27}O_3)$-O-CO(CH-CH)$_4$-COOH. It has an empirical formula of $C_{26}H_{34}O_7$ (M.W. 458.56) or $C_{27}H_{36}O_7$ (M.W. 472.59). The pure acid has been assigned a potency of 1,000 $\mu g./mg.$ It is insoluble in water, slightly soluble in ethanol, and soluble in chloroform and ether. It is light-sensitive and is subject to degradation by photolysis, photooxidation, and oxidation. It should therefore be protected from light and air. It exhibits a characteristic spectrum in the ultraviolet with absorption maximums at 336 and 351 $m\mu$ (see fig. 13, Section B, Chapter 17).

Assay of Fumagillin Capsules. Accurately weigh the contents of 20 capsules. Transfer an accurately weighed portion of the powder containing an estimated 100 mg. of fumagillin to a 100 ml. volumetric flask. Dissolve the fumagillin in 10 ml. of chloroform and make to volume with 95 per cent ethyl alcohol. Centrifuge and transfer a 20 ml. aliquot of the supernatant to a 100 ml. volumetric flask and make to volume with 95 per cent ethyl alcohol. Transfer a 5 ml. aliquot of this solution to a 250 ml. volumetric flask and dilute to volume with 95 per cent ethyl alcohol. Determine the absorbance of this solution in a suitable spectrophotometer in a 1 cm. cell at 351 $m\mu$ against 95 per cent ethyl alcohol as a blank.

$$\text{mg. per capsule} = \frac{\text{absorbance at 351 } m\mu}{0.586} \times \text{labeled potency per capsule}$$

where 0.586 is the theoretical absorbance at 351 $m\mu$ for a 4.0 $\mu g./ml.$ solution.

14 NYSTATIN

Section A: Microbiologic Assay Methods for Nystatin

Nystatin, originally called fungicidin, is an antifungal agent and because of its lack of activity against bacteria is assayed by using *Saccharomyces cerevisiae* as a test organism. The cylinder-plate methods, described later, using this test organism are conducted in a manner similar to those previously described in other chapters in which various bacteria have been used. One main difference that will be noted, however, is that the separate base layer and seed layer usually employed is changed. Only one layer of medium is used which contains the test organism. In Method 2 the inoculum is decreased to compensate for the inhibition of nystatin by blood serum.

METHOD 1: Cylinder-plate Method Using *Saccharomyces cerevisiae* as the Test Organism. (ATCC 9763.)

Cylinders (Cups). Use stainless steel cylinders with an outside diameter of 8 mm. (±0.1 mm.), an inside diameter of 6 mm. (±0.1 mm.), and a length of 10 mm (±0.1 mm.).

Culture Media. Use agar medium no. 12 for carrying the test organism, broth medium no. 13 for preparing the suspension, and agar medium no. 12 for preparing the test plates.

Working Standard. The primary standard is a special batch of nystatin that has been assigned a potency of 1,000 units/mg. The present working standard is crystalline nystatin and it has a potency of 3,700 units/mg. Dissolve a suitable weighed portion of this standard in an amount of formamide to give a 1,000 unit/ml. concentration. This stock solution may be used for three days when stored at 5 C. or less.

Preparation of Sample. Dissolve the sample to be tested in sufficient formamide to give a nystatin concentration of 400 units/ml. (estimated). Further dilute with phosphate buffer no. 1, pH 6, to 20 units/ml. Nystatin tablets are prepared as described in Section B of this Chapter.

Preparation of Test Organism. Maintain the test organism on agar medium no. 12 and transfer once a week. After transfer, the culture is incubated at

37 C. for 24 hours and then kept under refrigeration. Prepare the organism suspension by inoculating 100 ml. of broth medium no. 13 with a loopful of growth from the agar slant. Incubate the broth at 37 C. for 16 to 18 hours. Run test plates to determine the quantity of this suspension to be added to each 100 ml. of agar medium no. 12 to give clear, sharp zones of appropriate size. This quantity is usually about 2.5 ml. The broth culture is kept refrigerated and may be used for one week.

AN ALTERNATE METHOD FOR PREPARING THE TEST ORGANISM SUSPENSION. Wash the organism from the agar slant with 3 ml. of sterile physiologic saline solution onto a large surface, such as that provided by a Roux bottle containing 300 ml. of agar medium no. 12. Spread the suspension of organisms over the entire agar surface with the aid of sterile glass beads. Incubate for 24 hours at 37 C. and then wash the resulting growth from the agar surface with about 15 ml. of sterile physiologic saline solution. This suspension may be used for several weeks if kept refrigerated. Usually 0.1 ml. of this suspension is used in 100 ml. of agar medium no. 12, although test plates should be run to determine the exact amount necessary to give clear, sharp zones of appropriate size.

Preparation of Plates. Melt sufficient agar medium no. 12, cool to 48 C., and add the proper amount of the broth culture of *S. cerevisiae* prepared as just described. Add 6 ml. of this inoculated agar to each Petri dish (100 by 22 mm. flat bottom). Distribute the agar evenly in the plates, cover with porcelain covers glazed only on the outside or other suitable cover, and allow to harden. After the agar has hardened place six cylinders on the agar surface so that they are at approximately 60 degree intervals on a 2.8 cm. radius.

Standard Curve and Assay Procedure. STANDARD CURVE. Dilute the 1,000 unit/ml. standard solution in formamide to give concentrations of 100, 200, 300, 400, 600, and 800 units/ml. Dilute the formamide concentrations with phosphate buffer no. 1, *p*H 6, to make concentrations of 5, 10, 15, 20, 30, 40, and 50 units/ml. The 20 units/ml. solution is the reference point and is included on each plate. A total of 18 plates is used in the preparation of the standard curve, three plates for each concentration except the 20 units/ml. concentration. On each of three plates fill three cylinders with the 20 units/ml. standard and the other three cylinders with the concentration of the standard under test. Thus there will be 54 of the 20 units/ml. determinations and nine determinations for each of the other concentrations on the curve. Incubate the plates for 16 to 18 hours at 37 C. and measure the diameter of zones of inhibition. Average the readings of the 20 units/ml. concentration and the readings of the concentration tested for each set of three plates, and average also all 54 readings of the 20 units/ml. concentration. The average of the 54 readings of the 20 units/ml. concentration is the correction point for the curve. Correct the average value obtained for each concentration to the figure it would be if the 20 units/ml. reading for that set of three plates were the same as the correction point. Thus, if in correcting the 15 units/ml. concentration the average of the 54 readings of the 20 units/ml. concentration is 18 mm. and the average of the 20 units/ml. concentration of this set of three plates is 17.8

mm., the correction is plus 0.2 mm. If the average reading of the 15 units/ml. concentration of these same three plates is 15 mm., the corrected value is then 15.2 mm. Plot these corrected values, including the average of the 54 of the 20 units/ml. concentrations on two-cycle semilogarithmic paper, using the concentrations in units/ml. as the ordinate (logarithmic scale) and the diameter of the zone of inhibition as the abscissa. Draw the standard curve through these points.

ASSAY PROCEDURE. Use one or more plates for each sample (usually three) and fill three cylinders on each plate with the 20 units/ml. standard and three cylinders with the sample diluted to an estimated 20 units/ml. as already described, alternating standard and sample. Incubate the plates for 16 to 18 hours at 37 C. and measure the diameter of each circle of inhibition. Average the zone readings of the standard and average the zone readings of the sample on the plates used. If the sample gives a larger average zone size than the average of the standard, add the difference between them to the 20 units/ml. zone size of the standard curve. If the average sample zone size is smaller than the standard value, subtract the difference between them from the 20 units/ml. zone size of the standard curve. From the curve read the concentration corresponding to these corrected values of zone sizes.

METHOD 2: Modification of Method 1 for the Assay of Nystatin in Blood Serum and Other Substances.

Proceed as directed in the microbiologic assay in Method 1, Section A of this Chapter, except that the inoculum prepared is 1 per cent (1 ml. of broth culture per 100 ml. of agar medium no. 12). The standard curve and assay procedure are the same as described in Method 1.

Section B: **General Properties of Nystatin and Assay of its Pharmaceutical Dosage Form**

Nystatin has been isolated in crystalline form, although the commercial product is amorphous. The crystalline compound is insoluble in water, chloroform, acetone, and hexane. It is slightly soluble in methanol, ethanol, butanol, and dioxane. It is soluble in pyridine, formamide, and dimethylformamide. It is also soluble in glacial acetic acid, 0.05 N methanolic hydrochloric acid or sodium hydroxide, although these agents rapidly inactivate it. Crystalline nystatin has been reported to have an empirical formula of $C_{46}H_{83}NO_{18}$ with a M.W. of 938.2. It has both a basic and an acidic group. It has no methoxyl, phenolic hydroxyl, or acetyl groups. It gives a positive Molisch test indicating carbohydrate moieties. In methanol solution it exhibits absorption maximums at 291, 305, and 319 mμ (see fig. 15, Section B of Chapter 17).

Because the structure of nystatin is not known, the investigators of this drug have set aside a certain batch and assigned it a potency of 1,000 units/mg. This batch was impure and since then batches have been prepared with several times this potency. However, the unit designation is still used and the first primary standard is also still used as a reference point in assigning values to other working standards.

Nystatin Tablets. These tablets contain 500,000 units/tablet. To assay, place three tablets in a blending jar and add 150 ml. of formamide. Blend for two minutes in a high-speed blender and then dilute an aliquot with sufficient formamide to give a nystatin concentration of 400 units/ml. (estimated). Further dilute an aliquot of this solution with phosphate buffer no. 1, pH 6, to give a nystatin concentration of 20 units/ml. (estimated) and assay by the microbiologic assay in Method 1, Section A of this Chapter.

Section C: **Determination of Nystatin in Body Fluids**

Blood Serum. Use the microbiologic assay in Method 2, Section A of this Chapter. Further dilute the formamide solution of the working standard containing 1,000 units/ml. with normal serum for the standard curve using the same concentrations as directed in Method 2. The blood sample is prepared as in Section D, Chapter 2, and the serum is placed in the cups undiluted unless a concentration greater than 50 units/ml. is expected in which case the sample should be diluted to an estimated 20 units with normal serum.

Urine. Dilute the urine according to its estimated nystatin content with phosphate buffer no. 1, pH 6, to an estimated 20 units/ml. and assay using the microbiologic assay in Method 2, Section A of this Chapter.

15 ANISOMYCIN

Section A: Microbiologic Assay Methods for Anisomycin

Anisomycin like nystatin is an antifungal agent and because of its lack of activity against bacteria it is also assayed by using a yeast, *S. cerevisiae* as a test organism. The cylinder-plate methods, described later, using this test organism are conducted in a manner similar to those previously described for nystatin in Chapter 14. In the case of anisomycin, a heavier inoculum and *p*H 8 buffer are used. Attempts to increase the sensitivity of the assay in the presence of serum have been unsuccessful.

METHOD 1: Cylinder-plate Method Using *Saccharomyces cerevisiae* as the Test Organism. (ATCC 9763.)

Cylinders (Cups). Use stainless steel cylinders with an outside diameter of 8 mm. (±0.1 mm.), an inside diameter of 6 mm. (±0.1 mm.), and a length of 10 mm. (±0.1 mm.).

Culture Media. Use agar medium no. 12 for carrying the test organism, broth medium no. 13 for preparing the suspension, and agar medium no. 12 for preparing the test plates.

Working Standard. The standard is highly purified recrystallized anhydrous anisomycin base that has been assigned a potency of 1,000 µg./mg. Dissolve a suitable weighed portion of this standard in a small amount of methyl alcohol and further dilute with water to make a solution containing 1,000 µg./ml. This stock solution may be used for seven days when stored at 5 C. or less.

Preparation of Sample. Dissolve the sample to be tested in the same manner as described for the standard. Anisomycin preparations are prepared as described in Section B of this Chapter.

Preparation of Test Organism. Maintain the test organism on agar medium no. 12 and transfer once a week. After transfer, incubate at 37 C. for 24 hours and then keep under refrigeration. Prepare the organism suspension by inoculating 100 ml. of broth medium no. 13 with a loopful of growth from the agar slant. Incubate the broth at 37 C. for 16 to 18 hours. Run test plates to determine the quantity of this suspension to be added to each 100 ml. of agar medium no. 12 to give clear, sharp inhibitory zones of appropriate size. The broth culture is kept refrigerated and may be used for one week.

Preparation of Plates. Melt sufficient agar medium no. 12, cool to 48 C., and add the required amount as determined by test plates (usually about 2.5 ml./100 ml.) of the broth culture of *S. cerevisiae* prepared as already described. Add 10 ml. of this inoculated agar to each Petri dish (100 by 22 mm. flat bottom). Distribute the agar evenly in the plates, cover with porcelain covers glazed only on the outside or other suitable covers, and allow to harden. After the agar has hardened, place six cylinders on the agar surface so that they are at approximately 60 degree intervals on a 2.8 cm. radius.

Standard Curve and Assay Procedure. STANDARD CURVE. Dilute the 1,000 μg./ml. standard solution in phosphate buffer no. 3, *p*H 8, to make concentrations of 5, 10, 15, 25, 50, 75, and 100 μg./ml. The 25 μg./ml. solution is the reference point and is included on each plate. A total of 18 plates is used in the preparation of the standard curve, three plates for each concentration except the 25.0 μg./ml. concentration. On each of three plates fill three cylinders with the 25 μg./ml. standard and the other three cylinders with the concentration of the standard under test. Thus there will be 54 of the 25 μg./ml. determinations and nine determinations for each of the other concentrations on the curve. Incubate the plates for 16 to 18 hours at 37 C. and measure the diameter of zones of inhibition. Average the readings of the 25 μg./ml. concentration and the readings of the concentration tested for each set of three plates, and average also all 54 readings of the 25 μg./ml. concentration. The average of the 54 readings of the 25 μg./ml. concentration is the correction point for the curve. Correct the average value obtained for each concentration to the figure it would be if the 25 μg./ml. reading for that set of three plates were the same as the correction point. Thus, if in correcting the 15 μg./ml. concentration the average of the 54 readings of the 25 μg./ml. concentration is 18 mm. and the average of the 25 μg./ml. concentration of this set of three plates is 17.8 mm., the correction is plus 0.2 mm. If the average reading of the 15 μg./ml. concentration of these same three plates is 15 mm., the corrected value is then 15.2 mm. Plot these corrected values, including the average of the 54 of the 25 μg./ml. concentration on two-cycle semilogarithmic paper, using the concentrations in μg./ml. as the ordinate (logarithmic scale) and the diameter of the zone of inhibition as the abscissa. Draw the standard curve through these points.

ASSAY PROCEDURE. Use one or more plates for each sample (usually three) and fill three cylinders on each plate with the 25 μg./ml. standard and three cylinders with the sample diluted to an estimated 25 μg./ml. with phosphate buffer no. 3, *p*H 8, alternating standard and sample. Incubate the plates for 16 to 18 hours at 37 C. and measure the diameter of each circle of inhibition. Average the zone readings of the standard and average the zone readings of the sample on the plates used. If the sample gives a larger average zone size than the average of the standard, add the difference between them to the 25 μg./ml. zone size of the standard curve. If the average sample zone size is smaller than the standard value, subtract the difference between them from the 25 µg./ml. zone size of the standard curve. From the curve read the concentration corresponding to these corrected values of zone sizes.

METHOD 2: Modification of Method 1 for the Assay of Anisomycin in Blood Serum and Other Substances.

Proceed as directed in the microbiologic assay in Method 1, Section A of this Chapter, except that the reference point for the standard curve is 50 µg./ml. instead of 25 µg./ml.

Section B: Properties of Anisomycin and Assay of its Pharmaceutical Dosage Forms

Anisomycin is a white, crystalline, monobasic antibiotic. The base melts at 140 to 141 C. and has a specific rotation $[\alpha]\,_D^{23} = -30°$ (C = 1 per cent in methanol). It has an empirical formula of $C_{14}H_{19}NO_4$, M.W. = 265.31. The pure anhydrous base has been assigned a potency of 1,000 µg./mg. It is sparingly soluble in water and soluble in methanol. It shows a characteristic absorption spectrum in the ultraviolet with absorption maximums at 224, 277, and 283 mµ (see fig. 14, Section B, Chapter 17).

Anisomycin Vaginal Powder. This powder is a mixture of lactose and magnesium stearate with 1 mg. of anisomycin per Gm. of powder. To assay, accurately weigh about 5 Gm. of powder into a mortar, add 10.0 ml. of methanol, triturate thoroughly with a pestle, and allow to stand for 15 minutes with frequent agitation to dissolve the anisomycin. Dilute a 1.0 ml. aliquot of the supernatant alcohol solution with 19.0 ml. of phosphate buffer no. 3, pH 8, to give an anisomycin concentration of 25 µg./ml. (estimated) and assay by the microbiologic assay in Method 1, Section A of this Chapter.

Anisomycin Vaginal Tablets. These tablets contain 1.5 mg. of anisomycin per tablet. To assay reduce three tablets to a fine powder with a mortar and pestle. Add 10.0 ml. of methanol, triturate thoroughly, and allow to stand for 15 minutes with frequent agitation. Dilute a 1.0 ml. aliquot of the supernatant methanol solution with 17.0 ml. of phosphate buffer no. 3, pH 8, to give an anisomycin concentration of 25 µg./ml. (estimated) and assay by the microbiologic assay in Method 1, Section A of this Chapter.

Section C: Determination of Anisomycin in Body Fluids

Blood Serum. Use the microbiologic assay in Method 2, Section A of this Chapter. Dilute the 1,000 µg./ml. concentration of the working standard in normal serum for the standard curve using the concentrations as directed in

Method 2. The blood sample is prepared as in Section D, Chapter 2, and the serum is placed in the cups undiluted unless a concentration greater than 100 μg./ml. is expected in which case the sample should be diluted to an estimated 50 μg./ml. with normal serum.

Urine. Dilute the urine according to its estimated anisomycin content with phosphate buffer no. 3, pH 8, to an estimated 25 μg./ml. and assay using the microbiologic assay in Method 1, Section A of this Chapter.

16 ASSAY OF MIXTURES OF ANTIBIOTICS IN PHARMACEUTICAL DOSAGE FORMS

In the assay of two or more antibiotics in the presence of one another, the usual method is to use a microorganism as the test organism that is very sensitive to one of the antibiotics and insensitive to the others in the amounts present. An organism usually can be made resistant to an antibiotic by growing it in media containing increasing amounts of the antibiotic until the desired resistance is attained. The resistant organism can then be used as a test organism.

Another useful method for mixtures is the use of specific enzymes or chemical inactivators to eliminate certain antibiotics from the field of action. Penicillinase is used to inactivate penicillin and semicarbazide may be used for inactivation of streptomycin. Semicarbazide, however, will not inactivate dihydrostreptomycin. Erythromycin may be inactivated by allowing it to stand in mild acid, a property that has been found useful in eliminating this antibiotic when it interferes in the assay of other antibiotics stable in acid. Neomycin has been found to be unaffected when heated with barium hydroxide, while dihydrostreptomycin is inactivated. This method can therefore be used to remove dihydrostreptomycin, which interferes in the assay of neomycin, when these two antibiotics are present in a preparation.

Sometimes differences in solubilities of antibiotics in various solvents may be made use of in separating mixtures of antibiotics. Ion exchange resins may also be very useful in separating mixtures.

Finally if interference does occur between two antibiotics in the microbiologic assay and none of these procedures can be conveniently used to separate or determine them, the potency can be determined in some cases by adding the proper amount of the interfering antibiotic in the preparation of the standard curve of the antibiotic whose potency is desired. For example in the assay of antibiotics A and B, antibiotic A interferes with the determination of antibiotic B in that it is also sensitive to the test organism used for antibiotic B. Antibiotic B does not interfere with the determination of antibiotic A. The amount of antibiotic A can therefore be determined accurately. When the standard curve for antibiotic B is prepared, the proper amount of antibiotic A, found by assay, is added to each concentration of antibiotic B standard for each point on the curve. The standard curve obtained from the mixture of antibiotics A and B is then used to calculate the potency of antibiotic B. If the test organism is extremely sensitive to the interfering antibiotic, the method is not feasible.

Many mixtures of antibiotics contain other drugs in addition to the antibiotics, such as vasoconstrictors, antihistaminics, sulfonamides, and cortisone. None of these other drugs so far encountered interferes with the microbiologic assay procedures.

The methods given are designed to take care of the usual concentrations encountered in commercial preparations. However, if unusual concentrations are encountered, it may be necessary to modify the extraction volume or dilutions.

Procaine Penicillin in Streptomycin and/or Dihydrostreptomycin Sulfate Solution. PROCAINE PENICILLIN CONTENT. Shake the sample thoroughly, remove a 1.0 ml. aliquot of the suspension, and dilute with phosphate buffer no. 1, *p*H 6, to a penicillin concentration of 1 unit/ml. (estimated). Assay by penicillin Method 1, Section A, Chapter 2. The streptomycin or dihydrostreptomycin does not interfere with the penicillin assay.

The iodometric chemical assay, Section B, Chapter 2, may also be used to determine penicillin potency, but it is necessary to add one drop of 1.2 *N* hydrochloric acid to the blank immediately before the addition of the 0.01 *N* iodine. This step is required to prevent a slight interference caused by streptomycin or dihydrostreptomycin.

STREPTOMYCIN OR DIHYDROSTREPTOMYCIN CONTENT. Dilute a 1.0 ml. aliquot of the suspension with distilled water to a streptomycin or dihydrostreptomycin concentration of 100 μg./ml. (estimated) and assay by Method 2, Section A, Chapter 3. The procaine penicillin concentration present in these preparations does not interfere in this method.

STREPTOMYCIN AND DIHYDROSTREPTOMYCIN CONTENT. The preparation under discussion may be marketed in three ways, procaine penicillin suspended in streptomycin sulfate solution, procaine penicillin suspended in dihydrostreptomycin sulfate solution, and procaine penicillin suspended in streptomycin and dihydrostreptomycin sulfate solutions. In the last preparation the streptomycin and dihydrostreptomycin are present in a 50:50 ratio. In such a mixture determine the total content of streptomycin plus dihydrostreptomycin as already described. Determine the streptomycin content of the mixture by the maltol-ferric chloride colorimetric procedure in Method 1, Section B, Chapter 3. The dihydrostreptomycin content is obtained by subtracting the streptomycin content from the total streptomycin, dihydrostreptomycin potency.

Buffered Crystalline Penicillin (Sodium or Potassium Penicillin), Streptomycin and/or Dihydrostreptomycin Sulfate. BUFFERED CRYSTALLINE PENICILLIN CONTENT. Follow the same procedure described under procaine penicillin in streptomycin sulfate solution, in this Chapter.

STREPTOMYCIN OR DIHYDROSTREPTOMYCIN CONTENT. Follow the same procedure already described in this Chapter.

STREPTOMYCIN AND DIHYDROSTREPTOMYCIN CONTENT. Follow the same procedure already described in this Chapter.

Procaine Penicillin, Buffered Crystalline Penicillin (Sodium or Potassium) and Streptomycin and/or Dihydrostreptomycin Sulfate. TOTAL PENICILLIN CONTENT. Add the amount of water recommended in the labeling to the contents of a vial and shake well. Withdraw 1.0 ml. or other suitable aliquot of the suspension and follow the same procedure described under procaine penicillin in streptomycin sulfate solution, in this Chapter.

SODIUM OR POTASSIUM PENICILLIN CONTENT (BUFFERED CRYSTALLINE PENICILLIN). Follow the method described under procaine penicillin and buffered crystalline penicillin for aqueous injection, Section C, Chapter 2, except that in the iodometric chemical assay add one drop of 1.2 N hydrochloric acid to the blank immediately before the addition of the 0.01 N iodine.

PROCAINE PENICILLIN CONTENT. The difference between the total penicillin content and the sodium or potassium penicillin content represents the procaine penicillin content of the sample.

STREPTOMYCIN OR DIHYDROSTREPTOMYCIN CONTENT. Follow the same procedure already described in this Chapter.

STREPTOMYCIN AND DIHYDROSTREPTOMYCIN CONTENT. Follow the same procedure already described in this Chapter.

Benzathine Penicillin and Streptomycin and/or Dihydrostreptomycin Sulfate. These preparations exist either as dry powders to which water is added prior to use or as a suspension.

BENZATHINE PENICILLIN CONTENT. Follow the same procedure described under benzathine penicillin for aqueous injection, Section C, Chapter 2. If the iodometric chemical assay is used, add one drop of 1.2 N hydrochloric acid to the blank immediately before the addition of the 0.01 N iodine.

STREPTOMYCIN OR DIHYDROSTREPTOMYCIN CONTENT. Follow the same procedure already described in this Chapter.

STREPTOMYCIN AND DIHYDROSTREPTOMYCIN CONTENT. Follow the same procedure already described in this Chapter.

Buffered Crystalline Penicillin (Sodium or Potassium), Benzathine Penicillin, Streptomycin and Dihydrostreptomycin Sulfate. TOTAL PENICILLIN CONTENT, BUFFERED CRYSTALLINE PENICILLIN CONTENT, AND BENZATHINE PENICILLIN CONTENT. Follow the same procedures described under benzathine penicillin and buffered crystalline penicillin for aqueous injection, Section C, Chapter 2.

If the iodometric chemical assay method is used, add one drop of 1.2 N hydrochloric acid to the blank immediately before the addition of the 0.01 N iodine.

STREPTOMYCIN AND DIHYDROSTREPTOMYCIN CONTENT. Follow the same procedure already described in this Chapter.

Procaine Penicillin and Benzathine Penicillin in Streptomycin and/or Dihydrostreptomycin Sulfate Solution. TOTAL PENICILLIN CONTENT AND PROCAINE PENICILLIN CONTENT. Follow the same procedures described under benzathine penicillin, procaine penicillin, and buffered crystalline penicillin for aqueous injection, Section C, Chapter 2. If the iodometric chemical assay method is used, add one drop of 1.2 N hydrochloric acid to the blank immediately before the addition of the 0.01 N iodine.

BENZATHINE PENICILLIN CONTENT. The difference between the total penicillin content and the procaine penicillin content represents the benzathine penicillin content.

STREPTOMYCIN OR DIHYDROSTREPTOMYCIN CONTENT. Follow the same procedure already described in this Chapter.

STREPTOMYCIN AND DIHYDROSTREPTOMYCIN CONTENT. Follow the same procedure already described in this Chapter.

Procaine Penicillin, Benzathine Penicillin, Streptomycin and/or Dihydrostreptomycin Sulfate. These preparations exist as dry powders to which water is added just prior to use. When the amount of water recommended in the labeling has been added, assay an aliquot of the suspension as just described.

Buffered Crystalline Penicillin (Sodium or Potassium), Procaine Penicillin, Benzathine Penicillin, and Streptomycin and Dihydrostreptomycin Sulfate. TOTAL PENICILLIN CONTENT, BUFFERED CRYSTALLINE PENICILLIN CONTENT, AND BENZATHINE PENICILLIN CONTENT. Follow the same procedures described under benzathine penicillin, procaine penicillin, and buffered crystalline penicillin for aqueous injection, Section C, Chapter 2. If the iodometric chemical assay method is used, add one drop of 1.2 N hydrochloric acid to the blank immediately before the addition of the 0.01 N iodine.

STREPTOMYCIN AND DIHYDROSTREPTOMYCIN CONTENT. Follow the same procedure already described in this Chapter.

Penicillin and Streptomycin or Dihydrostreptomycin Ointment. PENICILLIN CONTENT. Use an accurately weighed sample of approximately 1 Gm. of ointment and follow the procedure described under penicillin ointment Section C, Chapter 2. The quantity of streptomycin or dihydrostreptomycin ordinarily encountered in penicillin-streptomycin or penicillin-dihydrostreptomycin ointments does not interfere in the *M. pyogenes* var. *aureus* cylinder-plate method.

STREPTOMYCIN OR DIHYDROSTREPTOMYCIN CONTENT. *Method 1.* Place an accurately weighed sample of approximately 1.0 Gm. into a separatory funnel containing approximately 50 ml. of peroxide-free ether. Shake ointment and ether until homogeneous. Shake with a 20 ml. portion of phosphate buffer no. 3, *p*H 8. Remove the buffer layer and repeat the extraction with three 20 ml. quantities of buffer. Combine the extracts and make up to 100 ml. with buffer. To a 5.0 ml. aliquot add sufficient penicillinase (see Chapter 21) and let stand for a half hour at 37 C. to inactivate the penicillin. After inactivation make the proper estimated dilutions in phosphate buffer no. 3, *p*H 8, to give a concentration of 1.0 µg./ml. and assay by the cylinder-plate microbiologic assay in Method 1, Section A, Chapter 3.

Method 2. Accurately weigh 1.0 to 2.0 Gm. of the sample into a separatory funnel containing approximately 50 ml. of peroxide-free ether. Shake ointment and ether until homogeneous. Shake with a 20 ml. portion of distilled water. Remove the aqueous layer and repeat the extraction with three 20 ml. quantities of distilled water. Combine the extracts and make to an appropriate measured volume. Remove an aliquot, and if the ratio of the content of penicillin to the content of streptomycin is equal to or greater than one unit for each µg., add sufficient penicillinase to inactivate completely the penicillin used in the test. Dilute an aliquot to 30.0 µg./ml. with distilled water, place 1 ml. amounts of this in tubes and assay by the turbidimetric assay in Method 2, Section A, Chapter 3.

As may be seen from this, one may either use the *B. subtilis* cylinder-plate or the *K. pneumoniae* turbidimetric procedure for measuring streptomycin or dihydrostreptomycin. In the cylinder-plate method, penicillin interferes and must be inactivated with the enzyme penicillinase. In the turbidimetric method, penicillin will not interfere unless it is present in a ratio to the streptomycin or dihydrostreptomycin equal to or greater than 1 unit of penicillin for each µg. of streptomycin or dihydrostreptomycin. The cylinder-plate method is the method of choice because the extraction is made in buffer solution assuring a constant *p*H, the plate method is less subject to interference from traces of solvents and any turbidity of the extract is without effect.

Procaine Penicillin and Streptomycin or Dihydrostreptomycin in Oil. PROCAINE PENICILLIN CONTENT AND STREPTOMYCIN OF DIHYDROSTREPTOMYCIN CONTENT. Use 1.0 ml. and follow the same procedures described under penicillin and streptomycin or dihydrostreptomycin ointment, which was previously described in this Chapter.

Benzathine Penicillin and Streptomycin or Dihydrostreptomycin in Oil. BENZATHINE PENICILLIN CONTENT. Place a representative sample (usually 1.0 ml.) of a multiple-dose container, or the entire contents of a single-dose container, in a blending jar containing sufficient formamide (previously adjusted to a *p*H of 6.5 ±0.5 with concentrated sulfuric acid) to give a final volume of 100 ml. Using a high-speed blender, blend the mixture for two minutes, dilute a suitable aliquot with phosphate buffer no. 1, *p*H 6, to give a penicillin concentration of 1.0 unit/ml. (estimated), and assay by the microbiologic assay in Method 1, Section A, Chapter 2.

STREPTOMYCIN OR DIHYDROSTREPTOMYCIN CONTENT. Follow the same procedure described under penicillin and streptomycin ointment in this Chapter.

Penicillin and Streptomycin or Dihydrostreptomycin Vaginal Suppositories. PENICILLIN CONTENT. Use five suppositories and follow the separatory funnel extraction procedure described under penicillin ointment, Section C, Chapter 2, using 150 ml. of ether to dissolve the suppositories. The blender method described under penicillin ointment may also be used, in which case 200 ml. of phosphate buffer no. 1, *p*H 6, is used in the blender for five suppositories.

STREPTOMYCIN OR DIHYDROSTREPTOMYCIN CONTENT. Use five suppositories and follow the same procedure described under penicillin and streptomycin ointment in this Chapter.

Penicillin and Streptomycin or Dihydrostreptomycin Tablets. PENICILLIN CONTENT. Follow the same procedure described under penicillin tablets, Section C, Chapter 2.

STREPTOMYCIN OR DIHYDROSTREPTOMYCIN CONTENT. Follow the procedure described under streptomycin tablets, Section C, Chapter 3, except that sufficient penicillinase (Chapter 21) is added to an aliquot of the extract and allowed to stand one-half hour at 37 C. to inactivate the penicillin.

Penicillin and Streptomycin or Dihydrostreptomycin Bougies. PENICILLIN CONTENT, STREPTOMYCIN OR DIHYDROSTREPTOMYCIN CONTENT. Follow the same procedures described under penicillin and streptomycin tablets in this Chapter.

Penicillin and Streptomycin or Dihydrostreptomycin Dental Cones. PENICILLIN CONTENT, STREPTOMYCIN OR DIHYDROSTREPTOMYCIN CONTENT. Follow the same procedures described under penicillin and streptomycin tablets in this Chapter.

Penicillin and Streptomycin or Dihydrostreptomycin Implantation Pellets. PENICILLIN CONTENT, STREPTOMYCIN OR DIHYDROSTREPTOMYCIN CONTENT. Follow the same procedures described under penicillin and streptomycin tablets in this Chapter.

Penicillin and Streptomycin or Dihydrostreptomycin Powder. PENICILLIN CONTENT, STREPTOMYCIN OR DIHYDROSTREPTOMYCIN CONTENT. Using accurately weighed samples of approximately 1 Gm., follow the same procedures described under penicillin and streptomycin tablets in this Chapter.

Penicillin and Bacitracin. A dry mixture of these two antibiotics to which a diluent is added is sold for parenteral use. Bacitracin does not interfere in the *M. pyogenes* var. *aureus* cylinder-plate assay method for penicillin. Penicillin does interfere in the *M. flavus* cylinder-plate method for bacitracin but can be removed by inactivation with penicillinase.

PENICILLIN CONTENT. Dilute the contents of a vial with distilled water to a volume of 100 ml. Dilute an aliquot of this solution with phosphate buffer no. 1, *p*H 6, to a concentration of 1 unit/ml. of penicillin (estimated) and assay by the microbiologic assay in Method 1, Section A, Chapter 2.

BACITRACIN CONTENT. Add sufficient penicillinase (Chapter 21) to an aliquot of the water solution just prepared and allow to stand for one-half hour at 37 C. to inactivate completely the penicillin present. Dilute the penicillin inactivated solution with phosphate buffer no. 1, *p*H 6, to a bacitracin concentration of 1 unit/ml. (estimated) and assay by the microbiologic assay in Method 1, Section A, Chapter 6.

Penicillin and Bacitracin Ointment. PENICILLIN CONTENT. Follow the same procedure described under penicillin ointment Section C, Chapter 2.

BACITRACIN CONTENT. Use an aliquot of the same phosphate buffer no. 1, *p*H 6, extract obtained for the penicillin content and inactivate the penicillin by allowing to stand one-half hour at 37 C. with sufficient penicillinase (see Chapter 21). Dilute the penicillin inactivated solution with phosphate buffer no. 1, *p*H 6, to give a bacitracin concentration of 1 unit/ml. (estimated) and assay by the microbiologic assay in Method 1, Section A, Chapter 6.

Penicillin and Bacitracin Troches. PENICILLIN CONTENT. Follow the same procedure described under penicillin tablets, Section C, Chapter 2.

BACITRACIN CONTENT. Use an aliquot of the same phosphate buffer no. 1, *p*H 6, extract obtained for the penicillin content and inactivate the penicillin by allowing to stand one-half hour at 37 C. with sufficient penicillinase (Chapter 21). Dilute the penicillin inactivated solution with phosphate buffer no. 1, *p*H 6, to give a bacitracin concentration of 1 unit/ml. (estimated) and assay by the microbiologic assay in Method 1, Section A, Chapter 6.

Penicillin, Streptomycin or Dihydrostreptomycin, and Bacitracin Ointment. In this combination, the penicillin interferes with the streptomycin or dihydrostreptomycin and bacitracin assays but can be eliminated by inactivation with penicillinase. Streptomycin or dihydrostreptomycin and bacitracin do not affect the penicillin assay. Streptomycin interferes with the bacitracin assay but can be eliminated by inactivation with semicarbazide. Dihydrostreptomycin interferes with the bacitracin assay, since it is also active against the *M. flavus* test organism, and it presents a problem because there is no enzyme or chemical inactivator available as yet for it. There are two ways, however, in which bacitracin may be determined in the presence of dihydrostreptomycin. One way is to add dihydrostreptomycin to the bacitracin standard during the preparation of the bacitracin standard curve and the other is to use a culture of *M. flavus* that has been made resistant or insensitive to dihydrostreptomycin as the test organism. The latter procedure is preferred in the presence of not only dihydrostreptomycin but also streptomycin. Both procedures are given in detail in the following paragraphs.

PENICILLIN CONTENT. Follow the same procedure described under penicillin ointment Section C, Chapter 2.

STREPTOMYCIN OR DIHYDROSTREPTOMYCIN CONTENT. Follow the same procedure described under penicillin and streptomycin ointment in this Chapter.

BACITRACIN CONTENT. Use an aliquot of the same phosphate buffer no. 1, *p*H 6, extract obtained for the penicillin content and inactivate the penicillin at 37 C. for 30 minutes with sufficient penicillinase (Chapter 21). Dilute with phosphate buffer no. 1, *p*H 6, to give a bacitracin concentration of 1 unit/ml. (estimated) and assay by the microbiologic assay in Method 1, Section A, Chapter 6, except use as the test organism a strain of *M. flavus*, which is resistant or insensitive to dihydrostreptomycin and streptomycin. Such a strain may be obtained from the American Type Culture Collection (10240A).

Various methods can be used to make a culture resistant to an antibiotic. The culture can be added to broth tubes containing increasing amounts of the antibiotic. The tube showing growth in the presence of the highest quantity of the antibiotic is used for preparing a new inoculum and the same process repeated until the desired resistance to the antibiotic is obtained. Another procedure that can be used is to grow the organism on agar slants containing gradually increased amounts of the antibiotic until the desired resistance is obtained. When an organism has been made resistant to an antibiotic, this resistance is maintained by carrying it on a medium containing the quantity of antibiotic to which it has been made resistant. Organisms made resistant to either streptomycin or dihydrostreptomycin have a cross resistance to the other. If the streptomycin-dihydrostreptomycin resistant strain of *M. flavus* is not available, the following methods may be used.

Streptomycin present. Use an aliquot of the same phosphate buffer no. 1, *p*H 6, extract obtained for the penicillin content and inactivate the penicillin at 37 C. for 30 minutes with sufficient penicillinase (Chapter 21). Next add to the same solution sufficient 0.5 per cent freshly prepared semicarbazide solution (use 1.0 ml. for each 1,000 µg. of streptomycin) and let stand for one hour at room temperature to inactivate the streptomycin. (Note that it is important not to use larger quantities of semicarbazide than as indicated since larger amounts of this chemical may have an action on the test organism.) Dilute the penicillin and streptomycin inactivated solution with phosphate buffer no. 1, *p*H 6, to give a bacitracin concentration of 1 unit/ml. (estimated) and assay by the microbiologic assay in Method 1, Section A, Chapter 6.

Dihydrostreptomycin present. Use an aliquot of the same phosphate buffer no. 1, *p*H 6, extract obtained for the penicillin content and inactivate the penicillin at 37 C. for 30 minutes with sufficient penicillinase (Chapter 21). Dilute the solution, which now contains only dihydrostreptomycin and bacitracin, with phosphate buffer no. 1, *p*H 6, to give a bacitracin concentration of 1 unit/ml. (based on label potency) and assay by the microbiologic assay in Method 1, Section A, Chapter 6, except prepare the bacitracin standard curve as follows: Calculate from the quantity of dihydrostreptomycin actually found, the quantity of dihydrostreptomycin that would be present when the sample is diluted to contain 1 unit/ml. of bacitracin (based on label potency). Prepare the bacitracin standard curve by adding this same calculated quantity of dihydrostreptomycin to each concentration of bacitracin used for the curve.

EXAMPLE. An ointment is labeled to contain 20,000 units penicillin, 10 mg. dihydrostreptomycin, and 1,000 units bacitracin per Gm. The dihydrostreptomycin content found by assay is 9.5 mg./Gm. When the extract containing the bacitracin is diluted to contain 1 unit/ml. (based on label potency), it will contain 9.5 µg./ml. of dihydrostreptomycin and an unknown amount (probably 1 unit) of bacitracin. In order to determine the effect 9.5 µg. of dihydrostreptomycin will have with varying concentrations of bacitracin, it is necessary to add this same quantity (9.5 µg.) to each concentration of bacitracin used in the standard curve. When the unknown is read from a standard curve so prepared, it will give the units of bacitracin present per 9.5 µg. of dihydrostreptomycin.

Penicillin, Streptomycin or Dihydrostreptomycin, and Bacitracin Dental Paste. This preparation, known as the Grossman formula or PBSC, is a mixture of these antibiotics with sodium caprylate in a silicone oil base and is used in dental practice for root canal therapy. To assay follow the same procedure described under penicillin, streptomycin, and bacitracin ointment, in this Chapter.

Penicillin, Bacitracin, and Neomycin Ointment. In this combination penicillin will interfere with the assay of bacitracin and neomycin but is eliminated with penicillinase. Bacitracin and neomycin do not interfere in the assay of penicillin in the concentrations encountered in commercial preparations. Bacitracin does not interfere in the neomycin assay and neomycin does not interfere in the bacitracin assay.

PENICILLIN AND BACITRACIN CONTENT. Follow the same procedure described under penicillin and bacitracin ointment in this Chapter.

NEOMYCIN CONTENT. Extract another accurately weighed portion of approximately 1 Gm. of the ointment as was just done for the penicillin and bacitracin content except use phosphate buffer no. 3, *p*H 8, to extract the neomycin. Add sufficient penicillinase (Chapter 21) to an aliquot of the extract, allow to stand for one-half hour at 37 C. to inactivate completely the penicillin present, dilute with phosphate buffer no. 3, *p*H 8, to give a neomycin concentration of 10.0 µg./ml. (estimated) and assay by the microbiologic assay in Method 1, Section A, Chapter 9.

Penicillin, Bacitracin, and Neomycin in Oil. Follow the same procedure described under penicillin, bacitracin, and neomycin ointment in this Chapter.

Penicillin, Streptomycin or Dihydrostreptomycin, and Neomycin in Oil. The interference of penicillin in the assay for streptomycin or dihydrostreptomycin and neomycin can be eliminated with penicillinase. Neomycin in the quantity encountered does not interfere in the assay of the penicillin, nor in the *B. subtilis* cylinder-plate assay for streptomycin or dihydrostreptomycin. Neomycin will, however, interfere in the *K. pneumoniae* turbidimetric assay method.

Streptomycin interferes with the assay of the neomycin but can be inactivated with semicarbazide. Dihydrostreptomycin also interferes with the neomycin assay but can be destroyed by heating with barium hydroxide, which action does not affect the neomycin potency. The interference caused by streptomycin or dihydrostreptomycin in the neomycin assay can also be overcome by using as the test organism a strain of *M. pyogenes* var. *aureus* that has been made resistant or insensitive to these antibiotics. This last mentioned technique is the preferred method.

PENICILLIN AND STREPTOMYCIN OR DIHYDROSTREPTOMYCIN CONTENT. Use 1.0 ml. of the preparation and follow the same procedure described under penicillin and streptomycin ointment, in this Chapter, using the *B. subtilis* cylinder-plate method for the streptomycin or dihydrostreptomycin content.

NEOMYCIN CONTENT. Place 1.0 ml. of the sample in a separatory funnel containing 50 ml. of peroxide-free ether and extract with four successive 20 ml. portions of phosphate buffer no. 3, pH 8. Make the combined extractions to 100 ml. with the buffer. Dilute an aliquot with phosphate buffer no. 3, pH 8, to give a neomycin concentration of 10 μg./ml. (estimated). To 5 ml. of this solution add sufficient penicillinase (Chapter 21) and let stand for one-half hour at 37 C. to inactivate the penicillin present. Then assay by the microbiologic assay in Method 1, Section A, Chapter 9, using a streptomycin and dihydrostreptomycin resistant strain of *M. pyogenes* var. *aureus* (ATCC 6538PR).

If this streptomycin and dihydrostreptomycin resistant organism is not available, the following alternate methods may be used.

Streptomycin present. Extract 1.0 ml. of the preparation as described under neomycin ointment, Section B, Chapter 9. Inactivate the penicillin in an aliquot of the extract by allowing to stand for one-half hour at 37 C. with sufficient penicillinase (Chapter 21). Next add to the same solution sufficient 0.5 per cent freshly prepared semicarbazide solution (use 1.0 ml. for each 125 μg. of streptomycin) and let stand for one hour at room temperature to inactivate the streptomycin. Dilute the penicillin and streptomycin inactivated solution with phosphate buffer no. 3, pH 8, to give a neomycin concentration of 10 μg./ml. (estimated) and assay by the microbiologic assay in Method 1, Section A, Chapter 9.

Dihydrostreptomycin present. Place 1.0 ml. of the sample in a separatory funnel containing approximately 50 ml. of peroxide-free ether and extract with four successive 20 ml. portions of distilled water. Make the combined aqueous extractions to 100 ml. with distilled water. Transfer a 10 ml. aliquot of the aqueous extract to a 25 ml. volumetric flask and add 1.0 ml. of 5 per cent barium hydroxide. Using a test-tube clamp, suspend the open flask in a steam bath so that the mouth of the flask is slightly above the level of the steam bath. Heat with steam for three hours; remove, cool, add one drop of 1 per cent phenolphthalein, and neutralize dropwise with 1.0 N sulfuric acid. Make to volume with distilled water and pour a reasonable aliquot into an appropriate centrifuge tube. Centrifuge for five minutes at approximately 4,000 r.p.m. and decant. Pipette an appropriate volume for assay and accurately add sufficient phosphate buffer no. 9, pH 8, to provide, after addition of distilled water, a solution having a molarity of 0.1 with respect to the potassium phosphate buffer and containing 10 μg./ml. of neomycin. Assay this solution by the microbiologic assay in Method 1, Section A, Chapter 9.

Since the concentration of buffer solution will affect the zone size in the assay, it is necessary to adjust the final solution so that the molarity of the buffer will be the same as that used in preparing the standard curve.

Penicillin, Streptomycin or Dihydrostreptomycin, and Neomycin Ointment. Use 1 Gm. of ointment and follow the same procedure described under penicillin, streptomycin, and neomycin in oil, in this Chapter.

Benzathine Penicillin, Procaine Penicillin, and Streptomycin or Dihydrostreptomycin in Oil. TOTAL PENICILLIN CONTENT. Place a representative sample (usually 1.0 ml.) of a multiple-dose container, or the entire contents of a single-dose container, in a blending jar containing sufficient formamide (previously adjusted to a *p*H of 6.5 ±0.5 with concentrated sulfuric acid) to give a final volume of 100 ml. Using a high-speed blender, blend the mixture for two minutes, dilute a suitable aliquot with phosphate buffer no. 1, *p*H 6, to give a penicillin concentration of 1.0 unit/ml. (estimated) and assay by the microbiologic assay in Method 1, Section A, Chapter 2.

PROCAINE PENICILLIN CONTENT. Dilute an aliquot of the formamide solution, as just prepared, with phosphate buffer no. 1, *p*H 6, to give a procaine penicillin concentration of 100 units/ml. (estimated) and determine the procaine colorimetrically by the method described for procaine penicillin and buffered crystalline sodium or potassium penicillin for aqueous injection under Section C, Chapter 2.

BENZATHINE PENICILLIN CONTENT. The benzathine penicillin content is determined by subtracting the procaine penicillin found from the total penicillin.

STREPTOMYCIN OR DIHYDROSTREPTOMYCIN CONTENT. Follow the same procedure as described under penicillin and streptomycin ointment in this Chapter.

Streptomycin, Polymyxin, and Bacitracin Tablets. In this combination streptomycin will not interfere with the polymyxin assay. It will interfere with the bacitracin assay but its effect can be eliminated with semicarbazide or by using the streptomycin resistant strain of *M. flavus* in the assay. Polymyxin does not interfere in the streptomycin or bacitracin assay and the bacitracin does not interfere in the streptomycin or polymyxin assay.

STREPTOMYCIN CONTENT. Use 12 tablets and follow the same procedure described under streptomycin tablets, Section C, Chapter 3.

POLYMYXIN CONTENT. Use 12 tablets and follow the same procedure described under polymyxin tablets, Section B, Chapter 8.

BACITRACIN CONTENT. *Method 1.* Dilute an aliquot of the phosphate buffer no. 1, *p*H 6, extract obtained from the polymyxin method to give a bacitracin concentration of 1 unit/ml. (estimated) and assay by the microbiologic assay in Method 1, Section A, Chapter 6, except use as the test organism a strain of *M. flavus* that is resistant to streptomycin. Such a strain may be obtained from the American Type Culture Collection (10240A).

Method 2. If the streptomycin resistant strain of *M. flavus* is not available, inactivate the streptomycin in an aliquot of the phosphate buffer no. 1, pH 6, extract obtained from the polymyxin content, by adding sufficient 0.5 per cent semicarbazide solution (use 1.0 ml. for each 1,000 μg. of streptomycin) and let stand for one hour. Dilute the solution with sufficient phosphate buffer no. 1, pH 6, to give a bacitracin concentration of 1 unit/ml. (estimated) and assay by the microbiologic assay in Method 1, Section A, Chapter 6.

Streptomycin, Polymyxin, and Bacitracin Gauze Pads. STREPTOMYCIN CONTENT. Soak 12 gauze pads of the ¾ by ¾ inch size or three pads of larger size in 50 ml. of phosphate buffer no. 3, pH 8, for one hour with frequent agitation. Assay the solution making the necessary dilutions in phosphate buffer no. 3, pH 8, by the microbiologic assay in Method 1, Section A, Chapter 3.

POLYMYXIN CONTENT. Soak 12 gauze pads of the ¾ by ¾ inch size or three pads of larger size in 50 ml. of phosphate buffer no. 6, pH 6, for one hour with frequent agitation. Dilute the solution with phosphate buffer no. 6, pH 6, to give a polymyxin concentration of 10 units/ml. (estimated) and assay by the microbiologic in Method 2, Section A, Chapter 8.

BACITRACIN CONTENT. Soak 12 gauze pads of the ¾ by ¾ inch size or three pads of larger size in 50 ml. of phosphate buffer no. 1, pH 6, for one hour with frequent agitation.

Method 1. Dilute an aliquot of the extract thus obtained to give a bacitracin concentration of 1 unit/ml. (estimated) and assay by the microbiologic assay in Method 1, Section A, Chapter 6, except use as the test organism a strain of *M. flavus* that is resistant to streptomycin (ATCC 10240A).

Method 2. If the streptomycin resistant strain of *M. flavus* is not available, inactivate the streptomycin in an aliquot of the phosphate buffer no. 1, pH 6, extract by adding sufficient 0.5 per cent semicarbazide solution (use 1.0 ml. for each 1,000 μg. of streptomycin) and let stand for one hour. Dilute the solution with sufficient phosphate buffer no. 1, pH 6, to give a bacitracin concentration of 1 unit/ml. (estimated) and assay by the microbiologic assay in Method 1, Section A, Chapter 6.

Streptomycin or Dihydrostreptomycin, Chlortetracycline, Chloramphenicol, and Bacitracin Dental Cement. STREPTOMYCIN OR DIHYDROSTREPTOMYCIN CONTENT. Place an accurately weighed portion of approximately 700 mg. of the dental cement in a sintered-glass filter funnel and wash with three successive 5 ml. portions of 0.3 per cent piperidine in acetone. Remove any residual piperidine with two 5 ml. portions of acetone and suck dry with vacuum. To the residue on the filter add 10 ml. of distilled water to dissolve the streptomycin or dihydrostreptomycin, add 10 ml. of oxidized nitroprusside solution, and proceed as directed in Method 3, Section B, Chapter 3.

CHLORTETRACYCLINE CONTENT. Use the fluorometric Method 4, Section B, Chapter 4, treating the sample as follows: Make a homogeneous slurry of 500 mg. of the dental cement in 500 ml. of water. Place a 10 ml. portion of the slurry in one of the matched tubes and add 2 ml. of the buffer reagent. Centrifuge for three minutes at 3,000 r.p.m. and read the blank fluorescence of this solution. Stir the solution and heat on the steam bath for five minutes. Cool and wipe the inside surface of the test tube with a swab of glass wool. Centrifuge for five minutes at 3,000 r.p.m. and read the fluorescence within one hour. Subtract the initial blank fluorescence reading. Calculate the chlortetracycline content by reference to a standard curve prepared by treating the chlortetracycline standards in a similar manner. It is not necessary to centrifuge the standard solutions.

CHLORAMPHENICOL CONTENT. Use the colorimetric Method 2, Section B, Chapter 5, treating the sample as follows: Place 500 mg. of the dental cement in a 50 ml. volumetric flask and add 25 ml. of ethyl acetate. Heat to boiling on a steam bath. Cool and dilute to mark with ethyl acetate. Centrifuge and place 15 ml. of the clear solution in a 100 ml. volumetric flask. Evaporate to dryness on a steam bath with the aid of a stream of air. Dissolve the residue in 3 ml. of 0.1 N sodium hydroxide, add 25 mg. of sodium hydrosulfite, and proceed as previously.

BACITRACIN CONTENT. Weigh 1 Gm. of the dental cement and transfer to a sintered-glass funnel of medium porosity. Wash the cement five times by shaking with 5 ml. portions of acetone, using a filtering flask and vacuum. Allow the vacuum to dry the residue. Discard the washings. Wash the residue five times by shaking with 5 ml. portions of phosphate buffer no. 1, pH 6, withdrawing each portion under vacuum. Combine the washings and add sufficient buffer to give a bacitracin concentration of 2 units/ml. (estimated).

Use a chromatographic column made from a glass test tube 100 by 15 mm. with an approximate 85 by 7 mm. glass tube blown into the bottom of the test tube. The end of the column is drawn to a tip. Place a plug of glass wool in the tip. Fill the column with a slurry of 6.5 Gm. of acid-washed alumina (chromatographic grade) and phosphate buffer no. 1, pH 6. Allow the alumina to settle in the tube and the excess buffer to drain off. When the liquid level nearly reaches the top of the column of alumina, add the sample solution (containing 2 units/ml.) dropwise from a dropping funnel at the same rate that the buffer is being released from the tip. Discard the first 15 ml. of effluent. Collect the remainder of the sample, dilute an aliquot with buffer to give a final bacitracin concentration of 1 unit/ml. (estimated) and assay by the microbiologic assay in Method 1, Section A, Chapter 6, except use as the test organism the streptomycin and dihydrostreptomycin resistant strain of *M. flavus* (ATCC 10240A).

Chloramphenicol and Streptomycin or Dihydrostreptomycin Capsules. Neither of these antibiotics interferes with the assay of the other.

CHLORAMPHENICOL CONTENT. Use 10 capsules and follow the same procedure described under chloramphenicol capsules, Section C, Chapter 5.

STREPTOMYCIN OR DIHYDROSTREPTOMYCIN CONTENT. Place the contents of 10 capsules and the empty capsules in a blender jar containing 500 ml. of phosphate buffer no. 3, pH 8, and blend in a high-speed blender for two minutes. Dilute an aliquot of the solution with phosphate buffer no. 3, pH 8, to give a streptomycin or dihydrostreptomycin concentration of 1,000 μg./ml. and assay by the microbiologic assay in Method 1, Section A, Chapter 3.

Chloramphenicol Palmitate and Streptomycin or Dihydrostreptomycin Oral Suspension. CHLORAMPHENICOL CONTENT. Follow the same procedure described under chloramphenicol palmitate oral suspension, Section C, Chapter 5.

STREPTOMYCIN OR DIHYDROSTREPTOMYCIN CONTENT. Dilute 1.0 ml. of the suspension with phosphate buffer no. 3, pH 8, to give a streptomycin or dihydrostreptomycin concentration of 1.0 μg./ml. (estimated) and assay by the microbiologic assay in Method 1, Section A, Chapter 3.

Bacitracin and Tyrothricin Troches. Neither of these antibiotics interferes with the assay of the other.

BACITRACIN CONTENT. Use five troches and follow the same procedure described under bacitracin tablets, Section B, Chapter 6.

TYROTHRICIN CONTENT. Use five troches and follow the same procedure described under tyrothricin troches, Section B, Chapter 7.

Bacitracin and Tyrothricin Ointment. BACITRACIN CONTENT. Follow the same procedure described under bacitracin ointment, Section B, Chapter 6.

TYROTHRICIN CONTENT. Follow the same procedure described under tyrothricin ointment, Section B, Chapter 7.

Bacitracin and Polymyxin Ointment. Neither of these antibiotics interferes with the assay of the other.

BACITRACIN CONTENT. Accurately weigh approximately 5 Gm. and transfer to a separatory funnel containing approximately 50 ml. of peroxide-free ether. Shake with four 25 ml. portions of phosphate buffer no. 1, pH 6, and combine the extracts. Dilute an aliquot with phosphate buffer no. 1, pH 6, to give a bacitracin concentration of 1 unit/ml. (estimated) and assay by the microbiologic assay in Method 1, Section A, Chapter 6.

POLYMYXIN CONTENT. Dilute, if necessary, another aliquot of the phosphate buffer no. 1, pH 6, extract obtained for the bacitracin content, with phosphate buffer no. 1, pH 6, to give a polymyxin concentration of 100 units/ml. (estimated) and assay by the microbiologic assay in Method 1, Section A, Chapter 8.

Bacitracin and Polymyxin Tablets. BACITRACIN CONTENT. Use five tablets and follow the same procedure described under bacitracin tablets, Section B, Chapter 6.

POLYMYXIN CONTENT. Dilute, if necessary, an aliquot of the phosphate buffer no. 1, *p*H 6, extract obtained for the bacitracin content, with phosphate buffer no. 1, *p*H 6, to give a polymyxin concentration of 100 units/ml. (estimated) and assay by the microbiologic assay in Method 1, Section A, Chapter 8.

Bacitracin and Polymyxin Troches. Follow the same procedure described under bacitracin and polymyxin tablets in this Chapter.

Bacitracin and Neomycin Ointment. Neither of these antibiotics interferes with the assay of the other in the proportions encountered.

BACITRACIN CONTENT. Follow the same procedure described under bacitracin ointment, Section B, Chapter 6.

NEOMYCIN CONTENT. Follow the same procedure described under neomycin ointment, Section B, Chapter 9.

Bacitracin and Neomycin Tablets. BACITRACIN CONTENT. Use five tablets and follow the same procedure described under bacitracin tablets, Section B, Chapter 6.

NEOMYCIN CONTENT. Use five tablets and follow the same procedure described under neomycin tablets, Section B, Chapter 9.

Bacitracin and Neomycin Troches. BACITRACIN CONTENT. Use five troches and follow the same procedure described under bacitracin tablets, Section B, Chapter 6.

NEOMYCIN CONTENT. Use five troches and follow the same procedure described under neomycin tablets, Section B, Chapter 9.

Bacitracin and Neomycin with Vasoconstrictor (Nose Drops). BACITRACIN CONTENT. Dilute the powder with the amount of diluent recommended in the labeling. Remove a suitable aliquot of the solution, dilute with phosphate buffer no. 1, *p*H 6, to give a bacitracin concentration of 1 unit/ml. (estimated), and assay by the microbiologic assay in Method 1, Section A, Chapter 6.

NEOMYCIN CONTENT. Remove another suitable aliquot of the solution just prepared, dilute with phosphate buffer no. 3, *p*H 8, to give a neomycin concentration of 10 *μ*g./ml. (estimated), and assay by the microbiologic assay in Method 1, Section A, Chapter 9.

Bacitracin Methylene Disalicylate and Streptomycin Powder (Veterinary). In this combination streptomycin interferes with the assay of bacitracin and is inactivated with semicarbazide. The bacitracin does not interfere with the streptomycin assay. As the bacitracin is present in the form of bacitracin methylene disalicylate it is brought into solution with sodium bicarbonate.

BACITRACIN CONTENT. Place an accurately weighed sample of approximately 5 Gm. in a blending jar, add 40 ml. of 2.0 per cent sodium bicarbonate solution, and swirl until the sample is thoroughly wetted. Allow to stand for 15 minutes with occasional swirling. Add 30 ml. of phosphate buffer no. 1, *p*H 6, and allow to stand for one hour with occasional swirling. Add 30 ml. of acetone and blend in a high-speed blender for two minutes. Allow to settle for 15 minutes and filter through filter paper on a Buchner funnel.

Method 1. Dilute an aliquot of the filtrate with sufficient phosphate buffer no. 1, *p*H 6, to obtain a concentration of 1 unit/ml. of bacitracin (estimated) and assay by the microbiologic assay in Method 1, Section A, Chapter 6, except use as a test organism a streptomycin resistant strain of *M. flavus.*

Method 2. If a streptomycin resistant strain of *M. flavus* is not available, remove an aliquot of the filtrate and add sufficient 0.5 per cent semicarbazide solution (1.0 ml. for each 1,000 μg. of streptomycin) to inactivate (one hour at room temperature) the streptomycin contained in the solution. After inactivation, remove an aliquot of the solution, dilute with phosphate buffer no. 1, *p*H 6, to give a bacitracin concentration of 1 unit/ml., and assay by the microbiologic assay in Method 1, Section A, Chapter 6.

STREPTOMYCIN CONTENT. Place an accurately weighed sample of approximately 5 Gm. in a blending jar, add 500 ml. of phosphate buffer no. 3, *p*H 8, and blend for two minutes in a high-speed blender. Allow the foam to subside, dilute an aliquot with phosphate buffer no. 3, *p*H 8, to give a streptomycin concentration of 1,000 μg./ml., and assay by the microbiologic assay in Method 1, Section A, Chapter 3.

Bacitracin or Zinc Bacitracin, Neomycin, and Polymyxin Troches. In this combination the bacitracin may be assayed without interference from the neomycin or polymyxin. The neomycin may also be assayed without interference from the bacitracin or polymyxin. The neomycin, however, does interfere with the polymyxin assay if the microbiologic assay in Method 1, Section A, Chapter 8, is used; in which case it is necessary to add neomycin to the polymyxin when preparing the standard curve. By using the microbiologic assay in Method 2, Section A, Chapter 8, and preparing the sample with phosphate buffer no. 6, *p*H 6 (10 per cent), polymyxin can be assayed without interference from neomycin.

POLYMYXIN CONTENT. Dissolve five troches in about 50 ml. of phosphate buffer no. 6, *p*H 6, add sufficient additional buffer to give a polymyxin concentration of 10.0 units/ml. (estimated), and assay by microbiologic assay in Method 2, Section A, Chapter 8.

BACITRACIN CONTENT. Dilute an aliquot of the phosphate buffer no. 6, *p*H 6, extract obtained for the polymyxin content, with phosphate buffer no. 6, *p*H 6, to give a bacitracin concentration of 10 units/ml. (estimated). Further dilute one part of this solution with nine parts of distilled water to obtain a concentration of 1 unit/ml. of bacitracin (estimated) and a buffer concentration of 1 per cent. Assay by the microbiologic assay in Method 1, Section A, Chapter 6.

NEOMYCIN CONTENT. Use five troches and follow the same procedure described under neomycin tablets, Section B, Chapter 9.

Bacitracin or Zinc Bacitracin, Neomycin, and Polymyxin Ointment. POLYMYXIN CONTENT. Accurately weigh approximately 5 Gm. of the ointment and transfer to a separatory funnel containing approximately 50 ml. of peroxide-free ether. Shake with four 25 ml. portions of phosphate buffer no. 6, *p*H 6, and combine the extracts. Dilute an aliquot with phosphate buffer no. 6, *p*H 6, to give a polymyxin concentration of 10 units/ml. (estimated) and assay by the microbiologic assay in Method 2, Section A, Chapter 8.

BACITRACIN CONTENT. Dilute another aliquot of the phosphate buffer no. 6, *p*H 6, extract obtained for the polymyxin content, with phosphate buffer no. 6, *p*H 6, to give a bacitracin concentration of 10 units/ml. (estimated). Further dilute one part of this solution with nine parts of distilled water to obtain a concentration of 1 unit/ml. of bacitracin (estimated) and assay by the microbiologic assay in Method 1, Section A, Chapter 6.

NEOMYCIN CONTENT. Accurately weigh approximately 1 Gm. of the ointment and transfer to a separatory funnel containing approximately 50 ml. of peroxide-free ether. Shake with four 25 ml. portions of phoshpate buffer. no 3, *p*H 8, and combine the extracts. Dilute an aliquot with phosphate buffer no. 3, *p*H 8, to give a neomycin concentration of 10 μg./ml. (estimated) and assay by the microbiologic assay in Method 1, Section A, Chapter 9.

Bacitracin, Neomycin, and Polymyxin Tablets. Follow the same procedure described for bacitracin, neomycin, and polymyxin troches in this Chapter.

Bacitracin, Neomycin, and Polymyxin with Vasoconstrictor (Nose Drops). Add the quantity of diluent recommended in the labeling and using suitable aliquots of the resultant solution assay for bacitracin, neomycin, and polymyxin as described under bacitracin, neomycin, and polymyxin troches in this Chapter.

Bacitracin, Tyrothricin, and Neomycin Troches. None of the antibiotics in this mixture interferes with the assay of the others.

BACITRACIN CONTENT. Use five troches and follow the same procedure described under bacitracin tablets, Section B, Chapter 6.

TYROTHRICIN CONTENT. Use five troches and follow the same procedure described under tyrothricin troches, Section B, Chapter 7.

NEOMYCIN CONTENT. Use five troches and follow the same procedure described under neomycin tablets, Section B, Chapter 9.

Oxytetracycline and Polymyxin Ointment. Polymyxin does not interfere with the assay of oxytetracycline but oxytetracycline does interfere with the assay of polymyxin. It has been found that oxytetracycline hydrochloride has a sufficient solubility in acetone to permit its separation from a number of antibiotics that are insoluble in this solvent. In the method to be described, the ointment base is removed with benzene and then the oxytetracycline hydrochloride is separated from the polymyxin by dissolving it in acetone.

OXYTETRACYCLINE CONTENT. Place an accurately weighed portion of approximately 1.0 to 1.5 Gm. of the ointment in a medium porosity sintered-glass filter funnel equipped with a ground glass stopper. Wash the ointment on the filter with five successive 10 ml. portions of warm benzene, removing each washing with vacuum. Discard the benzene washings. Shake the residue in the funnel with five successive 10 ml. portions of acetone, removing each portion under vacuum. Combine the acetone extracts and make to 100 ml. with acetone. Remove an aliquot of this solution, further dilute in phosphate buffer no. 4, pH 4.5, to give an oxytetracycline concentration of 0.24 µg./ml. (estimated), and assay by the microbiologic assay in Method 1, Section A, Chapter 4.

POLYMYXIN CONTENT. The polymyxin remaining in the funnel, after removal of the oxytetracycline, is dissolved as follows: Wash with five successive 10 ml. portions of phosphate buffer no. 6, pH 6, removing each washing with vacuum. Combine the washings, dilute with phosphate buffer no. 6, pH 6, to give a polymyxin concentration of 10 units/ml. (estimated), and assay by the microbiologic assay in Method 2, Section A, Chapter 8.

Oxytetracycline and Polymyxin Vaginal Tablets. OXYTETRACYCLINE CONTENT. Accurately weigh 20 tablets and grind to a powder with a mortar and pestle. Transfer approximately 1 Gm. (accurately weighed) of the powdered tablets to a medium porosity sintered-glass filter funnel equipped with a ground glass stopper. Shake the powder with five successive 10 ml. portions of acetone, removing each portion under vacuum. Combine the acetone extracts and make to 100 ml. with acetone. Remove an aliquot of this solution, further dilute in phosphate buffer no. 4, pH 4.5, to give an oxytetracycline concentration of 0.24 µg./ml. (estimated), and assay by the microbiologic assay in method 1, Section A, Chapter 4.

POLYMYXIN CONTENT. Wash the residue remaining in the funnel with five successive 10 ml. portions of phosphate buffer no. 6, pH 6, removing each washing with vacuum. Combine the washings, dilute with phosphate buffer no. 6, pH 6, to give a polymyxin concentration of 10 units/ml. (estimated), and assay by the microbiologic assay in Method 2, Section A, Chapter 8.

Oxytetracycline and Polymyxin Topical Powder. Determine the oxytetracycline and polymyxin content by the same procedure used for oxytetracycline and polymyxin vaginal tablets in this Chapter, using 2 Gm. of powder.

Oxytetracycline and Polymyxin with Vasoconstrictor (Nose Drops). This preparation is sold as a combination package. Determine the oxytetracycline and polymyxin content of the bottle containing the powdered antibiotics by the same procedure used for oxytetracycline and polymyxin vaginal tablets in this Chapter, using the entire contents of the bottle.

Oxytetracycline and Polymyxin Otic. This preparation is sold as a combination package. Determine the oxytetracycline and polymyxin content of the bottle containing the powdered antibiotics by the same procedure used for oxytetracycline and polymyxin vaginal tablets in this Chapter, using the entire contents of the bottle.

Tetracycline and Polymyxin Ointment. As was the case with oxytetracycline and polymyxin, it is necessary to separate these two antibiotics before they can be assayed. Tetracycline hydrochloride, however, is not soluble in acetone. It is soluble though in acetone that has been made alkaline with 0.3 per cent piperidine, while polymyxin is not.

Determine the tetracycline and polymyxin content by the same procedure described for oxytetracycline and polymyxin ointment in this Chapter, only use acetone containing 0.3 per cent piperidine.

Tetracycline and Nystatin Capsules. TETRACYCLINE CONTENT. Follow the same procedure described under tetracycline capsules, Section C, Chapter 4.

NYSTATIN CONTENT. Place five capsules in a blending jar with 150 ml. of formamide. Blend for two minutes in a high-speed blender and then dilute an aliquot with sufficient formamide to give a nystatin concentration of 400 units/ml. (estimated). Further dilute this solution with phosphate buffer no. 1, *p*H 6, to give a concentration of 20 units/ml. (estimated) and assay by the microbiologic assay in Method 1, Section A, Chapter 14.

Polymyxin and Gramicidin Troches. POLYMYXIN CONTENT. Place 12 troches in a blending jar containing 200 ml. of phosphate buffer no. 1, *p*H 6, and blend for two minutes with a high-speed blender. Dilute an aliquot of the solution, if necessary, with phosphate buffer no. 1, *p*H 6, to give a polymyxin concentration of 100 units/ml. (estimated) and assay by the microbiologic assay in Method 1, Section A, Chapter 8.

GRAMICIDIN CONTENT. Use five troches and follow the same procedure described under tyrothricin troches, Section B, Chapter 7.

Polymyxin and Gramicidin with Vasoconstrictor (Nose Drops). POLYMYXIN CONTENT. Dilute a suitable aliquot of the sample with phosphate buffer no. 6, *p*H 6, to give a polymyxin concentration of 10 units/ml. (estimated) and assay by the microbiologic assay in Method 2, Section A, Chapter 8.

GRAMICIDIN CONTENT. Follow the same procedure described under tyrothricin nose drops, Section B, Chapter 7.

Neomycin and Gramicidin Ointment. Neither of these antibiotics interferes with the assay of the other.

NEOMYCIN CONTENT. Follow the same procedure described under neomycin ointment, Section B, Chapter 9.

GRAMICIDIN CONTENT. Follow the same procedure described under tyrothricin ointment, Section B, Chapter 7.

Neomycin and Tyrothricin or Gramicidin Troches. NEOMYCIN CONTENT. Follow the same procedure described under neomycin tablets, Section B, Chapter 9.

TYROTHRICIN OR GRAMICIDIN CONTENT. Follow the same procedure described under tyrothricin troches, Section B, Chapter 7.

Neomycin and Gramicidin with Vasoconstrictor (Nose Drops). NEOMYCIN CONTENT. Dilute a suitable aliquot of the sample with phosphate buffer no. 3, pH 8, to give a neomycin concentration of 10 μg./ml. (estimated) and assay by the microbiologic assay in Method 1, Section A, Chapter 9.

GRAMICIDIN CONTENT. Follow the same procedure described under tyrothricin nose drops, Section B, Chapter 7.

Erythromycin and Polymyxin Ointment. Neither of these antibiotics interferes with the assay of the other.

ERYTHROMYCIN CONTENT. Follow the same procedure described under erythromycin ointment, Section C, Chapter 10.

POLYMYXIN CONTENT. Follow the same procedure described under polymyxin ointment, Section B, Chapter 8.

Erythromycin and Polymyxin Otic (Ear Drops). ERYTHROMYCIN CONTENT. Dilute a suitable aliquot of the preparation with phosphate buffer no. 3, pH 8, to give an erythromycin concentration of 1 μg./ml. and assay by the microbiologic assay in Method 1, Section A, Chapter 10.

POLYMYXIN CONTENT. Dilute a suitable aliquot of the preparation with phosphate buffer no. 6, pH 6, to give a polymyxin concentration of 10 units/ml. (estimated) and assay by the microbiologic assay in Method 2, Section A, Chapter 8.

Erythromycin and Streptomycin or Dihydrostreptomycin Ointment. Erythromycin interferes in the assay of streptomycin or dihydrostreptomycin and must be eliminated by inactivation with acid or by extraction with ether. The streptomycin or dihydrostreptomycin does not interfere with the assay of the erythromycin.

ERYTHROMYCIN CONTENT. Place an accurately weighed sample of approximately 1 Gm. of ointment into a glass blender jar containing 100 ml. of polyethylene glycol 400. Using a high-speed blender, blend the mixture for two minutes, and filter the solution through a cotton plug or filter paper. Dilute an aliquot of the filtrate with phosphate buffer no. 3, pH 8, to give an erythromycin content of 1.0 μg./ml. (estimated) and assay by the microbiologic assay in Method 1, Section A, Chapter 10.

STREPTOMYCIN OR DIHYDROSTREPTOMYCIN CONTENT. *Method 1.* Place an accurately weighed sample of approximately 1 Gm. of the ointment in a separatory funnel containing about 50 ml. of peroxide-free ether. Shake the ointment until homogeneous, add 20 ml. of phosphate buffer no. 3, *p*H 8, and shake well. Remove the buffer layer and repeat the extraction with three more 20 ml. portions of the buffer. Combine the buffer extracts and make to 100 ml. with buffer. Place the buffer solution into a second separatory funnel and wash with three 30 ml. portions of ether. Discard the ether washes, dilute an aliquot of the buffer layer with phosphate buffer no. 3, *p*H 8, and assay by the microbiologic assay in Method 1, Section A, Chapter 3.

Method 2. Place an accurately weighed sample of approximately 1 Gm. of the ointment in a blending jar containing sufficient phosphate buffer no. 3, *p*H 8, to make 100 ml. Using a high-speed blender, blend the mixture for three minutes. Adjust a suitable aliquot of the buffer extract with 1 *N* hydrochloric acid to give the solution a *p*H of 2 and allow to stand for three hours at 37 C. to inactivate the erythromycin. At the end of this time readjust the *p*H to 8 with 1 *N* sodium hydroxide, dilute with phosphate buffer no. 3, *p*H 8, and assay by the microbiologic assay in Method 1, Section A, Chapter 3.

Erythromycin and Neomycin Ointment. ERYTHROMYCIN CONTENT. Follow the same procedure described under erythromycin and streptomycin ointment in this Chapter.

NEOMYCIN CONTENT. Prepare the sample by the same procedure described under erythromycin and streptomycin ointment, Method 1 or 2 of this Chapter, only assay the extract by the microbiologic assay method 1, Section A, Chapter 9.

Chlortetracycline Hydrochloride or Tetracycline Hydrochloride, Neomycin Sulfate, Streptomycin Sulfate or Dihydrostreptomycin Sulfate, and Procaine Penicillin Ointment. In a mixture of this kind containing four different antibiotics, it is necessary to separate quantitatively some of the antibiotics from each other to avoid interference. In the method to be described, the ointment base can be separated with isooctane, which does not dissolve any of the antibiotics present. After removal of the ointment base, the procaine penicillin is separated by dissolving in chloroform, in which the other three antibiotics are insoluble. The chlortetracycline or tetracycline may be separated next by dissolving in acetone containing a little piperidine to keep it alkaline. The streptomycin or dihydrostreptomycin and neomycin content that remains may be determined by those methods that were described previously.

PENICILLIN CONTENT. Place an accurately weighed sample of approximately 1 Gm. in an extraction funnel prepared by fusing a ground glass joint to the top of a medium porosity sintered-glass filter funnel (30 mm. diameter). Wash with five 10 ml. portions of warm isooctane and draw off under vacuum. Discard the isooctane washings. Wash the residue with three 10 ml. portions of chloroform and draw off under vacuum. Combine the extracts and make to mark in a 250 ml. volumetric flask with absolute alcohol. Make the proper estimated dilutions in phosphate buffer no. 1, *p*H 6, and assay by the microbiologic assay in Method 1, Section A, Chapter 2.

CHLORTETRACYCLINE OR TETRACYCLINE CONTENT. Wash the residue in the funnel four times with 10 ml. portions of 0.3 per cent piperidine in acetone solution. Withdraw each washing under vacuum. Combine the four washings in a 100 ml. volumetric flask and make to mark immediately with phosphate buffer no. 4, pH 4.5. Dilute an aliquot of this solution with phosphate buffer no. 4, pH 4.5, and assay by the microbiologic assay in Method 1, Section A, Chapter 4.

NEOMYCIN CONTENT. The residue remaining in the funnel after the extractions contains the neomycin and streptomycin or dihydrostreptomycin. Wash this residue five times, using 10 ml. portions of phosphate buffer no. 3, pH 8, drawing each portion off under vacuum. Combine the washings in a 100 ml. volumetric flask and make to mark with phosphate buffer no. 3, pH 8. Dilute an aliquot of this solution with phosphate buffer no. 3, pH 8, to give a neomycin concentration of 10 μg./ml. (estimated) and assay by the microbiologic assay in Method 1, Section A, Chapter 9, using American Type Culture Collection 6538PR, strain of *M. pyogenes* var. *aureus* that is resistant to streptomycin and dihydrostreptomycin.

STREPTOMYCIN OR DIHYDROSTREPTOMYCIN CONTENT. Dilute an aliquot of the aqueous solution as just prepared with phosphate buffer no. 3, pH 8, to a potency of 1 μg./ml. (estimated) and assay by the microbiologic assay in Method 1, Section A, Chapter 3.

17 IDENTIFICATION OF THE ANTIBIOTICS

Section A: Qualitative Tests

Detailed descriptions of qualitative identity tests of each individual antibiotic are compiled in this section. For ease of reference, a summary of the data is presented in table II. Illustrative examples of the applicability and scope of the tests are included to demonstrate the manner in which these techniques may be applied.[16]

It should be borne in mind that the procedures described establish presumptive evidence for the presence of the antibiotics; however, for conclusive identification one must resort to standard criteria, such as melting points, crystallographic data, infrared and ultraviolet absorption characteristics, and the accepted bioassay techniques.

PROCEDURE 1: Maltol Test for Streptomycin.

Dissolve several milligrams of sample in about 2 ml. of water, add 2 drops 2 N sodium hydroxide, and heat in steam bath for three minutes. Cool, acidify with 1 N sulfuric acid, and add 2 drops of 5 per cent ferric sulfate or ferric chloride solution. A purple color denotes the presence of maltol, which is derived from streptomycin.[5]

PROCEDURE 2: Glucosamine Test for Streptomycin, Dihydro-streptomycin, and Neomycin.

Dissolve about 10 mg. of sample in 1 ml. of water, add 2 ml. 1 N hydrochloric acid, and heat in steam bath for 10 minutes to liberate glucosamine or N-methyl glucosamine from their respective glycosides. Add 2 ml. 2 N sodium hydroxide and 1 ml. of 2.0 per cent aqueous acetylacetone and heat on the steam bath for five minutes. Cool and add 1 ml. Ehrlich's reagent (500 mg. p-dimethylaminobenzaldehyde in 25 ml. ethanol and 25 ml. concentrated hydrochloric acid). Cherry color denotes glucosamine or N-methyl glucosamine. The initial acid hydrolysis is unnecessary in the case of streptomycin, since the treatment with alkali results in a rearrangement with direct liberation of N-methyl glucosamine.[17]

PROCEDURE 3: Guanido Test for Streptomycin, Dihydrostreptomycin, and Viomycin.

To 10 mg. of sample in 1 ml. of water, add 1 ml. of oxidized nitroprusside reagent.[8,9] (To 1 ml, 10 per cent sodium ferricyanide, add 1 ml. of 10 per cent sodium nitroprusside and 1 ml. of 2 N sodium hydroxide. After the initial dark color lightens to a light yellow dilute to 100 ml. with water.) A red color denotes the presence of streptomycin, dihydrostreptomycin, or viomycin. At low concentrations several minutes are required for color development.

PROCEDURE 4: Fluorescence Tests for Chlortetracycline, Oxytetracycline, and Tetracycline.

To several milligrams of sample in 5 ml. of water, add 1 ml. 2 N sodium hydroxide. With chlortetracycline the solution turns to a deep yellow-orange, with strong blue fluorescence under ultraviolet light. On heating, the yellow color fades and the blue fluorescence increases.[11]

With oxytetracycline a deep yellow-orange color develops with green fluorescence under ultraviolet light. On heating, the solution remains yellow-orange but the fluorescence changes to a deep blue. In mixtures of the two antibiotics, the initial blue fluorescence of the chlortetracycline dominates, masking the green of the oxytetracycline.

With tetracycline a deep yellow-orange color develops with no fluorescence. On heating a blue fluorescence develops under ultraviolet light.

To several milligrams of sample, add 2 ml. of concentrated hydrochloric acid. In approximately one minute, oxytetracycline acquires a green fluorescence while chlortetracycline and tetracycline do not fluoresce under ultraviolet light.

PROCEDURE 5: Ninhydrin Test for Bacitracin, Polymyxin B, Tyrothricin, Neomycin, Viomycin, and Ephenamine Penicillin G.

To several milligrams of sample, add 1 ml. of water, 1 ml. ninhydrin reagent (0.2 per cent ninhydrin in *n*-butanol) and about 0.5 ml. of pyridine. Heat in a steam bath for about five minutes. A deep purple color develops in the presence of these antibiotics. On prolonged heating, both streptomycin and dihydrostreptomycin furnish a weak response.

PROCEDURE 6: Diazotization Test for Chloramphenicol, Procaine Penicillin G, and Chloroprocaine Penicillin O.

To several milligrams of sample, add 2 ml. of water, 2 drops of 5 per cent sodium nitrite solution, and several drops of concentrated hydrochloric acid. After one-half minute, add 5 drops of 5 per cent sulfamic acid solution; shake and add a minute amount of N(1-naphthyl) ethylene diamine dihydrochloride. A deep purple color denotes the presence of the procaine or chloroprocaine salts and/or sulfonamides.

Add to several milligrams of sample, 2 ml. of water, 2 drops 2 N sodium hydroxide, and about 25 mg. of sodium hydrosulfite. After 10 minutes, add 0.5 ml. of 5 per cent sodium nitrite and 5 to 10 drops of concentrated hydrochloric acid. (The larger amount of sodium nitrite used in this step serves to destroy excess hydrosulfite.) After one-half minute, add 1 ml. of 5 per cent sulfamic acid. Add a minute amount of N(1-naphthyl) ethylene diamine dihydrochloride to develop color as previously.[12] A positive response to this with negative response to the method in the last paragraph denotes the presence of chloramphenicol. If the response to the procedure in the last paragraph is positive, extract the colored solution with 5 ml. of ethyl acetate. Repeat procedure in the last paragraph on a 1 ml. aliquot of the ethyl acetate extract to insure complete removal of primary aromatic amines. If the test is now negative, treat the remaining portion of the ethyl acetate extract by the procedure in this paragraph. This confirms the presence of chloramphenicol in a mixture containing procaine salts and/or sulfonamides.

PROCEDURE 7: Test for Erythromycin.

Dissolve about 3 mg. of sample in 2 ml. acetone and add an equal volume of concentrated hydrochloric acid. A rapid color development takes place initiating with orange, changing to red, and finally resulting in a deep purple. Shake with 2 ml. of chloroform. A portion of the color extracts into the chloroform layer, lending a purple color to it.

PROCEDURE 8: Test for Tyrothricin and Gramicidin.

Add 2 ml. of Ehrlich's reagent (Procedure 2) to about 2 mg. of sample. A cherry-red color develops in a few minutes. Add 2 drops of 5 per cent sodium nitrite solution. Color immediately changes to blue. The presence of tyrothricin and/or gramicidin is confirmed. If sample is negative to Procedure 13 A, then the response to this test confirms presence of gramicidin.[18]

PROCEDURE 9: Test for Carbomycin.

Dissolve about 5 mg. of sample in 1 ml. of water and add two volumes of concentrated hydrochloric acid. A deep purple color develops gradually within five minutes. Dilute with about 10 ml. of water; this dilutes the color. Extract with 2 ml. *n*-butanol. Both phases become colorless. Add 1 ml. of concentrated hydrochloric acid to the isolated butanol layer. The purple color is regenerated.

PROCEDURE 10: Test for Fumagillin.

To 5 mg. of the sample, add about 50 mg. of vanillin and 2 ml. of concentrated hydrochloric acid. A green color slowly develops in 10 to 15 minutes. The other antibiotics that react with these reagents tend mainly toward the red or purple.

To 5 mg. of sample, add 2 ml. of ethyl acetate and proceed as previously. Include a blank. A cherry-red color develops that intensifies with fumagillin but fades in the blank.

PROCEDURE 11: Test for Dihydrostreptomycin in the Presence of Streptomycin and/or Viomycin.

Dissolve 10 mg. of sample in 1 ml. of water and saturate with solid calcium chloride. Shake thoroughly with 15 ml. *n*-propanol and centrifuge for five minutes at about 4,000 r.p.m. The supernatant liquid contains most of the dihydrostreptomycin, a small portion of streptomycin, and none of the viomycin. To the supernatant liquid, add 5 ml. of ethyl acetate and shake. The presence of dihydrostreptomycin causes the solution to cloud, while the streptomycin remains in solution. Centrifuge for 10 minutes at about 4,000 r.p.m.; the dihydrostreptomycin is deposited as a coating on the sides of the centrifuge tube. Decant the clear liquid and discard. Rinse the tube with about 5 ml. of propanol; then apply Procedure 3 to the residue.

PROCEDURE 12: A Modified Biuret Test for Chloramphenicol, Bacitracin, Polymyxin, Viomycin, Gramicidin, and Tyrothricin.

Dissolve or suspend about 20 mg. of sample in 1 ml. of methanol. Add 2 ml. of 2 N sodium hydroxide, 1 drop of 1 per cent copper sulfate, and extract with 2 ml. of butanol. Note the color of both the aqueous and butanol phases (table I). In the case of chloramphenicol, use 5 drops of the copper sulfate solution.

Unlike the response of the polypeptide antibiotics to the biuret test with copper sulfate, chloramphenicol apparently forms a coordination complex with this reagent necessitating the use of the larger amount of copper sulfate.

PROCEDURE 13: Paper Chromatography for Identifying Bacitracin, Polymyxin B, Neomycin, Tyrothricin, and Viomycin.

These antibiotics cannot be readily characterized chemically nor do they contain diagnostic groupings that would permit ready identification. Consequently, their identity is established by comparison of their migration characteristics with those of standards by paper chromatography.

For these chromatographic procedures any airtight container, resistant to organic solvents, acids, and weak bases, may be used. The simplest type in use by this laboratory is a glass stoppered cylindrical museum jar 11½ inches high and 3½ inches in diameter. Eight inch squares of Whatman no. 1 paper were used throughout; these were fashioned into cylinders, held together at the top by a paper clip, and rested directly on the floor of the glass cylinder, immersed in a layer of about ¼ inch of the resolving solvent.

Place small drops, containing about 2 mg./ml. of sample and of known antibiotic dissolved in the proper solvent, 1 inch from the bottom of paper and spaced at least 1 inch apart. After air drying, place in the chromatographic chamber. In all cases allow the resolving solvent to ascend about 4 to 5 inches from the point of origin. Remove paper and dry either in 100 C. oven or in air. Spray the dried paper with 1 per cent ninhydrin in water-saturated butanol. Heat in 100 C. oven for 10 minutes.

PROCEDURE 13 A: Tyrothricin.

Dissolve sample in 75 per cent methanol.

Resolving solvent: 25 ml. of 9:1 acetone: water, 5 ml. of chloroform, 2 ml. of ethylene glycol, and 1 ml. of pyridine. Tyrothricin is recognized as a sharply defined band at an R_f 0.6 to 0.7. Polymyxin B sulfate remains at origin. The bulk of the bacitracin remains at the origin, but a small portion streaks from the origin to an R_f 0.5. The presence of ephenamine penicillin G is evidenced by a spot at the solvent front.

PROCEDURE 13 B: Bacitracin, Polymyxin B, and Ephenamine Penicillin.

Dissolve sample in 75 per cent methanol.

Resolving solvent: 25 ml. of 3:1 propanol: water, 5 ml. benzene, 1.5 ml. ethylene glycol, 1 ml. glacial acetic acid.

 Polymyxin is found at R_f 0.25 to 0.3.

 Bacitracin is found at R_f 0.5 to 0.6.

 Tyrothricin is found at solvent front.

 Ephenamine penicillin G is found at R_f 0.7 to 0.8.

PROCEDURE 13 C: Neomycin and Viomycin.

Dissolve sample in water.

Resolving solvent: 25 ml. 1:1 *n*-propanol: water, 1 ml. glacial acetic acid.

 Neomycin is found at R_f 0.25 to 0.3.

 Viomycin is found at R_f 0.4.

 Bacitracin is found at solvent front.

 Polymyxin is found at R_f 0.9 to the front.

PROCEDURE 14: Identification of the Individual Penicillin G Salts.

The data for the various penicillin salts supplied in the table pertain to the gross characteristics of the individual salt. However, mixtures of penicillin salts will not fall into clearly defined solubility categories. Nevertheless, certain aspects of their solubility behavior can be used for their characterization.

PROCEDURE 14 A: For All Penicillin G Salts.

Note slight characteristic flowery odor of the dry powder. Add 10 ml. water plus 2 drops of concentrated hydrochloric acid to about 10 mg. of sample and heat on steam bath. Note strong characteristic odor.

PROCEDURE 14 B: Sodium or Potassium Penicillin G.

Dissolve about 25 mg. sample in 2 ml. water. For powders that are not completely water soluble, suspend about 25 mg. of sample in 3 ml. of carbon tetrachloride and shake with 0.5 ml. of water. Correspondingly larger portions of material and solvents can be used as long as the water is kept to a minimum. Centrifuge and carefully draw off the aqueous layer. Add 1 drop of 1 *N* hydrochloric acid. A resultant white precipitate indicates the presence of sodium or potassium penicillin. The precipitate will dissolve on dilution with water. It should be noted that solutions of buffered penicillins other than the sodium or potassium salts will furnish sufficient ions to respond to this test. However, in this latter case the quantity of sodium or potassium penicillin formed under the test conditions is small and provides only a transitory precipitate. Identity of the cation as sodium or potassium can be determined by a flame test.

PROCEDURE 14 C: Procaine Penicillin G.

Responds to Procedure 6. Add 2 drops of 2 *N* sodium hydroxide to a suspension of 10 mg. of sample in about 10 ml. water. Solution occurs immediately. Heat on steam bath and note characteristic odor of diethylaminoethanol.

PROCEDURE 14 D: Diethylaminoethyl Ester of Penicillin G.

Repeat procedure 14 B, but add 1 drop of ammonium hydroxide to the aqueous phase instead of the 1 *N* hydrochloric acid. A white precipitate denotes the presence of the ester.

Dissolve about 10 mg. in 10 ml. of water. Add two drops of 2 *N* sodium hydroxide, causing a momentary precipitate that disappears rapidly as a result of hydrolysis. Heat on steam bath and note characteristic odor of diethylaminoethanol.

PROCEDURE 14 E: 1-Ephenamine Penicillin G.

Responds to Procedures 5 and 13 B.

Suspend about 10 mg. in 10 ml. of water and add two drops of 2 *N* sodium hydroxide. Unlike the other penicillin salts, this salt does not dissolve.

PROCEDURE 14 F: N,N'Dibenzylethylenediamine Dipenicillin.

This is the only penicillin salt that is insoluble in 95 per cent ethanol.

Dissolve about 10 mg. in 2 ml. methylcellosolve and add 5 ml. of water. In a few minutes crystals separate that, when observed under the microscope, appear as flat plates. Presence of other penicillin salts does not interfere.

PROCEDURE 15: Identification of Penicillin O Salts.

The therapeutic justification for penicillin O precludes the presence of the penicillin G salts. Consequently, any similar responses to the tests by penicillin G and penicillin O should not lead to confusion.

PROCEDURE 15 A: Note Characteristic Garlic-like Odor of All Penicillin O Salts.

Add 10 ml. of water to about 10 mg. penicillin O salt. Heat on steam bath and note the intensified garlic-like odor.

PROCEDURE 15 B: Differentiation Between the Potassium Penicillin O and the Chloroprocaine Salt.

Refer to solubilities in table I.

PROCEDURE 15 C: Chloroprocaine Penicillin O.

Responds to Procedure 6.

Application of Test Procedures. To demonstrate the manner in which the test procedures can be utilized, the identification of each component of an extremely complicated mixture, containing 100 mg. each of 14 antibiotics, is described. The formulation contained potassium penicillin G, streptomycin calcium chloride salt, dihydrostreptomycin sulfate, chloramphenicol, chlortetracycline hydrochloride, oxytetracycline hydrochloride, bacitracin, polymyxin B sulfate, neomycin sulfate, viomycin sulfate, erythromycin, tyrothricin, carbomycin hydrochloride, and fumagillin. Therapeutic and economic reasons would preclude the marketing of such a mixture. Nevertheless, this extreme case is used as an example to demonstrate the versatility of the identification scheme.

Procedure. The mixture was a light buff colored powder, suggestive of chlortetracycline, oxytetracycline, or some of the polypeptide-like antibiotics, which occasionally exhibit an off-color.

To about 10 mg. of mixture, add 5 ml. of water. Mixture partially dissolves in water to give a yellow solution, suggestive of chlortetracycline and oxytetracycline. Test by Procedure 4 to confirm presence of chlortetracycline. (The blue fluorescence of chlortetracycline masks the green fluorescence of oxytetracycline.)

Test about 10 mg. of the mixture by Procedure 4 to confirm presence of oxytetracycline.

Dissolve about 20 mg. mixture in 5 ml. water and note odor: slight characteristic odor of penicillin. Add several drops of concentrated hydrochloric acid and heat on steam bath for about five minutes. Strong characteristic penicillin odor (Procedure 14 A). This confirms the penicillin G.

Add about 10 ml. absolute methanol, containing one drop 1 N sulfuric acid * to about 100 mg. sample; shake, centrifuge, and decant. Dissolve residue in 3 ml. of water and divide into three equal portions and treat as follows:

Apply Procedure 2—positive glucosamine indicates presence of streptomycin, dihydrostreptomycin, and/or neomycin.

Apply Procedure 3—positive test indicates streptomycin, dihydrostreptomycin, and/or viomycin.

Apply Procedure 1—positive maltol verifies presence of streptomycin.

Add 50 mg. of the mixture to 2 ml. of water, shake, and centrifuge to separate the water soluble fraction. Test by Procedure 11. This confirms the presence of dihydrostreptomycin.

Treat about 5 mg. of the mixture by Procedure 5; suggests ephenamine

---

* Sulfuric acid added to convert methanol-soluble hydrochloride salts to methanol-insoluble sulfate streptomycin and dihydrostreptomycin salts.

penicillin, bacitracin, polymyxin B, tyrothricin, viomycin, and/or neomycin.

Add 10 ml. water to about 25 mg. of mixture, shake, and centrifuge. Discard supernatant liquid, add 10 ml. ethyl acetate, shake, centrifuge, and discard supernatant. Apply Procedure 8 to residue; this denotes presence of tyrothricin and/or gramicidin. Add 2 ml. of 75 per cent ethanol to about 100 mg. of mixture, shake, and centrifuge. Test the supernatant liquid by Procedures 13 A and 13 B; this verifies the presence of tyrothricin, bacitracin, and polymyxin. Dissolve this residue in 2 ml. of water, shake, and centrifuge. Decant the supernatant and test by Procedure 13 C. Confirms the presence of neomycin and viomycin.

Add 5 ml. benzene to about 50 mg. of mixture, shake, and centrifuge. Evaporate the supernatant liquid on steam bath and refer to Procedure 7; this confirms the presence of erythromycin.

Add 5 ml. ethyl acetate to about 50 mg. of mixture, shake, and filter through filter paper. Evaporate the filtrate to dryness on a steam bath and test by Procedure 9; this verifies the presence of carbomycin.

Treat 10 mg. of mixture directly by Procedure 6; this confirms the presence of chloramphenicol.

Shake about 50 mg. of the mixture with two 10 ml. portions of propanol water (1:3), centrifuge, pour off the solution. Treat the residue in the centrifuge tube by Procedure 10; this confirms the presence of fumagillin.

It is obvious that with less complex mixtures, which would normally be expected, it would be unnecessary to apply the full procedure stepwise. For example, a sample negative to the ninhydrin and maltol tests, but positive to the guanido test, immediately indicates that dihydrostreptomycin is present and streptomycin, bacitracin, polymyxin, tyrothricin, viomycin, and neomycin are absent. Again, in the absence of oxytetracycline and chlortetracycline, the modified biuret test described under Procedure 12 can be applied for screening six of the antibiotics. It will be noted that since gramicidin is a component of tyrothricin, the tests for gramicidin have diagnostic value only in the absence of tyrothricin.

Dosage Forms. The various dosage forms in which the antibiotics are marketed impose an additional burden on these identification procedures. Obviously, the main problem is one of removing interfering excipients prior to applying the identity techniques already described. In the majority of cases, however, the test procedures can be applied to the dosage form either directly or with a minimum of preliminary treatment.

In view of the great number and diversity of dosage forms on the current market, it is impractical to attempt consideration of each one in this report. Nevertheless, by discussing several actual examples, we can impart to the reader an insight to the reasoning, which will permit the resolution of an individual identification problem. Practical consideration governs the manipulation which need be applied to the normal sample to identify the constituent antibiotics. For example, more painstaking technique is required to identify tyrothricin in an ointment than bacitracin in the same ointment because of the relative quantities present.

EXAMPLE 1: *Tablets of erythromycin and sulfonamides.* Grind a tablet to a

TABLE II: *Summary of Data*

Antibiotic	Organoleptic			Solubility				Ninhydrin test	Modified Biuret		Test procedures
	Color*	Odor	Odor After Acid Heating	Water	Ethyl alcohol	Chloroform	Ethyl acetate		Color in aqueous phase	Color in butanol phase	
Potassium and sodium penicillin G	White	Slight flowery	Characteristic † penicillin G	+	+	−	−	−	−	−	14 A, 14 B
Diethylaminoethyl ester penicillin HI	White	Slight flowery	Characteristic † penicillin G	+	+	+	−	−	−	−	14 A, 14 D
Potassium penicillin O	White	Garlic	Garlic	+	+	−	−	−	−	−	15 A, 15 B
Procaine penicillin G	White	Slight flowery	Characteristic	−	+	+	−	−	−	−	6, 14 A, 14 C
N,N′ Dibenzylethylenediamine dipenicillin	White	Slight	Characteristic	−	−	−	−	−	−	−	14 A, 14 F
Ephenamine penicillin	White	Slight flowery	Characteristic	−	+	−	−	+	−	−	5, 13 B, 14 A, 14 E
Chloroprocaine penicillin O	White	Garlic	Garlic	−	+	+	−	−	−	−	6, 15 A, 15 C
Streptomycin sulfate	White	−	−	+	−	−	−	++‡	−	−	1, 2, 3
Streptomycin calcium chloride salt	White	−	−	+	+	−	−	++‡	−	−	1, 2, 3
Dihydrostreptomycin salt	White	−	−	+	−	−	−	++‡	−	−	2, 3, 11
Chlortetracycline	Yellow & fluorescent	−	−	+	Slight	−	−	−	−§	−§	4
Oxytetracycline	Yellow & sl. fluorescent	−	−	+	Slight	−	−	−	−§	−§	4
Tetracycline	Yellow & fluorescent	−	−	+	Slight	−	−	−	−§	−§	4

Antibiotic	Appearance*	Odor					Color	Color	References
Chloramphenicol	White	—	—	—	+	+	—	Blue	6, 12
Bacitracin	White	—	+	+	+	+	Pink	—	5, 12, 13 B
Polymyxin B	White	—	+	+	—	—	—	Pink	5, 12, 13 B
Neomycin	White	—	+	+	—	—	—	—	2, 5, 13 C
Viomycin	White	—	+	—	—	—	Pink	—	3, 5, 12, 13 C
Erythromycin	White	—	Slight	+	+	—	—	—	7
Carbomycin	White	—	+	+	+	—	—	—	9
Fumagillin	White	Musty	—	Slight	+	—	—	—	10
Gramicidin	White	—	—	—	+	—	—	Pink	8, 12
Tyrothricin‖	White	—	—	+	+	+	—	Pink	5, 8, 12, 13 A

* Some samples of the "white" antibiotics may exhibit a buff or tan tinge depending on the state of purity.
† Compare with known material.
‡ Positive ninhydrin after about 30 minutes heating.
§ Chlortetracycline, tetracycline, and oxytetracycline interfere with the biuret test.
‖ Tyrocidine, which with gramicidin makes up tyrothric n, is not reported as such, since it was not found in any commercial formulations.

powder. Apply Procedure 7 directly, demonstrating the presence of erythromycin. In some tablets, it may be desirable to remove the coating, e.g., in the case of a dye that might interfere with the fluorescence tests.

EXAMPLE 2: *Injectable suspension of procaine penicillin G, potassium penicillin G, pectin, and aluminum monostearate in peanut oil.* Apply Procedure 14 A to several drops. Penicillin G salts present.

Add 3 ml. of water to about 1 ml. sample and extract with two 10 ml. portions of ethyl ether in a glass stoppered tube; centrifuge, discard ether layers, and draw off the clear aqueous phase. Apply Procedure 14 B to 1 ml. showing the presence of sodium or potassium penicillin G.

Apply Procedure 3 to another portion of aqueous phase. Negative response indicates the absence of streptomycin, dihydrostreptomycin, and viomycin.

Apply Procedure 6 to another portion of aqueous phase. Indicates presence of procaine penicillin.

Shake these centrifuged solids with about 5 ml. of ethanol, centrifuge, and remove clear ethanol phase. Add 10 ml. of water to about 2 ml. of ethanol phase and heat on a steam bath to remove the ethanol. Apply Procedure 14 C; this verifies the presence of procaine salt. Negative response to 14 E shows absence of ephenamine salt. Apply Procedure 14 F to the alcohol-insoluble residue (which in this case is aluminum monostearate). Negative response indicates absence of dibenzylethylenediamine dipenicillin.

EXAMPLE 3: *Ointments (applicable to all ointments examined).* If ointment is yellow in color, apply Procedure 4 directly for chlortetracycline, tetracycline, and oxytetracycline.

Apply Procedure 14 A directly to about 0.5 Gm. of sample to establish presence or absence of penicillins.

Apply Procedure 5 directly to about 0.5 Gm. of sample to screen for those antibiotics listed under this test.

Dissolve about 1.0 Gm. of sample in 10 ml. of chloroform and extract with 2 ml. 0.1 N hydrochloric acid. Test a portion of aqueous layer by Procedure 3 for streptomycin, dihydrostreptomycin, and viomycin. If the response to Procedure 5 was positive, apply Procedure 13 B (bacitracin and polymyxin B), and 13 C (neomycin and viomycin) to another portion of the aqueous phase.

Dissolve about 1.0 Gm. of the sample in 2 ml. 90 per cent methanol, extract with two 10 ml. portions of petroleum ether, and discard the ether phase. Add 4 ml. of water to the methanol layer, saturate with sodium sulfate and extract with 1 ml. of ethyl acetate. Apply Procedure 13 A for tyrothricin to the ethyl acetate phase. For nongrease ointments, warm and stir the initial 1.0 Gm. of sample with 3 ml. of 90 per cent methanol. Centrifuge, remove the liquid, dilute with 3 ml. of water, saturate with sodium sulfate, and extract with 10 ml. of benzene; discard the benzene layer, extract with 1 ml. of ethyl acetate, and proceed as previously.

EXAMPLE 4: *Applicable to those preparations that contain tyrothricin in low concentrations. (Troches, ear, nose, and tooth drops.)* Treat sample in such a manner as to obtain about 5 ml. of solution containing about 0.5 mg. tyrothricin in 25 to 35 per cent methanol or ethanol. For troches, dissolve one or two troches in 3 ml. of water and add the appropriate amount of methanol. In the case of an alcoholic solution, add the proper amount of water to achieve these concentrations. Proceed as in Example 3 for nongrease ointments.

Section B: *Ultraviolet Absorption Spectra*

, Many of the antibiotics have characteristic absorption spectra in the ultraviolet. Such spectra can be used for identification purposes, if the antibiotic is available in relatively pure form. Figures 4 to 21 give ultraviolet curves for penicillin G, streptomycin, dihydrostreptomycin, chlortetracycline, oxytetracycline, tetracycline, chloramphenicol, erythromycin, carbomycin, viomycin, fumagillin, anisomycin, nystatin, neomycin, gramicidin, and tyrocidine.

Section C: *Infrared Absorption Spectra*

One of the most valuable methods of identifying organic compounds is by means of their infrared absorption spectra. The infrared spectra of sodium penicillin G, potassium penicillin O, streptomycin sulfate, dihydrostreptomycin sulfate, chlortetracycline hydrochloride, oxytetracycline hydrochloride, tetracycline hydrochloride, chloramphenicol, bacitracin, polymyxin B sulfate, neomycin B sulfate, erythromycin, carbomycin, viomycin sulfate, fumagillin, nystatin, anisomycin, gramicidin, tyrocidine hydrochloride, and tyrothricin are given in figures 22 to 41. The spectra were obtained on mineral oil mulls of the solid compounds and the Food and Drug Administration's working standards of the antibiotics were used as samples.

Section D: *Optical Rotations of Antibiotics*

The ability of solutions of certain organic compounds to rotate the plane of polarized light has been used for many years as a means of not only identifying the compound, but in many cases as a quantitative method for evaluating purity.

The formula for calculating the specific rotation of optically active organic compounds in solution is:

$$[\alpha]_D^t = \frac{100a}{1c}$$

where [α] = specific rotation.
  t = temperature.
  D = the D line of the sodium spectrum.
  a = the observed angular rotation in degrees in the polariscope on the solution under test.
  1 = the length of the polariscope tube used in decimeters.
  c = the concentration of the solution expressed as the number of grams of substance in 100 ml. of solution.

Table III presents the specific rotations of some of the antibiotics and their salts.

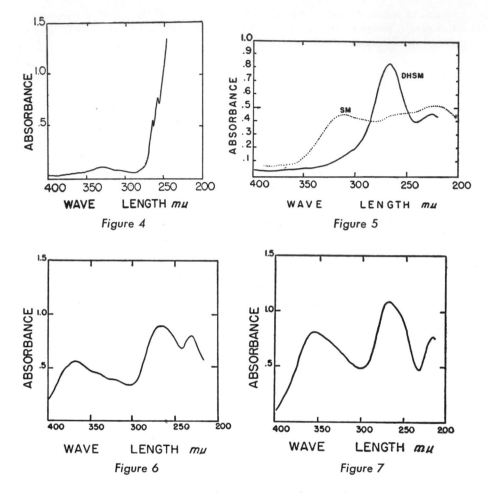

Figure 4

Figure 5

Figure 6

Figure 7

Fig. 4. Sodium penicillin G (benzylpenicillin), 1 mg./ml. in 1 per cent phosphate buffer, pH 6, 1 cm. cell.

Fig. 5. Dihydrostreptomycin sulfate is indicated by solid line (_____). Three ml. aqueous solution containing 2 mg. (activity) plus 3 ml. 0.5 N sulfuric acid, refluxed two hours, plus water to 25 ml. (see Method 3, Section B, Chapter 3). Streptomycin sulfate is indicated by broken line (........). Same quantity as for dihydrostreptomycin and treated in the same manner. Both solutions read in 1 cm. cell.

Fig. 6. Chlortetracycline hydrochloride, 25 mg/liter in 1 N hydrochloric acid. (Run within 10 minutes after addition of acid.) One cm. cell.

Fig. 7. Oxytetracycline hydrochloride, 25 mg. of activity (oxy-tetracycline base) per liter in 1 N hydrochloric acid. (Run within 10 minutes after addition of acid.) One cm. cell.

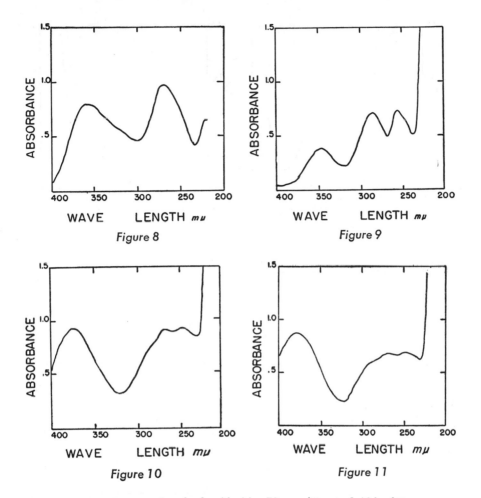

Figure 8

Figure 9

Figure 10

Figure 11

Fig. 8. Tetracycline hydrochloride, 25 mg./liter in 1 N hydrochloric acid. (Run within 10 minutes after addition of acid.) One cm. cell.

Fig. 9. Chlortetracycline hydrochloride, 25 mg./liter in 0.25 N sodium hydroxide. (Run within 10 minutes after addition of sodium hydroxide.) One cm. cell.

Fig. 10. Oxytetracycline hydrochloride, 25 mg. of activity (oxytetracycline base) per liter in 0.25 N sodium hydroxide. (Run within 10 minutes after addition of sodium hydroxide.) One cm. cell.

Fig. 11. Tetracycline hydrochloride, 25 mg./liter in 0.25 N sodium hydroxide. (Run within 10 minutes after addition of sodium hydroxide). One cm. cell.

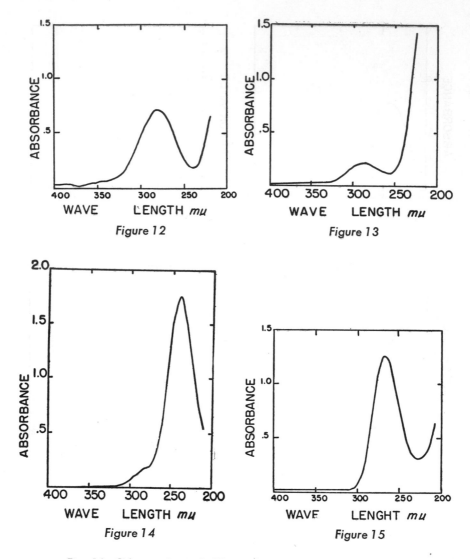

Figure 12

Figure 13

Figure 14

Figure 15

Fig. 12. Chloramphenicol, 25 mg./liter in water. One cm. cell.
Fig. 13. Erythromycin, 5 mg./ml. in methanol. One cm. cell.
Fig. 14. Carbomycin, 111 mg./liter in ethanol. One cm. cell.
Fig. 15. Viomycin sulfate, 41 mg./liter in water. One cm. cell.

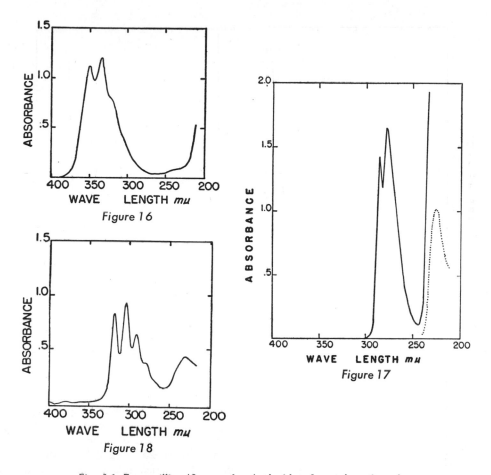

Figure 16

Figure 17

Figure 18

Fig. 16. Fumagillin, 40 mg. plus 4 ml. chloroform plus ethanol to 100 ml. Then 5 ml. (2 mg.) of this to 25 ml. with ethanol. Then 5 ml. (0.4 mg.) of this to 50 ml. with ethanol. Curve was run on this last solution containing 0.008 mg./ml. One cm. cell.

Fig. 17. Anisomycin, 0.25 mg./ml. in absolute ethanol. Absorption at 224 mμ shown at right using 0.025 mg./ml. One cm. cell.

Fig. 18. Nystatin, 0.02 mg./ml. (30.7 units) in methanol. One cm. cell.

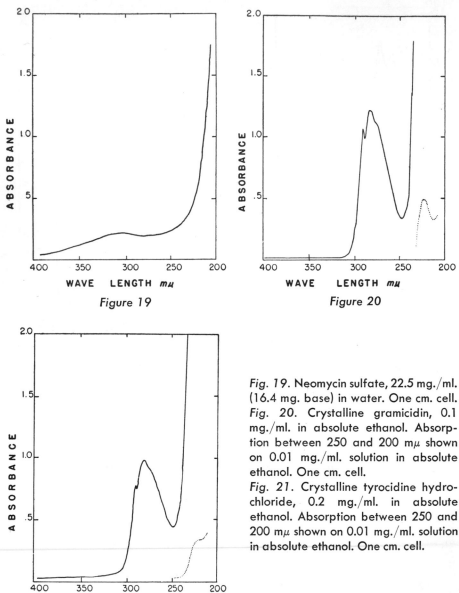

Figure 19

Figure 20

Figure 21

Fig. 19. Neomycin sulfate, 22.5 mg./ml. (16.4 mg. base) in water. One cm. cell.

Fig. 20. Crystalline gramicidin, 0.1 mg./ml. in absolute ethanol. Absorption between 250 and 200 mμ shown on 0.01 mg./ml. solution in absolute ethanol. One cm. cell.

Fig. 21. Crystalline tyrocidine hydrochloride, 0.2 mg./ml. in absolute ethanol. Absorption between 250 and 200 mμ shown on 0.01 mg./ml. solution in absolute ethanol. One cm. cell.

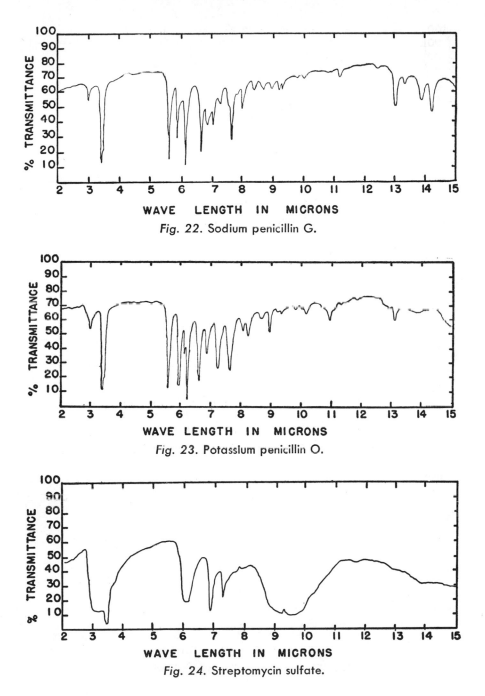

Fig. 22. Sodium penicillin G.

Fig. 23. Potassium penicillin O.

Fig. 24. Streptomycin sulfate.

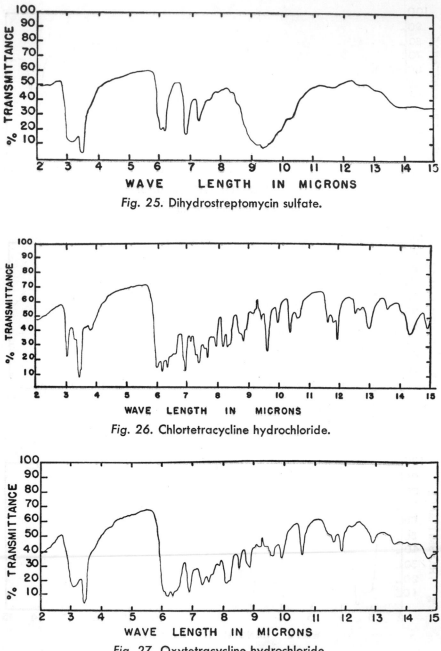

Fig. 25. Dihydrostreptomycin sulfate.

Fig. 26. Chlortetracycline hydrochloride.

Fig. 27. Oxytetracycline hydrochloride.

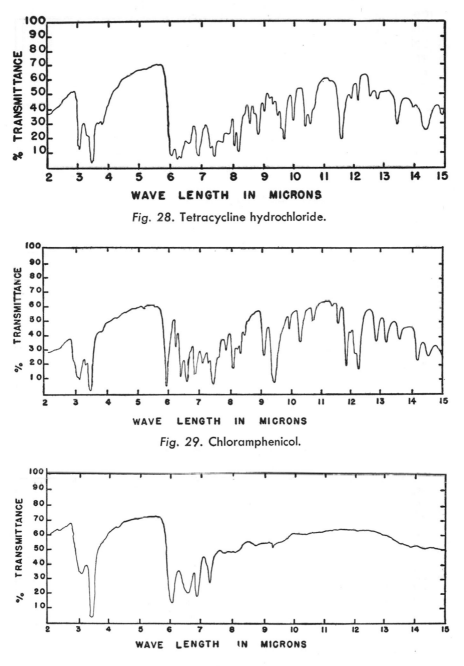

Fig. 28. Tetracycline hydrochloride.

Fig. 29. Chloramphenicol.

Fig. 30. Bacitracin.

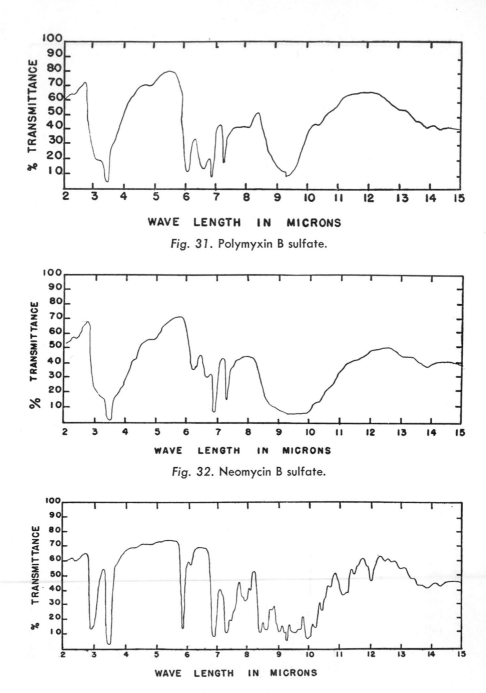

Fig. 31. Polymyxin B sulfate.

Fig. 32. Neomycin B sulfate.

Fig. 33. Erythromycin.

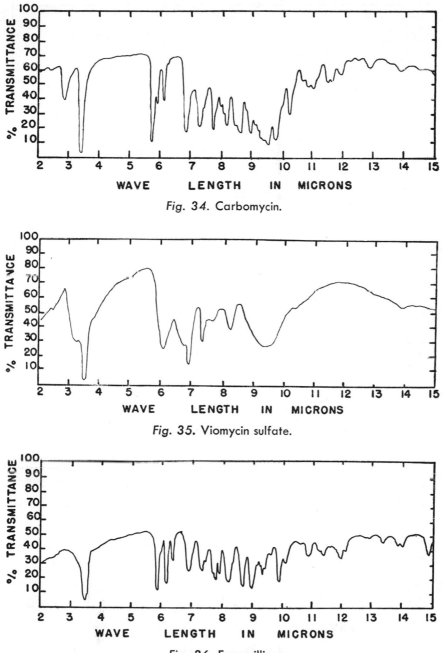

Fig. 34. Carbomycin.

Fig. 35. Viomycin sulfate.

Fig. 36. Fumagillin.

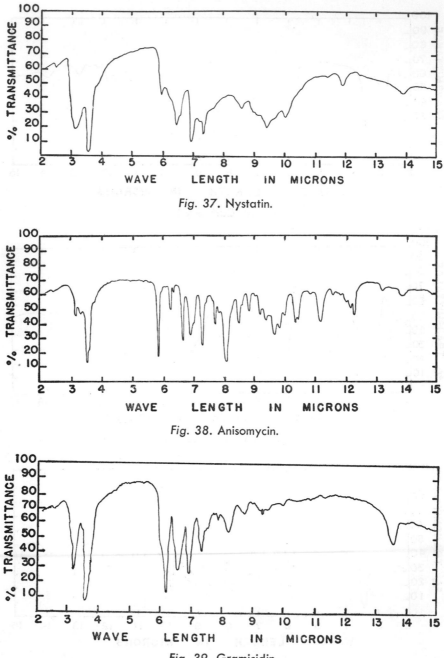

Fig. 37. Nystatin.

Fig. 38. Anisomycin.

Fig. 39. Gramicidin.

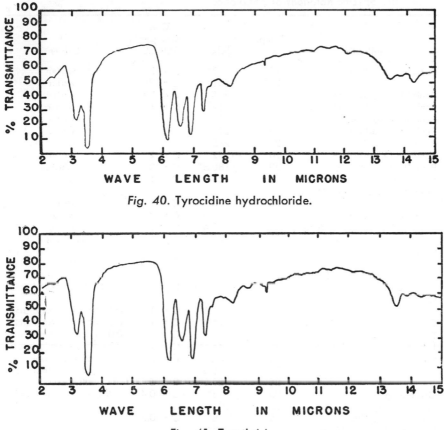

Fig. 40. Tyrocidine hydrochloride.

Fig. 41. Tyrothricin.

Section E: Optical-Crystallographic Method for the Identification of Crystalline Antibiotics

The crystalline antibiotic substances can be readily and specifically identified from their optical-crystallographic properties, which can be determined within certain limits by means of the polarizing microscope. The identification involves microscopic-crystallographic observations of optical phenomena and measurements of physical constants, which are compared to data on known substances. Such data are usually arranged in determinative tables. The discussion of the procedure is necessarily limited as to details because of the wide scope of material that is encompassed in measurements of microscopic-crystallographic properties. These details are covered in a number of texts.[19–21]

Table IV lists the microscopic-crystallographic properties of various crystalline antibiotics determined by the procedure to be described. Table V

TABLE III: *Specific Rotations of Antibiotics*

Antibiotic	Temp. C.	$[\alpha]_D^t$	C in Gm. per 100 ml.	Solvent
Penicillin G sodium	20	+298°	C = 2	water
	24.8	+301°	C = 2	water
Penicillin G potassium	22	+285°	C = 0.7	water
Penicillin dihydro F sodium	23	+319°	C = 1	water
Penicillin F sodium	25	+305°		water
Penicillin X sodium	25	+260°		water
Penicillin K sodium	25	+275°		water
Penicillin O potassium	20	+252°	C = 2	water
Penicillin G procaine	20	+180.8°	C = 3	methanol
Streptomycin hydrochloride	25	−84°	C = 1	water
Streptomycin calcium chloride complex	25	−76°	C = 1	water
Streptomycin sulfate	20	−84.8°	C = 3	water
Dihydrostreptomycin sulfate	20	−92.4°	C = 1	water
Chlortetracycline base	23	−275°		methanol
Chlortetracycline hydrochloride	25	−240°	C = 0.5	water
Oxytetracycline base (anhydrous)	25	−211.5°	C = 1	0.1 N hydrochloric acid
Oxytetracycline base dihydrate	25	−196.6°	C = 1	0.1 N hydrochloric acid
Oxytetracycline hydrochloride	25	−196°	C = 1	0.1 N hydrochloric acid
Tetracycline base (anhydrous)	20	−270°	C = 1	0.01 N hydrochloric acid
Tetracycline hydrochloride	25	−244.6°	C = 1	0.01 N hydrochloric acid
Chloramphenicol	20	+20°	C = 5	abs. ethanol
	25	+18.5°	C = 5	abs. ethanol
	25	−25.5°	C = 5	ethyl acetate
Gramicidin	25	+5°	C = 0.4	95 per cent ethanol
Tyrocidine hydrochloride	25	−101°	C = 1	95 per cent ethanol
Neomycin B sulfate	25	+58°	C = 0.5	water
Neomycin B hydrochloride	22	+54°		water
Neomycin C hydrochloride	22	+80°		water
Erythromycin (anhydrous)	20	−75.6°	C = 2	ethanol
Carbomycin base	25	−58.6°	C = 1	chloroform
Viomycin sulfate (hydrated)	25	−32°	C = 1	water
Anisomycin base	23	−30°	C = 1	methanol
Nystatin	25	−10°		glacial acetic acid
	25	+21°		pyridine
	25	+12°		dimethylformamide
	25	−7°		0.1 N hydrochloric acid in methanol

is a determinative table arranged according to the ascending value of the lowest (alpha) index. These values have been compiled from the literature and from files of W. V. Eisenberg and A. H. Tillson of the Division of Microbiology, Food and Drug Administration, Department of Health, Education, and Welfare.

Method. APPARATUS. Polarizing microscope fitted with polarizing prisms below and above a rotating, graduated circular stage and with accessories

(Bertrand lens or pinhole eyepiece, first order red or quartz wedge compensators) for observation of interference figures, optic sign, and sign of elongation. Refractometers for measuring refractive indices of liquids at 20 C. from 1.300 to 1.840 with accuracy of ±0.0005.

REAGENTS. *Immersion media*. Ideally, immersion media, which are to be used for refractive index determinations should have the same color and intensity of color as the substance being examined. The liquids should be chemically stable. Their refractive indices should not vary perceptibly with ordinary changes of temperature with the exception of the special liquids used in index-variation methods. A permanent set of liquids covering the range 1.430 to 1.790 in 0.005 intervals made with the following mixtures is very useful for inorganic and organic drug substances:

Mixture	n_D
Kerosene and mineral oil	1.435 to 1.480
Mineral oil and α-monochlornaphthalene	1.485 to 1.640
α-monochlornaphthalene and methylene iodide	1.645 to 1.740
Methylene iodide and sulfur	1.740 to 1.790

Substances that are soluble in these liquids will require preparing a special set of liquids.

PROCEDURE. *Refractive indices*. Determine the refractive indices by mounting the crystalline material in suitable immersion liquids and making observations of the Becke line. For the determination of the refractive indices, the crystals or crystal fragments of a given substance are successively suspended in immersion liquids of known refractive indices, advantage being taken of the fact that the greater the difference between the indices of refraction of crystal and liquid, the more prominently the one will stand out in bold relief from the other. By repeatedly mounting such crystals in oils of successively lower or higher index, it will be found that ultimately the zone of contact of crystal and liquid becomes practically invisible, thus demonstrating that the refractive index of liquid and solid has been matched. In the case of substances crystallizing in the isometric (cubic) system, there is only one refractive index, designated by the symbol n. Such substances are not doubly refractive when examined with crossed nicols. Substances crystallizing in other systems, namely, the hexagonal, tetragonal, monoclinic, triclinic, and orthorhombic systems, in the ideal cases, have more than one measurable refractive index. In the case of uniaxial substances such as those crystallizing in the hexagonal and tetragonal systems, two significant indices can be determined, designated as n_e and n_w. The indices of refraction in the monoclinic, triclinic, and orthorhombic systems, in the ideal cases, are three in number, and designated as $n\alpha$, $n\beta$, and $n\gamma$.

The determination of the refractive index of isometric substances is simpler than in the case of doubly refractive material. The substance is successively immersed in liquids of known refractive index until ultimately the zone of contact of crystal with liquid becomes invisible. Then the refractive index of liquid has been matched against that of the solid.

Extinction and extinction angle of anisotropic substances. Anisotropic crystals,

TABLE IV: Optical-crystallographic properties of Antibiotics *

Antibiotic	α	β	γ	Optic sign	Extinction	Elongation	2V	Remarks
Penicillin sodium G	1.550	1.609	1.620	−	p	+	large	nβ common
Penicillin potassium G	1.550	—	1.603	−	p	+		elongated rectangular plates
Penicillin potassium O	1.545	—	1.593		p	+		
Penicillin procaine G	1.545	1.570	1.685	+	p,i	+		nβ common
Penicillin ephedrine G	1.575	—	1.610		p	−		
Penicillin 1-ephenamine G	1.583	1.590	1.648	+	i		very small	acute bisectrix figures
Penicillin benzathine G	1.523	1.622	1.630	−	p	+	very small	nα and nβ common
Penicillin G hydriodide diethylaminoethyl ester	1.601	1.608	1.632	+	p	−	moderate	
Penicillin dibenzylamine G	1.567	—	1.613		p	+		
Penicillin hydrabamine G	1.556	about 1.590	1.619		p,i	−		
Penicillin chloroprocaine O	1.541	1.585	1.656	+	p	±	very large	ext. angle = 18°
Dihydrostreptomycin sulfate	1.552	1.558	1.566	+	p,i		89°	
Dihydrostreptomycin hydrochloride	1.522	1.548	1.566	−	p	+	80°	
Chlortetracycline hydrochloride	1.635	1.706	1.730	−	p,s		59°	
Oxytetracycline dihydrate	1.634	1.646	1.700	+	p		28°	
Oxytetracycline hydrochloride	1.546	1.635	1.730	+	p,i	+	very large	Op. ax. figs. common
Tetracycline trihydrate	1.538	1.646	sl > 1.787	+	p,i		large	Occasional op. ax. figs.
Tetracycline hydrochloride	1.603	1.685	1.714	−	p		large	Bx. ac. and op. ax. figs.
Chloramphenicol	1.523	1.608	1.659	−	p	−	70–80°	
Chloramphenicol palmitate	1.527	—	1.569		p	±		
Gramicidin	1.541	about 1.553	1.573	+		+		
Tyrocidine hydrochloride	1.553	—	1.584		p	−		
Erythromycin dihydrate	1.512	1.523	1.532	−	p	+	84°	
Erythromycin oxalate dihydrate	1.484	1.492	1.516	+	p	+	60°	
Erythromycin ethyl carbonate	1.496	1.506	1.510	−	p	+	moderate	Op. ax. figs. common
Erythromycin glucoheptonate	1.506	—	1.528		p	+		
Erythromycin hydriodide hydrate	1.528	1.538	1.550	+	p	+	75°	
Carbomycin	1.474	1.484	1.513	+	p	±		
Fumagillin	1.518	about 1.572	> 1.780	+	p,i		small	

* Abbreviations: p = parallel; s = symmetrical; i = inclined; n = index; Bx. ac. = acute bisectrix; Op. ax. = optic axis; fig. = figure.

TABLE V: *Determinative Table for Antibiotics Arranged According to Ascending Value of the Lowest Index*

α	β	γ	Antibiotic
1.474	1.484	1.513	Carbomycin
1.484	1.492	1.516	Erythromycin oxalate dihydrate
1.496	1.506	1.510	Erythromycin ethyl carbonate
1.506	—	1.528	Erythromycin glucoheptonate
1.512	1.523	1.532	Erythromycin dihydrate
1.518	about 1.572	> 1.780	Fumagillin
1.522	1.548	1.566	Dihydrostreptomycin hydrochloride
1.523	1.608	1.659	Chloramphenicol
1.523	1.622	1.630	Penicillin benzathine G
1.527	—	1.569	Chloramphenicol palmitate
1.528	1.538	1.550	Erythromycin hydriodide hydrate
1.538	1.646	sl > 1.787	Tetracycline trihydrate
1.541	about 1.553	1.573	Gramicidin
1.541	1.585	1.656	Penicillin chloroprocaine O
1.545	—	1.593	Penicillin potassium O
1.545	1.570	1.685	Penicillin procaine G
1.546	1.635	1.730	Oxytetracycline hydrochloride
1.550	1.609	1.620	Penicillin sodium G
1.550	—	1.603	Penicillin potassium G
1.552	1.558	1.566	Dihydrostreptomycin sulfate
1.553	—	1.584	Tyrocidine hydrochloride
1.556	about 1.590	1.619	Penicillin hydrabamine G
1.567	—	1.613	Penicillin dibenzylamine G
1.575	—	1.610	Penicillin ephedrine G
1.583	1.590	1.648	Penicillin 1-ephenamine G
1.601	1.608	1.632	Penicillin G hydriodide diethyl-aminoethyl ester
1.603	1.685	1.714	Tetracycline hydrochloride
1.634	1.646	1.700	Oxytetracycline dihydrate
1.635	1.706	1.730	Chlortetracycline hydrochloride

when rotated through 360 degrees on the stage, become dark four times. The positions of darkness are known as extinction positions and correspond to positions in which the vibrations of the birefringent rays produced by the crystal are mutually parallel to the vibration directions of the polarizer and analyzer indicated by the cross hairs in the eyepiece. If the crystal extinguishes when the crystal edge or face is parallel to one of the cross hairs, the extinction is *parallel.* If the bisector of a silhouette angle is parallel to one of the cross hairs, the crystal has *symmetrical* extinction. Crystals showing extinction differing from these two are said to have *inclined* extinction. Extinction angles may be measured on those crystals showing inclined extinction. This is performed by rotating the crystal so that a crystal edge or face is parallel to one of the cross hairs. The stage is then rotated until the crystal extinguishes. The extinction angle between the face or edge at extinction and the nearest cross hair is read on the stage vernier. The extinction angles are expressed with relationship to the principal vibration directions of light and the crystallographic axes.

Elongation. Many crystals are frequently elongated in one direction. The relationship between the direction of elongation and the vibration directions of the slow and fast rays of an anisotropic crystal is sometimes of determinative value. If the substance is length slow, i.e., the slow ray or higher index of refraction is parallel to the direction of elongation, the sign of elongation is positive; if the substance is length fast, the sign is negative.

The sign of elongation (positive or negative) is determined with the gypsum plate and crossed nicols. A long and narrow crystal, showing very little color with crossed nicols, is so oriented that its long dimension is parallel to direction "z" of the plate (slow ray) which is inserted in the slit of the microscope tube. (Direction "z" is indicated by an arrow on the plate.) If the crystal appears blue or other color of a higher order than the red-violet due to the plate, the elongation is positive; if the crystal appears yellow, white, or gray, that is, of lower order color than the red-violet field, the elongation is negative.

Optic character and optic sign. Determine the optic character (uniaxial or biaxial) and the optic sign (positive or negative) using first order red or quartz wedge compensators in conjunction with interference figures. Interference figures are obtained from conoscopic images of crystals suitably oriented. In the absence of interference figures, determine these properties from the relationship of the principal refractive indices.

Optic axial angle (2V). Calculate the axial angle (2V) from the values of the three indices of refraction according to the formula

$$\text{Cos}^2 V_\alpha = \frac{\gamma^2(\beta^2 - \alpha^2)}{\beta^2(\gamma^2 - \alpha^2)}$$

in which $2V_\alpha$ is the axial angle about α, or estimate the approximate value of 2V from the curvature of the isogyre referring to diagrams of substances with known angles.

18 TESTS FOR TOXICITY, PYROGENS, HISTA-MINE, AND STERILITY

The toxicity test to be described is in reality a safety test. Only one dosage concentration is given and the LD_{50} is not determined. The dose given, however, is considerably in excess of that which would be administered to humans on a weight basis.

The solutions or suspensions prepared for the pyrogen test may also be used for the toxicity test. Therefore, all glassware, such as syringes, stirring rods, and flasks, and needles should be rendered pyrogen-free by heating for not less than 30 minutes at 250 C. Certain antibiotics because of their insolubility are given as a suspension. If the product is a powder, it is pulverized in a pyrogen-free glass mortar with a pyrogen-free glass pestle and then suspended in the diluent to be used, or it is homogenized with the diluent in a suitable homogenizer. Either pyrogen-free distilled water or normal saline solution is used as a diluent. In the case of mixtures of antibiotics, the dilution is made on the basis of only one of the antibiotics for both the toxicity and pyrogen tests. For example, a mixture of penicillin and streptomycin is diluted on the basis of the streptomycin activity of the preparation only.

In the production of some of the antibiotics, like streptomycin or the tetracyclines, an occasional batch may contain a blood pressure lowering substance believed to be histamine or a histamine-like compound. Therefore, it is necessary to test each batch of these drugs to be sure these substances are absent, or, if present, are there in quantities not to exceed a prescribed amount considered to be safe.

In testing for sterility there is no one medium that is optimum for the growth of all bacteria, molds, and yeasts. As the use of various media for each test would make it too cumbersome, one has to select media in which the majority of organisms will grow. In the test to be described thioglycollate medium is used for detecting bacterial growth and Sabouraud's medium for molds and yeasts. Only one antibiotic, penicillin, has a specific enzyme, penicillinase, which will inactivate it and keep it from acting on penicillin sensitive organisms during the sterility test. In testing other antibiotics for sterility only those organisms will be detected that are insensitive to the antibiotic under test.

Since it is always possible to introduce contaminants during the sampling operation, particularly of bulk powders, and also during the actual sterility

itself, allowances are made for such chance contamination in
method by allowing repeated examinations. If three or more
be run, the sample is considered to be sterile if not more than
all tubes run show growth.

Toxicity Test. Inject in the tail vein of each of 5 mice, within the weight
range of 18 to 25 Gm., with the volume of solution designated in table VI. The
injection should be made over a period of not more than five seconds. If no
animal dies within 48 hours, the sample is nontoxic. If one or more animals
die within 48 hours, repeat the test with five unused mice weighing 20 Gm.
(±0.5 Gm.) each; if all of the animals survive the repeat test, the sample is
nontoxic.

Certain antibiotics are administered orally instead of intravenously, in
which case the suspension of the drug is given by means of a cannula or other
suitable device.

Pyrogen Test. TEST ANIMAL. Use healthy rabbits, weighing 1,500 Gm. or
more, which have been maintained for at least one week on a uniform, un-
restricted diet and have not lost weight during this period. For subsequent
tests, animals utilized for previous tests may be used after a rest period of not
less than two days. Use a clinical rectal thermometer after it has been tested
in a rabbit to determine the time required to reach maximum temperature.
(Other recording devices of equal sensitivity are acceptable.) Insert the
thermometer or other recording device beyond the internal sphincter and
allow it to remain a sufficient time to reach maximum temperature as just
determined. Make four rectal temperature readings on each of the animals
to be used in the test at two hour intervals, one to three days before such use
(this may be omitted for any animal that has been used in such tests during
a preceding period of two weeks). House the test animal in individual cages
and protect them from disturbances likely to cause excitement. Exercise
particular care to avoid exciting the animals on the day of taking the control
temperatures and on the test day. Maintain the animals in an environment of
uniform temperature (±5 F.) at all times.

CONDUCT OF TEST. Heat all syringes and needles or equipment to be used in a
muffle furnace at 250 C. for not less than 30 minutes to render them pyrogen-
free and sterile. Perform the test in a room held at the same temperature as
that in which the animals are housed. During the test restrain the animals in
individual stocks. On the day of the test do not feed the animals used until
after completion of the test. Take a control temperature reading not more than
15 minutes after the animal is removed from the cage. Use 3 animals for each
test, but do not use those with control temperatures of less than 38.8 C. or
more than 39.9 C. Inject intravenously the volume of sample designated in
table VI through an ear vein within 15 minutes subsequent to the control
temperature reading. Read temperatures one hour after injection and each
hour thereafter until three readings have been made. The sample is nonpyrogenic if, when so tested, no animal shows a rise in any of the temperature
readings, after injection, of 0.6 C. or more above the control temperature of
such animal. If one or more of the animals shows such a rise in temperature,

or if the sum of the temperature rises of the three animals exceeds 1.4 C., repeat the test on 5 additional animals. The sample is nonpyrogenic if not more than 1 of these 5 animals shows a rise in temperature of 0.6 C. or more above the control temperature of such animal.

Histamine Test. Use a healthy adult cat as the test animal. Weigh it and place it under general anesthesia by employing sufficient (150 mg./Kg.) sodium phenobarbital administered intraperitoneally. Surgically expose the right carotid artery, separating it completely from all surrounding structures, including the vagus nerve, by blunt dissection and cannulate. Surgically expose the femoral vein. Start the recording kymograph and inspect the tracings for amplitude of excursion and relative stability of pressure. Determine the sensitivity of the animal by injecting into the femoral vein standard solutions of histamine made to contain the equivalent of 1.0 μg./ml. of histamine base. Make injections at not less than five minute intervals using doses of 0.05, 0.1, and 0.15 μg./Kg. of histamine base. Repeat these injections, disregarding the first series of readings, until the drop given by equivalent doses of histamine is relatively uniform. The fall in blood pressure given by 0.1 μg./Kg. of histamine base (not less than 20 mm. of mercury) is subsequently employed as the standard in testing samples. Inject the quantity of solution designated in table VI maintaining the five minute injection schedule. If a significant drop is encountered, the dose is repeated after the animal has been retested with the standard histamine. The animal may be used as long as it remains reasonably stable and responsive to histamine. The product is satisfactory if the fall in blood pressure obtained with the sample is no greater than the fall obtained with 0.1 μg. of histamine base per Kg. of body weight. (Dogs may be substituted for cats in this test provided the ratio of the doses of antibiotic and histamine employed is the same.)

Sterility Test. PENICILLIN. *Culture media.* In the test for bacteria, use fluid thioglycollate medium no. 14. In the test for molds and yeasts use Sabouraud's liquid medium no. 13.

Conduct of test for bacteria. Add not more than 10 ml. of sterile distilled water, or sterile physiologic salt solution, to each immediate container in the sample to be tested. From each of not less than seven immediate containers transfer aseptically the equivalent of approximately 300 mg., or the entire contents if the container is packaged to contain less than 300 mg., to individual tubes (38 by 200 mm.) each containing 75 to 100 ml. of thioglycollate medium no. 14 and sufficient penicillinase (see Chapter 21) to inactivate completely the penicillin used in the test. (Prior to use, the tubes containing the medium with added penicillinase are incubated at 30 to 32 C. for not less than 24 hours and examined for sterility.) After adding the penicillin to the tubes, let them stand at room temperature for two hours, with frequent shaking. To one of such tubes add 1.0 ml. of a 1:1000 dilution of an 18 to 24 hour broth culture of *M. pyogenes* var. *aureus* (ATCC 6538P). Incubate all tubes at 30 to 32 C. for five days. The batch meets the requirements of the test for bacteria if on the first or second test the control tube and no other tube shows growth, or if the number of tubes (excluding the control tubes) that show growth in three or more consecutive tests is not more than 10 per cent (to compensate

TABLE VI: *Dosages in the Tests for Toxicity, Pyrogens, Histamine, and Sterility*

Antibiotic	Dosage			
	Toxicity * per mouse	Pyrogen per Kg.	Histamine per Kg.	Sterility † per tube
Aluminum penicillin	0.5 ml. (1.5 mg.) suspension in normal saline	1.0 ml. (3 mg.) suspension in normal saline	—	300 mg.
Benzathine penicillin G	0.25 ml. (1000 u.) suspension in normal saline	0.5 ml. (2000 u.) suspension in normal saline	—	300 mg.
Benzathine penicillin G for aqueous injection or benzathine penicillin G in aqueous suspension	0.25 ml. (1000 u.) suspension in normal saline	0.5 ml. (2000 u.) suspension in normal saline	—	300 mg.
Benzathine penicillin G and buffered crystalline penicillin sodium or potassium for aqueous injection	0.25 ml. (1000 u.) suspension in normal saline	0.5 ml. (2000 u.) suspension in normal saline	—	300 mg.
Benzathine penicillin G and procaine penicillin for aqueous injection	0.25 ml. (1000 u.) suspension in normal saline	0.5 ml. (2000 u.) suspension in normal saline	—	300 mg.
Benzathine-procaine-buffered crystalline penicillin sodium or potassium for aqueous injection	0.25 ml. (1000 u.) suspension in normal saline	0.5 ml. (2000 u.) suspension in normal saline	—	300 mg.
Benzathine penicillin G-crystalline penicillin sodium or potassium procaine penicillin and dihydrostreptomycin-streptomycin sulfates	0.25 ml. (1000 u.) suspension in normal saline	0.5 ml. (2000 u.) suspension in normal saline	—	300 mg.
Buffered crystalline penicillin sodium or potassium	0.5 ml. (2000 u.) solution in water	1.0 ml. (2000 u.) solution in water	—	300 mg.
Chloroprocaine penicillin O	0.5 ml. (1000 u.) solution in normal saline	1.0 ml. (2000 u.) solution in normal saline	—	300 mg.

Preparation	Dose A	Dose B		Amount
Chloroprocaine penicillin O for aqueous injection	0.25 ml. (1000 u.) solution in normal saline	1.0 ml. (2000 u.) solution in normal saline	—	300 mg.
Dibenzylamine penicillin G	0.25 ml. (1000 u.) solution in normal saline	1.0 ml. (2000 u.) solution in normal saline	—	300 mg.
Diethylaminoethyl ester penicillin G hydriodide	0.5 ml. (1000 u.) solution in normal saline	1.0 ml. (2000 u.) solution in normal saline	—	300 mg.
Diethylaminoethyl ester penicillin G hydriodide for aqueous injection	0.5 ml. (1000 u.) solution in normal saline	1.0 ml. (2000 u.) solution in normal saline	—	300 mg.
Ephedrine penicillin G	0.5 ml. (2000 u.) solution in water	1.0 ml. (2000 u.) solution in water	—	300 mg.
l-Ephenamine penicillin G	1.0 ml. (800 u.) solution in normal saline (inject in 10 seconds)	2.0 ml. (1600 u.) solution in normal saline	—	300 mg.
l-Ephenamine penicillin G for aqueous injection	1.0 ml. (800 u.) solution in normal saline (inject in 10 seconds)	2.0 ml. (1600 u.) solution in normal saline	—	300 mg.
l-Ephenamine penicillin G in oil	—	—	—	300 mg.
Hydrabamine penicillin G	0.25 ml. (1000 u.) suspension in normal saline	—	—	—
Penicillin sodium, calcium, or potassium	0.5 ml. (2000 u.) solution in water	1.0 ml. (2000 u.) solution in water	—	300 mg.
Penicillin and bacitracin	0.5 ml. (2000 u. penicillin) solution in normal saline	1.0 ml. (300 u. bacitracin) solution in normal saline	—	500 mg.
Penicillin salts used: Crystalline sodium or potassium penicillin				
Penicillin and sulfonamide powder	—	—	—	500 mg.
Penicillin and streptomycin	0.5 ml. (0.5 mg. streptomycin activity) solution in water	2.0 ml. (10 mg. streptomycin activity) solution in water	—	500 mg.
Penicillin salts and combinations used: Procaine, crystalline sodium or potassium, l-ephenamine, procaine and crystalline sodium or potassium, benzathine				

TABLE VI: *Continued*

| | Dosage | | | |
Antibiotic	Toxicity * per mouse	Pyrogen per Kg.	Histamine per Kg.	Sterility † per tube
Penicillin and dihydrostreptomycin				
Penicillin salts and combinations used:				
Procaine, crystalline sodium or potassium, l-ephenamine, procaine and crystalline sodium or potassium, benzathine	0.5 ml. (0.5 mg. dihydrostreptomycin activity) solution in water	2.0 ml. (10 mg. dihydrostreptomycin activity) solution in water	—	500 mg.
Penicillin and Dihydrostreptomycin-streptomycin sulfates	0.5 ml. (0.5 mg. combined streptomycin-dihydrostreptomycin activity) solution in water	2.0 ml. (10 mg. combined streptomycin-dihydrostreptomycin activity) solution in water	—	500 mg.
Penicillin salts and combinations used:				
Crystalline sodium or potassium, procaine, benzathine, crystalline sodium or potassium and procaine, crystalline sodium or potassium and benzathine, procaine and benzathine				
Penicillin-streptomycin-bacitracin dental paste	—	—	—	300 mg.
Procaine penicillin G	0.5 ml. (1000 u.) solution in normal saline	1.0 ml. (2000 u.) solution in normal saline	—	300 mg.
Procaine penicillin for aqueous injection; procaine penicillin in aqueous suspension	0.25 ml. (1000 u.) solution in normal saline	1.0 ml. (2000 u.) solution in normal saline	—	300 mg.
Procaine penicillin and buffered crystalline penicillin sodium or potassium for aqueous injection	0.25 ml. (1000 u.) solution in normal saline	1.0 ml. (2000 u.) solution in normal saline	—	300 mg.
Procaine penicillin in oil	—	—	—	300 mg.
Procaine penicillin and crystalline penicillin sodium or potassium in oil	—	—	—	400 mg.

Procaine penicillin in streptomycin sulfate solution	0.5 ml. (0.5 mg. streptomycin activity) solution in water	2.0 ml. (10 mg. streptomycin activity) solution in water	—	500 mg.
Procaine penicillin in dihydrostreptomycin sulfate solution or in crystalline dihydrostreptomycin sulfate solution	0.5 ml. (0.5 mg. dihydrostreptomycin activity) solution in water	2.0 ml. (10 mg. dihydrostreptomycin activity) solution in water	—	500 mg.
Procaine penicillin and benzathine penicillin G in streptomycin sulfate solution	0.5 ml. (0.5 mg. streptomycin activity) solution in water	2.0 ml. (10 mg. streptomycin activity) solution in water	—	300 mg.
Procaine penicillin and benzathine penicillin G in dihydrostreptomycin sulfate solution or in crystalline dihydrostreptomycin sulfate solution	0.5 ml. (0.5 mg. dihydrostreptomycin activity) solution in water	2.0 ml. (10 mg. dihydrostreptomycin activity) solution in water	—	300 mg.
Procaine penicillin in dihydrostreptomycin-streptomycin sulfates solution	0.5 ml. (0.5 mg. combined streptomycin-dihydrostreptomycin activity) solution in water	2.0 ml. (10 mg. combined streptomycin-dihydrostreptomycin activity) solution in water	—	300 mg.
Streptomycin sulfate, hydrochloride, phosphate, or trihydrochloride calcium chloride	0.5 ml. (1 mg. activity) solution in water	1.0 ml. (10 mg. activity) solution in water	1.0 ml. (3 mg. activity) solution in normal saline	500 mg.
Streptomycin for topical use	0.5 ml. (1 mg. activity) solution in water	1.0 ml. (10 mg. activity) solution in water	1.0 ml. (3 mg. activity) solution in normal saline	500 mg.
Streptomycin sulfate solution	0.5 ml. (0.75 mg. activity) solution in water	1.0 ml. (10 mg. activity) solution in water	1.0 ml. (3 mg. activity) solution in normal saline	500 mg.
Streptomycin for inhalation therapy	0.5 ml. (1 mg. activity) solution in water	—	1.0 ml. (3 mg. activity) solution in normal saline	—

TABLE VI: Continued

Antibiotic	Dosage			
	Toxicity * per mouse	Pyrogen per Kg.	Histamine per Kg.	Sterility † per tube
Streptomycin sulfate oral veterinary	0.5 ml. (1 mg. activity) solution in water	—	—	—
Streptomycylidene isonicotinyl hydrazine sulfate	0.5 ml. (0.5 mg. activity) solution in water	1.0 ml. (10 mg. activity) solution in water	1.0 ml. (3 mg. activity) solution in normal saline	500 mg.
Streptomycin hydrochloride solution oral veterinary	0.5 ml. (1 mg. activity) solution in water	—	—	—
Streptomycin-bacitracin-polymyxin gauze pads	—	—	—	One pad
Dihydrostreptomycin sulfate, crystalline dihydrostreptomycin sulfate, dihydrostreptomycin hydrochloride	0.5 ml. (1 mg. activity) solution in water	1.0 ml. (10 mg. activity) solution in water	1.0 ml. (3 mg. activity) solution in normal saline	500 mg.
Dihydrostreptomycin sulfate solution, crystalline dihydrostreptomycin sulfate solution	0.5 ml. (1 mg. activity) solution in water	1.0 ml. (10 mg. activity) solution in water	1.0 ml. (3 mg. activity) solution in normal saline	500 mg.
Dihydrostreptomycin for inhalation therapy	0.5 ml. (1 mg. activity) solution in water	—	1.0 ml. (3 mg. activity) solution in normal saline	—
Dihydrostreptomycin-streptomycin sulfates	0.5 ml. (1 mg. activity) solution in water	1.0 ml. (10 mg. activity) solution in water	1.0 ml. (3 mg. activity) solution in normal saline	500 mg.
Dihydrostreptomycin-streptomycin sulfates solution	0.5 ml. (1 mg. activity) solution in water	1.0 ml. (10 mg. activity) solution in water	1.0 ml. (3 mg. activity) solution in normal saline	500 mg.

Dihydrostreptomycin-streptomycin sulfates with isonicotinic acid hydrazide	0.5 ml. (0.5 mg. activity) solution in water	1.0 ml. (10 mg. activity) solution in water	1.0 ml. (3 mg. activity) solution in normal saline	500 mg.
Chlortetracycline hydrochloride	0.5 ml. (1 mg. activity) solution in water	1.0 ml. (5 mg. activity) solution in water	0.6 ml. (3 mg. activity) solution in water	40 mg.
Chlortetracycline hydrochloride solely for manufacture of a veterinary drug for non-parenteral use	0.4 ml. (0.8 mg. activity) solution in water	—	—	—
Chlortetracycline calcium oral drops	Oral—a volume to contain 25 mg.	—	—	—
Chlortetracycline calcium syrup	Oral—a volume to contain 25 mg.	—	—	—
Chlortetracycline ophthalmic		—	—	Entire bottle
Chlortetracycline surgical powder		—	—	500 mg. powder
Chlortetracycline gauze packing		—	—	One gauze packing
Chlortetracycline dressing		—	—	¼ dressing
Oxytetracycline hydrochloride	0.5 ml. (1.5 mg. activity) solution in water	1.0 ml. (10 mg. activity) solution in water	1.0 ml. (3 mg. activity) solution in water	40 mg.
Oxytetracycline ophthalmic		—	—	Entire bottle
Oxytetracycline surgical powder		—	—	500 mg. powder
Oxytetracycline gauze pads		—	—	One pad
Tetracycline hydrochloride	0.5 ml. (1 mg. activity) solution in water	1.0 ml. (0.5 mg. activity) solution in water	0.6 ml. (3 mg. activity) solution in water	40 mg.
Tetracycline	0.5 ml. (1 mg. activity) dissolve 40 mg. in 2 ml. 0.1 N hydrochloric acid, dilute with water to 2 mg./ml.	—	—	—
Chloramphenicol	0.5 ml. (1 mg. activity) solution in normal saline (heat to dissolve)	1.0 ml. (5 mg. activity) solution in normal saline (heat to dissolve)	0.6 ml. (3 mg. activity) solution in normal saline (heat to dissolve)	40 mg.

Antibiotic	Dosage			Sterility† per tube
	Toxicity* per mouse	Pyrogen per Kg.	Histamine per Kg.	
Chloramphenicol palmitate	Oral—1 ml. (60 mg. activity) suspension in 10 per cent acacia solution	—	—	Entire bottle
Chloramphenicol ophthalmic	—	—	—	Entire vial
Chloramphenicol solution	0.5 ml. (1 mg. activity) solution in normal saline	1.0 ml. (5 mg. activity) solution in normal saline	0.6 ml. (3 mg. activity) solution in normal saline	
Chloramphenicol for aqueous injection	0.5 ml. (1 mg. activity) solution in normal saline	1.0 ml. (5 mg. activity) solution in normal saline	0.6 ml. (3 mg. activity) solution in normal saline	Entire contents dissolved in sterile 40 per cent (w/v) dimethyl acetamide 10 ml./Gm. powder
Bacitracin	0.5 ml. (100 u.) solution in normal saline	1.0 ml. (300 u.) solution in normal saline	—	500 mg.
Bacitracin methylene disalicylate	Oral—1.0 ml. (1000 u.) suspension in 10 per cent acacia solution		—	—
Bacitracin ophthalmic	—	—	—	Entire bottle
Zinc bacitracin	Oral—0.5 ml. (2000 u.) suspension in water	—	—	
Polymyxin sulfate	0.5 ml. (600 u.) solution in normal saline	1.0 ml. (20,000 u.) solution in normal saline	—	Entire bottle
Neomycin sulfate	0.5 ml. (100 µg. activ-	1.0 ml. (1 mg. activity)	—	—

	...ity] solution in normal saline	solution in normal saline		Entire bottle
Neomycin hydrochloride	—			
Neomycin ophthalmic		—	—	
Erythromycin	1.0 ml. (30 mg.) oral, suspension in water	—	—	
Erythromycin stearate	1.0 ml. (30 mg.) oral, suspension in water	—		
Erythromycin lactobionate	0.5 ml. (1.0 mg. activity) solution in water	0.5 ml. (50 mg. activity) solution in water	1.0 ml. (4 mg. activity) solution in water	300 mg.
Erythromycin glucoheptonate	0.5 ml. (1.0 mg. activity) solution in water	0.5 ml. (50 mg. activity) solution in water	1.0 ml. (4 mg. activity) solution in water	300 mg.
Erythromycin ethylcarbonate	1.0 ml. (30 mg.) oral, suspension in water			
Carbomycin	0.5 ml. (3 mg. activity) dissolve 120 mg. in 2 m. 0.1 N hydrochloric acid, dilute with water to 6 mg./ml.	—	—	
Viomycin sulfate	0.5 ml. (1.0 mg.) solution in water	1.0 ml. (10 mg.) solution in water	0.6 ml. (3.0 mg.) solution in normal saline	500 mg.
Fumagillin	Oral—1.0 ml. (40 mg.) suspension in water	—	—	
Anisomycin	0.5 ml. (2.0 mg.) solution in water	—	—	
Nystatin	0.5 ml. (600 u.) intraperitoneal, suspension in 0.5% acacia solution	—	—	

* All intravenous injections unless otherwise designated.
† If single-dose containers, use entire contents of container.

for contamination that may have been induced during the test) of the total number of samples tested.

Conduct of test for molds and yeasts. Add not more than 10 ml. of sterile distilled water or sterile physiologic salt solution to each immediate container in the sample to be tested. From each of not less than four immediate containers transfer aseptically the equivalent of approximately 300 mg., or the entire contents if the container is packaged to contain less than 300 mg., to individual tubes each containing 75 to 100 ml. of Sabouraud's liquid medium no. 13. Incubate all tubes at approximately 25 C. for five days. The batch meets the requirements of the test for molds and yeasts if on the first or second test no tube shows growth, or if the number of tubes that show growth in three or more consecutive tests is not more than 10 per cent (to compensate for contamination that may have been induced during the test) of the total number of samples tested.

Benzathine penicillin or preparations containing it are tested for sterility as previously except prior to sterilization add 0.5 ml. of polysorbate 80 to each tube of thioglycollate medium no. 14 and Sabouraud's medium no. 13, and after sterilization add sufficient penicillinase (see Chapter 21) to each tube of Sabouraud's medium no. 13 to inactivate completely the penicillin used in the test. This procedure is used to solubilize the benzathine penicillin.

Diethylaminoethyl ester penicillin G hydriodide or preparations containing it are tested for sterility, as under conduct for test for bacteria, molds, and yeasts. Except in the test for bacteria, prior to sterilization add 0.5 ml. of polysorbate 80 and a sufficient quantity of 2 N sodium hydroxide to each 100 ml. of thioglycollate medium no. 14 to give a pH of 7.9 after sterilization. (The 2 N sodium hydroxide should be added prior to adding the polysorbate 80.) The pH of the medium has to be adjusted to pH 7.9 to allow the ester to hydrolyze to free penicillin.

STREPTOMYCIN, DIHYDROSTREPTOMYCIN, BACITRACIN, OR VIOMYCIN. Use the entire contents of single-dose containers or the equivalent of approximately 0.5 Gm. (activity) from each multiple-dose container and proceed as directed under penicillin, except that neither penicillinase nor the control tube is used in the test for bacteria.

CHLORTETRACYCLINE, OXYTETRACYCLINE, TETRACYCLINE, OR CHLORAMPHENI-COL. Use 40 mg. (activity) from each container tested and proceed as directed under penicillin, except that neither penicillinase nor the control tube is used in the test for bacteria.

POLYMYXIN OR ERYTHROMYCIN. Use the entire contents of single-dose containers or the equivalent of approximately 300 mg. (activity) from each multiple-dose container and proceed as directed under penicillin, except that neither penicillinase nor the control tube is used in the test for bacteria.

An example of how the sterility test is interpreted is as follows: If in the first test for bacteria none of the tubes out of the six tested shows growth, the sample is satisfactory. If one tube out of six shows growth, the test is repeated on another six tubes and if none of these six shows growth, the sample is satisfactory. If on the second test, one tube out of six shows growth, then a third test is run. The total of the tubes run and the tubes showing growth from the first and second tests are now considered, in our example we have two tubes showing growth out of 12. This means on the third test at least eight more tubes should be run. If all eight are clear, then we would have a total for all three tests of two tubes showing growth out of 20 or not more than 10 per cent and the sample would pass.

For easy reference table VI has been prepared which lists the various antibiotic preparations and the amounts of them to be used in the tests for toxicity, pyrogens, histamine, and sterility.

19 METHODS FOR THE DETERMINATION OF BACTERIAL SUSCEPTIBILITY TO ANTIBIOTICS

The determination of the sensitivity of microorganisms to antibiotics in vitro is now a common laboratory procedure. The results of these sensitivity tests are widely used in the selection of the proper antibiotic to be used for specific therapy of patients with bacterial infections. The sensitivity of any given strain of organism to an antimicrobial agent is usually expressed as the concentration of the agent that inhibits the growth of the organism either partially or completely or that kills the organism within a certain time period.

Several methods for determining this value are currently used and the results obtained with a given strain by these different methods may show wide differences depending on the details of the method and the choice of the end point.[22]

It has been pointed out [23] that the astute and experienced clinician can often guess the probable species of bacteria producing certain clear-cut clinical categories of infection. For example, the internist may quickly decide that a patient with a cough, fever, chest pain, and rusty sputum has pneumococcal pneumonia. However, an extensive chronic ulcer of the leg may harbor a variety of different pathogenic microorganisms that play a role in the pathogenesis of the condition. Certainly the clinician cannot properly or intelligently treat cases of infection unless he knows which antibiotic or combination of antibiotics is most effective in stopping the activity of the invading organisms. It is therefore a more rational approach to depend on the laboratory to identify the microorganism and determine what its sensitivity is to the various antibiotics, rather than to attempt to predict on the basis of past experience. The introduction of new antibiotics, and the changing patterns of resistance of microorganisms to the older ones, further emphasizes the importance of antibiotic sensitivity testing.

General Principles Governing the Performance of Antibiotic Sensisivity Tests. If possible, the physician should decide when the patient is first visited whether cultures should be taken *before* any antibiotic is given. If antibiotics are administered before actual identification of the organism causing the infection and then the culture is taken, the causative organism may be suppressed and other secondary contaminating organisms not responsible for the original infection may be isolated instead. The isolation of cultures prior to administration of antibiotics will thus avoid errors due to unnecessary attention to contaminants. It is also highly desirable for the director or person in charge of the laboratory to be fully informed of the details of the clinical history, which may suggest to him the causative agent and the proper culture medium to use.

There are three general methods for determining antibiotic sensitivity currently in use: The tube or broth serial dilution technique, the agar diffusion method (the medicated disc method), and the agar plate dilution method. The first two methods enjoy the widest use. The broth serial dilution method is considered the most reliable and accurate if care is taken to insure constant conditions and proper controls. The agar diffusion or medicated disc method is the most widely used and simplest to perform. The agar plate dilution method is preferred by some laboratories and the choice between this procedure and the tube dilution method is one of individual preference. There has been some controversy as to the reliability of in vitro tests because the translation of in vitro results into clinical practice has not always resulted in the selection of the best drug for treatment. Nevertheless, while there have been some instances reported in which there was a lack of correlation between in vitro tests and clinical responses, the majority of cases show good correspondence. Frequently this results in economic and lifesaving measures for the patient.

Each of these methods will be considered separately; however, there are certain features common to all of them.

COLLECTION OF SPECIMEN. If deemed necessary, specimens of blood should be taken for cultures if the temperature is 101 F. or higher. Cultures from the throat, wounds, or ulcers may be taken up on a sterile cotton swab. Exudates in a body cavity, such as the pleura, peritoneum, and joint space, or in an abscess cavity may be obtained by aspiration with a sterile syringe. Cultures from areas of cellulitis may be obtained by injecting 1 ml. of nutrient broth into the area and immediately aspirating as much of it as possible. Urine is collected as aseptically as possible and the centrifuged sediment used for culture. For antibiotic sensitivity testing, it is preferable to use pure cultures.

CULTURE MEDIA. The selection of isolation media is beyond the scope of this discussion. A wide variety of isolation media for various species of bacteria is covered thoroughly in the manuals issued by Baltimore Biological Laboratories and by Difco Laboratories. Many laboratories make initial isolations on blood agar plates and incubate one aerobically and the other anaerobically. Medium no. 17 is useful for this purpose. After incubation, colonies are inoculated into a suitable nutrient broth. The selection of the broth medium depends on the growth requirements of the organism under test. We have found medium no. 3 generally satisfactory for most organisms and fluid thioglycollate medium no. 14 a good alternative, especially for streptococci, pneumococci, and anaerobic bacteria. Some fastidious pathogens may require the addition of blood, serum, or other growth factors, such as the "X" or "V" factors necessary for the growth of *H. influenzae*. The broth medium selected for isolation is usually used in the serial broth dilution method and can also be used in the agar diffusion technique by incorporating 1.5 per cent agar in the nutrient broth.

Each laboratory usually selects the sensitivity method that is best suited to its needs. Once this is decided upon, every effort should be made to maintain all test conditions as uniform as possible. The choice of culture media should be limited as much as possible to enable the laboratory to prepare the same formulation consistently. Dehydrated media have a great advantage in this respect, since they are more likely to be of uniform composition and *p*H. The *p*H of the medium should be carefully checked from batch to batch. Generally, a *p*H of from 6.6 to 7.2 is satisfactory. Streptomycin and chlortetracycline are strongly influenced by the *p*H. A heightened *p*H increases the activity of streptomycin while decreasing that of chlortetracycline. Even though oxytetracycline, penicillin, and chloramphenicol are not notably affected, a definite *p*H should be selected and adhered to for all antibiotics.

TIME AND TEMPERATURE OF INCUBATION. In our laboratories we use a temperature of 36 to 37 C. and an incubation time of 16 to 18 hours for conducting sensitivity tests. Most bacteria will grow well at this temperature for this length of time, and the currently used antibiotics do not suffer marked loss of potency. Even though some antibiotics deteriorate more rapidly than others, the initial impact of the fully potent antibiotic on the test organism in the broth dilution test and the rapid diffusion (3 to 4 hours) in the agar diffusion test are sufficient to produce an effect that lasts during the test period.

ANTIBIOTIC STOCK SOLUTIONS.* Dilute a weighed quantity of the antibiotic in sterile distilled water (carbomycin and erythromycin should first be put in solution with a minimal amount of methyl alcohol and then diluted with water) to make a concentration of 100 units or *μ*g./ml. or higher if resistant organisms are anticipated. Sterilize the antibiotic solutions by passing through a sintered-glass bacteriologic filter. Dispense small amounts, 1 or 2 ml., into 13 by 100 mm. test tubes or other suitable containers. Store these in a deep freezer at − 20 C. or in a solid carbon dioxide chest until needed. When needed, remove an amount sufficient for the day's test from the freezer and thaw. After thawing, mix thoroughly. If a freezer or carbon dioxide box is not available, use the freezing compartment of an ordinary refrigerator. As an additional check on the proper strength of the antibiotic, a standard organism may be included for each antibiotic used. *M. pyogenes* var. *aureus*, ATCC 6538P, the organism used for penicillin assay, is satisfactory for most currently used antibiotics.

Methods. SERIAL BROTH DILUTION METHOD. *Conduct of the test.* Prepare twofold serial dilutions of the antibiotic as follows: Place 10 sterile 13 by 100 mm. test tubes (Wassermann tubes) in a rack. To each of the last nine tubes add 0.5 ml. of the broth employed in the test. To the first tube (empty) add 0.5 ml. of the 100 or 1,000 unit or *μ*g./ml. solution of the antibiotic. To the second tube (containing 0.5 ml. of broth) also add 0.5 ml. of the same

---

* An "Antibiotic Diagnostic Kit" containing buffered, preweighed small amounts of all commonly used antibiotics is available from Chas. Pfizer & Co., Inc., Brooklyn, New York.

solution of the antibiotic. Mix and transfer 0.5 ml. from the second tube to the third tube. Continue this process until the last tube is reached and discard the last 0.5 ml. Prepare a 1:100, 1:1,000 or higher dilution of a broth culture or suspension of the organism to be tested in the same broth used in the test. Add 1.5 ml. of this inoculated broth to each tube of the series and also to another tube without antibiotic for the organism growth control. The first tube will then contain 25 units or μg./ml., if the 100 unit or μg. solution of antibiotic was used, the second 12.5, and the third 6.25, and so on. Incubate the tubes at optimum temperature (37 C.) overnight and observe for inhibition of growth of the organism in each tube. The least amount of antibiotic resulting in complete inhibition of growth is the end point and is recorded as the M.I.C. (minimal inhibitory concentration). Partial degrees of inhibition may be recorded if desired.

The concentration of antibiotic used to prepare the stock solution which is then further diluted depends in part on the nature and site of the infection. It is obvious that an organism requiring 25 μg./ml. of an antibiotic to inhibit growth would be considered resistant if present in the blood stream where such antibiotic concentrations can seldom be obtained, while the same organism causing a superficial infection in a wound or ulcer would be considered sensitive because high concentrations of antibiotic are readily obtained in compresses or ointments that could be applied to the local area. Organisms causing urinary tract infections might be considered sensitive if the relatively high concentrations of antibiotic obtainable in the urine are used in classifying the sensitivity or resistance of the infecting strain. However, it should be remembered that most urinary tract infections have foci of infection within the tissues, and, even though the urine may be free of bacteria as long as the antibiotic is administered, the organism may reappear in the urine when medication is stopped.

Synergistic or antagonistic combinations can be determined by mixing the stock solutions of the antibiotics before diluting. When either single antibiotics or combinations are tested, additional information can be obtained by subculturing in fluid thioglycollate medium no. 14 all of the tubes showing inhibition of growth. This is done by transferring the entire contents of the 2.0 ml. in the tubes into tubes containing 15 ml. of fluid thioglycollate medium no. 14. These tubes are incubated and observed for growth of the organism under test. In this way it can be determined whether the antibiotic or combination of antibiotics has a bactericidal or bacteriostatic effect.

An alternate method of performing the tube dilution test is to prepare dilutions of the antibiotics in broth and keep them at -20 C. or lower until used. Make bulk dilutions of the antibiotics in any suitable broth, such as broth medium no. 3 or brain-heart infusion broth no. 15, to obtain 100, 10, 5, 1.0, and 0.1 units or μg./ml. Transfer 1.0 ml. of these bulk dilutions to small 13 by 100 mm. test tubes (Wassermann tubes) and store at -20 C. or lower. When needed, the tubes containing the desired antibiotic are removed from the freezer, thawed, shaken thoroughly to mix, and inoculated with a loopful of a broth culture of the organism under test or with a small quantity from growth on solid media.

Interpretation of results. In the serial broth dilution method the difference in the antibiotic concentration from one tube to another is twofold, that is, each tube in the descending series has one half of the concentration of antibiotic contained in the preceding tube. Even when every effort is made to maintain constant test conditions variations will often occur. Extensive studies have shown that under rigid test conditions duplication of results may be obtained within a twofold error, that is, a minimal inhibitory concentration of antibiotic may be recorded as 2.5, 5, or 10 μg. in replicate tests. It is possible to use smaller increments of antibiotic concentrations, but this type of test is time consuming and unnecessary for the usual purpose of the clinical laboratory. The results of the serial broth dilution may be reported as the minimal inhibitory concentration in units or μg. of the antibiotic or the organism may be classified as being sensitive or resistant. Some have further broken down the sensitive classification into the categories "very sensitive," "sensitive," "moderately sensitive," and "slightly sensitive." We would suggest three categories, "sensitive," "moderately sensitive," and "resistant." Table VII is an example of how different categories can be related to broth dilution inhibitory tests, and these provide only a rough guide to the laboratory in reaching their own decisions as to the relative sensitivity or resistance of a given microorganism.

TABLE VII: *Method of Classifying Broth Dilution Inhibitory Tests* *

	Sensitive			Resistant	
	Very sensitive	Sensitive	Moderately sensitive	Slightly sensitive	Resistant
Penicillin	< 0.1 u.	0.1–0.5 u.	0.5–1 u.	1–10 u.	> 10 u.
Tetracycline Oxytetracycline } Chlortetracycline	< 1 μg.	1–5 μg.	5–10 μg.	10–20 μg.	> 20 μg.
Chloramphenicol	< 5 μg.	5–15 μg.	15–25 μg.	25–50 μg.	> 50 μg.
Bacitracin	< 0.5 u.	0.5–1 u.	1–2.5 u.	2.5–5 u.	> 5 u.
Streptomycin or di-hydrostreptomycin	< 1 μg.	1–5 μg.	5–10 μg.	10–20 μg.	> 20 μg.
Polymyxin B	< 10 u.	10–25 u.	25–50 u.	50–100 u.	> 100 u.
Erythromycin or carbomycin	< 1 μg.	1–2 μg.	—	2–5 μg.	> 5 μg.

* M.I.C. in μg. or u./ml.

AGAR DIFFUSION (MEDICATED DISC) METHOD. The medicated disc method is widely used for determining the sensitivity of microorganisms to antibiotics because of its simplicity, rapidity, and reproducibility. Numerous investigations have shown that there is a good correlation between the broth dilution method and the medicated disc technique if the latter is properly done and interpreted.

In the disc method, the specimen or exudate is suspended in broth, or a suspension of isolated culture is smeared evenly with a sterile cotton swab over the surface of an agar plate containing a suitable medium, such as heart infusion agar no. 16 or heart infusion agar with blood no. 17. Greater uniformity of inoculum may be obtained by using a young broth culture of a standard turbidity. One-half ml. of this culture is added to the plate and spread evenly over the surface with a sterile cotton swab or nichrome spatula. In either case the inoculated plate is placed in the incubator and allowed to dry thoroughly. This is *most important* because extra moisture will tend to leach out the antibiotics in the filter paper disc and give erroneous results. It is also important that the same amount of agar is added to each Petri dish so that the depth of the medium is constant. Discs saturated with the antibiotics (wet method) or previously saturated discs that have been properly dried are placed on the surface of the agar after inoculation. In this way, as many as 5 to 10 antibiotics may be tested against the same culture. After incubation, the relative sensitivity of the culture is clearly demonstrated by zones of inhibition surrounding the discs. With some organisms a zone of growth stimulation will be noted at the edge of the clear zone, and in some instances secondary zones of growth stimulation may be noted in areas beyond the clear zone. In some instances resistant colony variants can be found within the clear zones. These may be naturally resistant mutants or penicillinase producers if they occur around the penicillin impregnated disc.

The clear zones of inhibition will vary in size, and, although some workers have attempted to relate zone size with degree of sensitivity or resistance, it is at best a relative measure of susceptibility. Antibiotics vary in their ability to diffuse in an agar medium and this diffusion rate is not necessarily related to theraputic efficacy. Thus, mere zone size is a measure of diffusability rather than sensitivity. It is true, however, that under standard conditions the zone size given by a specific antibiotic is a measure of the sensitivity of a given organism. Zone sizes will vary with the thickness of the agar medium, the density of inoculum, and also with different culture media. It is generally conceded that zone sizes should be disregarded and only the *presence* or *absence* of any zone be taken into account. If this is done and only one concentration of antibiotic used, the result is reported as "resistant" or "susceptible." If two or three suitable concentrations are used, the result may be reported as sensitive, moderately sensitive, or resistant.

Preparation of discs. These may be prepared by cutting discs 5 to 10 mm. in diameter out of good absorbent filter paper (Whatman no. 2), or they may be purchased, ½ inch (12.7 mm.) in diameter. The concentration of the antibiotic solution used to saturate the disc depends on the quantity of fluid absorbed by the disc and the concentration of each particular antibiotic that will differentiate between "susceptible" or "resistant" in terms of the clinical end result. The ½ inch discs absorb 0.1 ml. of solution, and the concentrations of antibiotic solutions are based on this absorptive capacity. Thus if a disc absorbs 0.1 ml. and the concentration of antibiotic desired in the disc is 1 μg., the antibiotic solution used to saturate the disc must be 10 μg./ml. The final concentration of the antibiotic present in the disc is based on the diffusability of the drug and the blood concentration obtained with currently used clinical dosage schedules.

Table VIII lists the final concentration of antibiotic in the ½ inch disc for each of the antibiotics. The solutions used to prepare the discs should contain 10 times/ml. the quantities shown in the table, since the discs absorb 0.1 ml. These concentrations are based on the concentrations contained in the antibiotic impregnated filter paper discs prepared commercially by Difco Laboratories.

Conduct of sensitivity test. Use the clinical specimen itself or inoculate the clinical specimen on suitable isolation media and after incubation transfer

TABLE VIII: *Final Concentration of Antibiotic per Disc*

Bacitracin	2 u.	10 u.	20 u.
Carbomycin	0.5 μg.	1 μg.	10 μg.
Chloramphenicol	10 μg.	30 μg.	60 μg.
Chlortetracycline	10 μg.	30 μg.	60 μg.
Dihydrostreptomycin and streptomycin	1 μg.	10 μg.	100 μg.
Erythromycin	0.5 μg.	1 μg.	10 μg.
Neomycin	10 μg.	30 μg.	60 μg.
Oxytetracycline	10 μg.	30 μg.	60 μg.
Penicillin	0.5 u.	1 u.	10 u.
Polymyxin B	5 u.	10 u.	30 u.
Tetracycline	10 μg.	30 μg.	60 μg.
Viomycin	1 μg.	10 μg.	100 μg.

portions of well-isolated colonies into nutrient broth and incubate. Spread the specimen or culture over the surface of a blood agar plate (medium no. 17), using a cotton swab, until the entire surface of the plate has been covered. Allow to dry thoroughly. Pick up a sterile disc with a hypodermic or dissecting needle or a pair of fine tipped forceps. Bring the edge of the disc in contact with the antibiotic solution and hold there until the disc is thoroughly saturated. Then gently place on the surface of the inoculated plate and press gently so that all parts of the disc are in contact with the agar surface.

If prepared dry discs are used, they are simply placed on the agar surface and gently pressed. If a large number of antibiotics of various concentrations are to be tested, more than one inoculated plate may be necessary. Incubate the plates overnight at 37 C. and examine for zones of growth inhibition around the discs.

Interpretation. The disc method does not allow exact quantitative readings to be made. The diameter of the zone of inhibition varies with the antibiotic and with the test organism. These variations do not permit too much importance to be attached to zone size, and it is suggested that actual measurement of zone size be disregarded. The results of the disc test can be placed in the same categories as those described under the serial broth dilution test.[24]

VERY SENSITIVE. Large zone of inhibition around the disc of lowest concentration and large zones around the discs of intermediate and greatest concentration.

SENSITIVE. Small zone around the disc of lowest concentration and moderately large zones around the other two.

MODERATELY SENSITIVE. No zone around the disc of lowest concentration, but zones around the other two.

SLIGHTLY SENSITIVE. A zone only around the disc of highest concentration.

RESISTANT. No zones around any disc.

In practice it is suggested that "very sensitive" and "sensitive" be called "sensitive," and "slightly sensitive" and "resistant" be called "resistant," if the infecting organism is obtained from a systemic infection that can only be reached by the antibiotic by way of the blood stream. If the infecting organism is susceptible to local application of the antibiotic then "slightly sensitive" may be considered "sensitive."

PLATE DILUTION METHOD. The plate dilution method is similar in principle to the tube dilution method except that a solid medium is used. The agar medium used depends on the growth requirements of the organism under test. Agar medium no. 1 is a good general purpose medium, and, since it is used in many of the assay methods, it is always available. We have found that the plate dilution method is not satisfactory for those organisms that grow poorly on solid media, that grow in the form of fine, discrete colonies (streptococci and pneumococci), or that have a spreading tendency (*Proteus and Pseudomonas*).

Conduct of the test. Melt agar medium no. 1 sufficient for the tests, cool to 48 C., and hold at this temperature in a water bath. Prepare serial dilutions of the antibiotic in water starting at 1,000 units or μg./ml. The initial concentration is prepared as described under "preparation of standard" under the various chapter headings. The volume of each dilution needed will depend on the number of cultures to be tested. One ml. of each concentration is needed for every 10 cultures tested.

Mark Petri dishes into 10 approximately equal segments by drawing a line with a glass marking crayon from the center of the bottom underside of the dish to the periphery. If desired, a rubber stamp can be made and the dish marked in red glass marking ink to divide the dish into 10 equal segments. Add 1.0 ml. of each antibiotic solution to the dish and then add 9.0 ml. of agar medium no. 1, melted and cooled to 48 C. Mix by rotating each dish and allow to harden. Then using a sterile cotton swab, streak a segment on each of the plates containing a different antibiotic concentration with a broth culture of the test organism. Repeat with the other organisms under test until nine of the the segments have been treated. On the tenth segment, streak a culture of an organism of known sensitivity, such as *M. pyogenes* var. *aureus*, ATCC 6538P. A control plate without antibiotic is inoculated with each culture tested. Incubate 18 to 24 hours at 37 C. and examine the plates for growth. If 12 plates are used, the concentration of antibiotic will decrease by halves from 100 to 50 to 25 to 12.5 and so on to 0.04 unit or μg./ml. The concentration of antibiotic producing complete inhibition of growth is taken as the end point. Partial inhibition can be readily observed by noting a decrease in the amount of growth until complete inhibition is obtained.

The importance of antibiotic sensitivity tests properly conducted and interpreted is brought sharply into focus when we consider the tetracyclines. The similarity of molecular structure of the tetracyclines plus the fact that all three have wide antimicrobial spectra has led to the arbitrary substitution of one for the other. However, extensive in vitro studies [25,26] have shown that these three tetracycline drugs *do not* possess equal antibacterial activity and that laboratory tests should be utilized, except for highly sensitive organisms, such as the beta-hemolytic streptococci and pneumococci, to determine the drug of choice. In vitro sensitivity tests prior to and during treatment of chronic infections, such as osteomyelitis and subacute endocarditis, are particularly desirable. In these conditions the selection of the proper antibiotic is of vital importance. If the *most* active drug or drug combination is not selected and the proper quantities administered, the blood concentrations achieved may not be sufficient to penetrate the relatively avascular areas of the lesion and destroy the invading microorganism. Further, in these conditions, the antibiotic selected, or at least one of them if a combination is used, should be bactericidal (penicillin, streptomycin, bacitracin) and frequent sensitivity determinations must be made to detect a possible in vivo emergence of resistance. It is indeed an unwise procedure to disregard habitually laboratory control if one is to avoid indiscriminate and unwise use of the antibiotics.

20 MISCELLANEOUS TESTS AND METHODS

Determination of the Penicillin G Content of Sodium, Potassium, Ephedrine, Procaine, 1-Ephenamine, and Dibenzylamine Penicillin G

The penicillin mold is capable of producing a wide variety of different kinds of penicillin. Some of the more commonly known ones are penicillin G, X, K, F, dihydro F, and O. They all have the same penicillin nucleus and differ only in the side chain substituent. Table IX shows the relationship of these penicillins and gives the molecular weights of their sodium salts. The complete structure for penicillin G is given in Chapter 2, Section C.

If commercial penicillin is to be labeled as the penicillin G type, it must contain not less than 85 per cent penicillin G. Various methods have been developed for the determination of penicillin G, such as a gravimetric procedure in which the G type is precipitated as the N-ethyl piperidine salt (commonly known as the N.E.P. method), ultraviolet and infrared spectrophotometric methods, measurement of phenylacetic acid, isotope dilution methods, and radioactive tracer methods. Several of these methods are reported in the methods which follow. The isotope dilution and radioactive tracer methods are not given because they require special equipment and procedures not generally available to most laboratories.

None of the methods developed for the determination of penicillin G are perfect. All of the methods just mentioned, with the exception of the N.E.P. method, would measure as active penicillin G, any small amount of phenylacetic acid (used as precursor) or penicillin G degradation products that might be present. N-ethyl piperidine is a fairly specific precipitant for the G type of penicillin, but under certain conditions some of the other types of penicillin can coprecipitate with or have a solubilizing effect on the N.E.P. penicillin G precipitate. The chief cause of variation in results sometimes obtained by the N.E.P. method seems to be due to the amyl acetate used. Amyl acetate is quite variable in composition and studies are now in progress to select a boiling range specification for this solvent that will give more consistent and truer penicillin G values.

Method 1, to be described, is the official N.E.P. method. It is believed that results of studies now being made will require a specification that the amyl acetate should be redistilled and only the fraction distilling between 138.5 to 141.5 C. be used. The N-ethyl piperidine reagent should also be redistilled

TABLE IX: *Relationship of the Penicillins*

Common Name	Side Chain Linkage	M.W., Sodium Salt
Penicillin G	Benzyl	356.4
Penicillin X	p-Hydroxybenzyl	372.4
Penicillin F	$\triangle^2$-Pentenyl	334.4
Penicillin dihydro F	n-Amyl	336.4
Penicillin K	n-Heptyl	364.4
Penicillin O	Allylmercaptomethyl	352.4

and the fraction between 129.5 to 131 C. used. The official method specifies that the amyl acetate extract of the penicillin be dried by filtering through sodium sulfate. It has been found that dry silica gel (mesh size 6–16 Tyler standard) is a more effective drying agent and 0.5 Gm. in the filter funnel may be used in place of the sodium sulfate.

METHOD 1: N-Ethyl Piperidine Method for the Determination of the Penicillin G Content of Sodium, Potassium, or Ephedrine Penicillin G.

Reagents. The reagents to be described are freshly prepared every three days and are of such quality that when used in this procedure with a known penicillin G not less than 97 per cent of penicillin G is recovered.

AMYL ACETATE SOLUTION. Saturate the amyl acetate with the N-ethyl piperidine salt of penicillin G by adding 2 mg. of the salt for each 1 ml. of the solvent. Cool this solution to 0 to 8 C. and filter it through a sintered-glass filter immediately before use.

ACETONE SOLUTION. Saturate reagent grade acetone with the N-ethyl piperidine salt of penicillin G using 3 mg. of salt for each 1 ml. of acetone. Cool this solution to from 0 to 8 C. and filter it through a sintered-glass filter immediately before use.

N-ETHYL PIPERIDINE SOLUTION. N-ethyl piperidine should be stored in brown bottles in a refrigerator. Dilute 1.0 ml. of this reagent with 4.0 ml. of amyl acetate. Saturate this solution with the N-ethyl piperidine salt of penicillin G using about 3 mg. of the salt for each 1.0 ml. of solution. Cool this solution to 0 to 8 C. and filter it through a sintered-glass filter immediately before use.

PHOSPHORIC ACID SOLUTION. Prepare by dissolving 1.0 ml. of reagent grade phosphoric acid (85 per cent) in 4.0 ml. of water. Cool to 0 to 8 C. and shake before using.

SODIUM SULFATE. The powdered anhydrous, reagent grade, sodium sulfate is used.

Procedure.[27] Accurately weigh from 60 to 70 mg. of the sample to be tested in a glass test tube or glass vial of approximately 10 ml. capacity. Add 2.0 ml.

of water to dissolve the penicillin and cool the solution to 0 to 5 C. Add 2 ml. of the amyl acetate solution and 0.5 ml. of the phosphoric acid solution, stopper and shake vigorously for approximately 15 seconds. Centrifuge to obtain a clear separation of the two layers (approximately 20 seconds). After centrifuging remove as much of the amyl acetate layer as possible (usually about 1.7 to 1.8 ml.) with a 2 ml. hypodermic syringe equipped with a suitable needle. Place about 0.1 Gm. of the sodium sulfate in a microfilter funnel (approximately 10 mm. diameter) having a fritted glass disc of medium porosity and add the amyl acetate solution from the hypodermic syringe. Allow it to stand in contact with the drying agent for exactly 20 seconds, then apply suction and collect the filtrate in a small test tube placed in a suction flask, which is surrounded by cracked ice. Pipette a 1.0 ml. aliquot of the amyl acetate filtrate into a tared flat bottom glass tube (approximately 15 by 50 mm.) containing 1.0 ml. of the acetone solution and 0.5 ml. of the N-ethyl piperidine solution. The time elapsing between acidification and the addition of the filtrate to the reagents should not be more than three minutes. Place the glass tube containing this mixture in a large weighing bottle, stopper the bottle, and allow to stand for not less than two hours in a refrigerator at 0 to 8 C. Remove the liquid from the precipitate by means of a tared microfilter stick and wash with a total of 1 ml. of the acetone solution adding the latter by means of a hypodermic syringe equipped with a fine needle. Place the filter stick inside the glass tube, dry under vacuum at room temperature for not less than one hour, and weigh. (Save all N-ethyl piperidine penicillin G residues for saturating reagents.)

Per cent of sodium penicillin G =

$$\frac{\text{mg. N-ethyl piperidine penicillin precipitate} \times 159.3}{\text{Weight of sample mg.}}$$

Per cent of potassium penicillin G =

$$\frac{\text{mg. N-ethyl piperidine penicillin precipitate} \times 166.5}{\text{Weight of sample mg.}}$$

Per cent of ephedrine penicillin G =

$$\frac{\text{mg. N-ethyl piperidine penicillin precipitate} \times 223.2}{\text{Weight of sample mg.}}$$

METHOD 2: N-Ethyl Piperidine Method for the Determination of the Penicillin G Content of Procaine, 1-Ephenamine, and Dibenzylamine Penicillin G.

The penicillin G content of procaine penicillin G, l-ephenamine penicillin G, and dibenzylamine penicillin G may also be determined by Method 1, but, because of their sparing solubility, the following modification of the extraction procedure is required.

Accurately weigh approximately 100 mg. of the sample to be tested in a glass test tube or glass vial of approximately 10 ml. capacity. Add 2 ml. of water and cool to 0 to 5 C. Add 2 ml. of the amyl acetate solution and 0.5 ml. of the phosphoric acid solution, stopper, and shake vigorously for approximately 15 seconds. Add a second 0.5 ml. portion of the phosphoric acid solution and shake vigorously again. Centrifuge to obtain a clear separation of the two layers (approximately 20 seconds). If any procaine penicillin remains undissolved, add a third portion of 0.5 ml. of the phosphoric acid solution and repeat the shaking and centrifugation. Proceed as in Method 1 starting with the removal of the amyl acetate layer.

Per cent of procaine penicillin G =

$$\frac{\text{mg. N-ethyl piperidine penicillin precipitate} \times 263.1}{\text{Weight of sample mg.}}$$

Per cent of l-ephenamine penicillin G =

$$\frac{\text{mg. N-ethyl piperidine penicillin precipitate} \times 251}{\text{Weight of sample mg.}}$$

Per cent of dibenzylamine penicillin G =

$$\frac{\text{mg. N-ethyl piperidine penicillin precipitate} \times 245.5}{\text{Weight of sample mg.}}$$

Determination of the Penicillin G Content of Benzathine Penicillin G.

Penicillin G gives a characteristic absorption maximum in the ultraviolet at 263 mμ due to its phenyl group. The penicillin G content of penicillin may be determined by measuring this absorption. However, as previously mentioned, the method could also measure any other phenyl compounds other than active penicillin G which might be present. The penicillin G content of benzathine penicillin G cannot be determined by the N.E.P. method because of the insolubility of this salt in water. It has thus been necessary to resort to the ultraviolet spectrophotometric method for determining the penicillin G content of benzathine penicillin G, in spite of its possible disadvantages. In the method, allowance is made for the absorption due to the N,N'-dibenzylethylenediamine portion of the benzathine penicillin.

METHOD 3: Ultraviolet Spectrophotometric Method for the Determination of the Penicillin G Content of Benzathine Penicillin.

Dissolve 50 mg. of the sample, accurately weighed, in absolute methyl alcohol and make to a volume of 100 ml. with absolute methyl alcohol. With a suitable spectrophotometer determine the absorbance of the solution in a 1 cm. cell at 263 mμ compared with absolute methyl alcohol as a blank. Multiply the absorbance obtained by the appropriate factor to obtain the absorbance value of a 1 per cent solution. The $E_{1\,cm.}^{1\%}$ value of the sample multiplied by 100, divided by 7.0, represents the per cent penicillin G in the sample.

Another method for determining the benzathine penicillin G content of benzathine penicillin G is to measure the phenylacetic acid formed when the salt is heated with strong alkali. The N,N'-dibenzylethylenediamine portion of the molecule does not form phenylacetic acid under the conditions of the test. The phenylacetic acid formed is extracted and measured spectrophotometrically. The details of the procedure are described in Method 4. If any free phenylacetic acid or any penicillin degradation products which would form phenylacetic acid are present, high results would be obtained. However, the amount of such inactive material can be judged from potency assays. The method has an advantage over the ultraviolet Method 3, in that the N,N'-dibenzylethylenediamine portion of the salt does not interfere.

METHOD 4: Phenylacetic Acid Method for the Determination of the Penicillin G Content of Benzathine Penicillin.

Reagents. The following reagents are used: 10 N sodium hydroxide; benzene, A.C.S.; chloroform, U.S.P.; 18 N sulfuric acid; and absorbent cotton, washed with chloroform and dried.

Procedure.[28] Accurately weigh approximately 65 mg. of benzathine penicillin G and place in a 20 mm. test tube. Add 5.0 ml. of 10 N sodium hydroxide. Heat in a boiling water bath for 15 minutes with occasional swirling. Add 1 ml. of distilled water and mix by swirling. Add 5 ml. of benzene, mix by swirling, and allow the benzene to come to a boil for 15 seconds. Remove the tube from the bath, centrifuge, and pipette off the benzene layer. Add another 5 ml. of benzene, mix, and place the tube in the bath. Allow the benzene to come to a boil for 15 seconds, again remove the tube from the bath, centrifuge, and pipette off the benzene layer. Replace the tube in the bath. After one and one-half hours, remove the tube from the bath, restore the volume to 5 ml. with distilled water, and chill in an ice bath. Add 3.0 ml. of 18 N sulfuric acid drop-wise with agitation. Wash the contents of the tube into a separatory funnel with 3.0 ml. more of 18 N sulfuric acid and 20 ml. of distilled water. Extract the acid solution with three 15 ml. portions of chloroform. Filter each extract through cotton previously moistened with chloroform and collect them in a 50 ml. volumetric flask. Make to 50 ml. with water-washed chloroform and mix. With a suitable spectrophotometer determine the absorbance of this chloroform solution at 253 (max.), 255 (min.), 259 (max.), 263 (min.), and 265 (max.) mμ, using as a blank chloroform previously shaken with an equal volume of water and filtered through cotton.

Calculations. The per cent penicillin G can be calculated from any one of the absorption peaks. If three different figures are obtained, the lowest one is still the highest possible value for penicillin G, since the values obtained represent the maximum penicillin G content.

$$\text{Per cent penicillin G} = \frac{A}{\text{Gm. of sample} \times 2} \times \frac{100}{E}$$

where A = absorbance observed at 253, 259, or 263 mμ.

E = theoretical $E_1^{1\%}$ $_{\text{cm.}}$ value at 253, 259, or 263 mμ for the particular penicillin salt.

Absorbancy ratios should agree substantially with those of phenylacetic acid.

$$\frac{A_{259} \text{ m}\mu}{A_{255} \text{ m}\mu} = 1.38; \qquad \frac{A_{259} \text{ m}\mu}{A_{263} \text{ m}\mu} = 1.52.$$

The $E_{1\text{ cm.}}^{1\%}$. values for benzathine penicillin are 3.00 at 253 mμ, 3.72 at 259 mμ, and 2.83 at 263 mμ.

(Note that Method 4 may also be used for other penicillin salts in which case the treatment with benzene is omitted and also with procaine penicillin the total amount of 18 N sulfuric acid used must be 16 ml. and the amount of water limited to 4 ml.)

The Determination of the Penicillin G Content of the Diethylaminoethyl Ester of Penicillin G.

The penicillin G content of diethylaminoethyl ester penicillin G hydriodide cannot be satisfactorily determined by the N.E.P. method. A method has been developed in which the ester is first hydrolyzed, the penicillin extracted into chloroform, and the penicillin G in the chloroform determined by its ultraviolet absorption. Penicillin G in chloroform solution shows a maximum at 265 mμ and a minimum at 280 mμ. By using both wave lengths, the method is made more specific.

METHOD 5: Determination of the Penicillin G Content of Diethylaminoethyl Ester Penicillin G Hydriodide.

Accurately weigh approximately 50 mg. of the sample and dissolve in 25 ml. potassium phosphate buffer no. 3, pH 8. Allow to stand at room temperature for not less than one and a half hours and not more than two hours. Transfer a 5.0 ml. aliquot to a 25 ml. glass stoppered test tube. Place the tube in an ice bath and add 10.0 ml. of chloroform (previously washed with water). After cooling, adjust the pH of the aqueous phase to 2.0 by adding 0.5 ml. of 1 to 4 phosphoric acid. Shake the tube thoroughly for two minutes, centrifuge, and withdraw the lower chloroform layer with the aid of a 10 ml. hypodermic syringe and a three inch needle. Superficially dry the chloroform by filtering through a pledget of cotton, using a U-shaped funnel to reduce evaporation during filtration. Determine the absorbance of the filtered chloroform solution in a 1 cm. cell at 265 mμ and 280 mμ, using a suitable spectrophotometer. Treat the working standard of sodium penicillin G in the same manner, using an accurately weighed sample of approximately 30 mg.

$$\text{Per cent penicillin G} = \frac{(\text{A of x at 265 m}\mu - \text{A of x at 280 m}\mu)\ (\text{wt.S})\ (100)}{(\text{A of S at 265 m}\mu - \text{A of S at 280 m}\mu)\ (\text{wt.x})\ (0.635)}$$

where A = absorbance.
    x = diethylaminoethyl ester penicillin G hydriodide.
    S = sodium penicillin G working standard.

Determination of the Penicillin G Content of Hydrabamine Penicillin G.

The N.E.P. procedure, as described in Method 1 of this chapter, also cannot be used to determine the G content of hydrabamine penicillin G because of the slight solubility of this salt in water. A modification of the N.E.P. method is used in which the extraction from and solution into amyl acetate is eliminated by dissolving the salt directly in pyridine and the N-ethyl piperidine precipitation is done in this solvent after adding petroleum ether to decrease the solubility of the N.E.P. penicillin precipitate.

METHOD 6: Pyridine N.E.P. Method for the Determination of the Penicillin G Content of Hydrabamine Penicillin G.

Reagents. The following reagents are used: pyridine, purified; N-ethyl piperidine (B.P. 129.5–131.0 C.); and petroleum ether (B.P. 30–60 C.)

Procedure.[29] Accurately weigh a glass weighing bottle of approximately 10 ml. capacity, together with its top, a stirring rod, and a medium porosity immersion filter stick. Transfer to the weighing bottle approximately 225 mg. of the sample to be tested and reweigh. Add 1.5 ml. of pyridine and stir until the solution is complete. Add 0.25 ml. of N-ethyl piperidine and stir until precipitation begins. When precipitation is complete, dilute with 2.5 ml. of petroleum ether, stir well, and allow to stand for 15 minutes. Attach the filter stick to a vacuum line equipped with a suitable trap and withdraw the liquid from the precipitate. Add 2.5 ml. of petroleum ether to the precipitate and withdraw the liquid from the precipitate. Repeat the procedure with two more 2.5 ml. portions of petroleum ether. Leave the stirring rod and the filter stick in the bottle, dry for 30 minutes in a vacuum desiccator, stopper, and weigh.

Per cent of hydrabamine penicillin G =

$$\frac{\text{mg. N-ethyl piperidine penicillin precipitate} \times 141.4}{\text{Weight of sample mg.}}$$

Determination of the Penicillin G Content of Potassium Penicillin O.

Penicillin O may be used to treat patients who are allergic or sensitive to penicillin G. For this reason, the quantity of penicillin G permitted in penicillin O must be kept at a minimum. The law permits not more than 0.5 per cent penicillin G in penicillin O. None of the methods for the determination of penicillin G already described are delicate enough to detect accurately such small quantities of penicillin G in penicillin O. If penicillin G is oxidized with potassium permanganate, the benzyl group is converted to benzoic acid. Penicillin O (allylmercaptomethyl penicillin) does not form benzoic acid under such treatment. In such a method the measurement of the benzoic acid formed would not necessarily mean that it all came from active penicillin G, since degradation products of penicillin G or other phenyl compounds may also give benzoic acid. However, it does give a measure of the maximum amount of penicillin G that could be present.

METHOD 7: Permanganate Oxidation Method for the Determination of Penicillin G in Potassium Penicillin O.

Reagents. The following reagents are used: 2.5 per cent w/v potassium hydroxide, 4.5 per cent w/v potassium permanganate, 10.0 per cent w/v oxalic acid, 18 N sulfuric acid, sodium chloride (reagent grade), chloroform (U.S.P.), and 0.1 N ammonium hydroxide.

Procedure.[30] Accurately weigh approximately 300 mg. of the sample to be tested in a 250 ml. Erlenmeyer flask, dissolve in 1.0 ml. of 2.5 per cent potassium hydroxide solution, add with swirling 50.0 ml. of 4.5 per cent potassium permanganate solution, and heat on the steam bath for two hours, covering the flask with a watch glass. Cool to room temperature and add 25.0 ml. of 10 per cent oxalic acid solution. When the reaction has ceased, add 15.0 ml. of 18 N sulfuric acid stepwise with agitation and cooling. Add 30.0 Gm. of sodium chloride and agitate until a clear, colorless solution is obtained. Transfer to a separatory funnel and extract with three portions of chloroform, 30 ml., 20 ml., and 10 ml. in that order. Filter the extract through a pledget of cotton previously moistened with chloroform and collect in a second separatory funnel. Add 50.0 ml. of 0.1 N ammonium hydroxide to the combined extracts, shake five minutes, and allow the phases to separate for 10 minutes. Discard all but a few ml. of the chloroform layer. Draw off the last few milliliters of chloroform and about 15 ml. of the ammonium hydroxide layer into a glass stoppered test tube and centrifuge two minutes to obtain a clear aqueous layer. Prepare a blank by shaking 50.0 ml. of 0.1 N ammonium hydroxide with 60.0 ml. of chloroform as just described. Determine the absorbance of the blank compared with 0.1 N ammonium hydroxide at 220 and 224 mμ. Determine the absorbance of the sample at 220 and 224 mμ compared with the blank. Calculate the quantity of benzoic acid in the solution from the equation

$$X = \frac{RE\ 224 - E220.}{RB - A}$$

X = concentration in mg./ml. of benzoic acid in sample.
A = absorbance per mg. of benzoic acid U.S.P. per ml. 0.1 N ammonium hydroxide at 220 mμ.
B = absorbance per mg. of benzoic acid U.S.P. per ml. of 0.1 N ammonium hydroxide at 224 mμ.
R = $\dfrac{\text{absorbance of blank at 220 m}\mu.}{\text{absorbance of blank at 224 m}\mu.}$
E220 = absorbance of sample at 220 mμ.
E224 = absorbance of sample at 224 mμ.
Calculate the quantity of penicillin G in the sample from the equation

$$\frac{3.05 \times (50)\ (100)}{\text{weight of sample in milligrams}} = \text{per cent penicillin G}$$

(Note that the common proprietary stopcock lubricants give rise to end absorption. Therefore, the stopcocks of the separatory funnels must be used dry, or be Teflon plugs, or lubricated with white petrolatum, which is satisfactory.)

Explanation of Calculations. The final step in the method is the measurement of benzoic acid in an aqueous ammonium hydroxide solution saturated with chloroform. A chloroform containing blank is used but compensation is not always perfect. The intense end absorption of chloroform therefore makes it necessary to correct for any chloroform imbalance at the analytical wave length. This is accomplished by treating the ammonium hydroxide solution as a two-component mixture, the components being benzoic acid and chloroform.

If we let:

A = absorbance of 1 mg. of benzoic acid U.S.P. per ml. 0.1 N ammonium hydroxide at 220 mμ.

B = absorbance of 1 mg. of benzoic acid U.S.P. per ml. 0.1 N ammonium hydroxide at 224 mμ.

a = absorbance of chloroform saturated 0.1 N ammonium hydroxide at 220 mμ.

b = absorbance of chloroform saturated 0.1 N ammonium hydroxide at 224 mμ.

R = ratio $\dfrac{a}{b}$.

x = concentration, mg./ml. benzoic acid in sample.

y = concentration, mg./ml. chloroform in sample.

E_{220} = absorbance of sample at 220 mμ.

E_{224} = absorbance of sample at 224 mμ.

Two equations may be established

(1) $Ax + ay = E_{220}$

(2) $Bx + by = E_{224}$

In equation (1) $y = \dfrac{E_{220} - Ax}{a}$ and in equation (2) $y = \dfrac{E_{224} - Bx}{b}$; therefore

$$\frac{E_{220} - Ax}{a} = \frac{E_{224} - Bx}{b} \text{ or } \frac{a}{b}(E_{224} - Bx) = E_{220} - Ax$$

As $R = \dfrac{a}{b}$, we have:

$$RE_{224} - RBx = E_{220} - Ax$$
$$RE_{224} - E_{220} = x(RB - A)$$
$$x = \frac{RE_{224} - E_{220}}{RB - A}$$

To convert the concentration of benzoic acid (x) into potassium penicillin G, it is necessary to multiply by 3.05 and the dilution factors.

Determination of the Penicillin G Content of Chloroprocaine Penicillin O.

To determine the penicillin G content of chloroprocaine penicillin O, Method 7 may be used after a preliminary extraction, which eliminates the chloroprocaine portion of the salt. This is necessary because chloroprocaine would also yield benzoic acid during the permanganate oxidation.

METHOD 8: Determination of the Penicillin G Content of Chloroprocaine Penicillin O.

Accurately weigh approximately 500 mg. of the sample in a 25 ml. glass stoppered test tube. Add 6.0 ml. of distilled water and 6.0 ml. of amyl acetate.

Place the tube in an ice bath for five minutes and then add 4.0 ml. of 1 to 4 phosphoric acid, shake vigorously for two minutes, centrifuge for one minute to separate the layers, and withdraw 5.0 ml. of the amyl acetate layer. Place the amyl acetate in a 250 ml. Erlenmeyer flask and evaporate to dryness by directing a stream of air into the flask. Dissolve the residue in 2.0 ml. of 2.5 per cent potassium hydroxide and proceed as in Method 7 of this Chapter, beginning with the addition, with swirling, of 50.0 ml. of 4.5 per cent potassium permanganate.

Calculate the per cent of penicillin G in the sample from the equation:

$$\frac{(5.10) \, (x) \, (50) \, (100)}{(\text{Wt. sample milligrams}) \, (0.833)} = \text{Per cent chloroprocaine penicillin G}$$

Determination of the Penicillin O Content of Potassium Penicillin O.

In the case of penicillin O, the law also requires a determination of its penicillin O content. The most suitable method thus far developed for this determination is an infrared absorption method. When a suspension or mull of crystalline potassium penicillin O in mineral oil is examined in the infrared, it gives a characteristic absorption maximum at 10.1 μ. The other types of penicillin do not give absorption maximums at this wave length. If penicillin O is diluted with another type of penicillin, such as penicillin G, the height of the absorption peak is reduced quantitatively. A standard curve can thus be prepared using a standard potassium penicillin O and known mixtures of this standard with a standard penicillin G. From this standard curve, the O content of an unknown sample of potassium penicillin O can be determined. The method has an accuracy of about ±5 per cent.

METHOD 9: Infrared Method for the Determination of the Potassium Penicillin O Content of Potassium Penicillin O.

Grind the sample to a uniform powder using a mortar and pestle. Weigh by difference 100 to 150 mg. of liquid petrolatum into an agate mortar. Divide the actual weight of the liquid petrolatum by three and add exactly this amount of the powdered penicillin O to the liquid petrolatum in the mortar. Mix with a small spatula and then mull thoroughly with the pestle until a uniform consistency is obtained. Use two circular rock-salt plates, each 2 inches in diameter, as the absorption cell. Place a small drop of the mull in the center of one of the rock-salt plates. Place a brass spacer, 0.0036 inch thick, on the plate. (This spacer is cut in the shape of a circular gasket with a 1 inch center hole and a slit to permit the escape of air when the two plates are pressed together.) Put on the top salt plate gently and slowly squeeze together to spread the mull uniformly. Clamp the two plates firmly together in a metal cell holder. (The cell holder consists of two metal plates, one containing a rectangular center slit ¼ inch wide by ⅝ inch long, the other with a center hole 1 inch in diameter. The two plates are clamped together by means of threaded studs and nuts.) Examine the assembled cell by holding it up to the light. The mull should appear smooth, free of any air bubbles, and not in contact with the spacer. Adjust the amplification of the spectrometer to full-scale deflection for 1 microvolt, set the slit opening to about 0.300 and run the spectrum from 9.4 to 10.7 μ, using an automatic slit-control mechanism and taking a zero reading (shutter closed) at the beginning and at the end of the run. Draw a base line between two points, one on each side of the analytical band (10.1 μ) and calculate the base-line optical density, using the following formula:

$$D_B = \log_{10} \frac{I_B}{I_p}$$

where:

D_B = base-line optical density.

I_p = distance from the zero line to the maximum absorption of the band.

I_B = distance from the zero line to the base line, measured at the same wave length as I_p.

Using known mixtures of penicillin G working standard and penicillin O working standard, prepare a standard curve by plotting the base-line optical densities obtained against the per cent penicillin O. Obtain the per cent penicillin O in the sample under test from this standard curve.

An illustration of how the base-line density is drawn is shown in figure 42.

Determination of the Penicillin O Content of Chloroprocaine Penicillin O.

The chloroprocaine penicillin O content of chloroprocaine penicillin O is also determined by an infrared method. Chloroprocaine penicillin O gives a somewhat different absorption spectrum than potassium penicillin O and therefore cannot be compared with the potassium penicillin O standard. In order to make a direct comparison, the free penicillin O acid is extracted from the chloroprocaine and read directly in a chloroform solution. A standard potassium penicillin O is also extracted in a similar manner and the extinction coefficient obtained on the standard is divided into that obtained on the sample to obtain its percentage of penicillin O. The penicillin O content of potassium penicillin O can also be determined by this method.

METHOD 10: Infrared Method for the Determination of the Chloroprocaine Penicillin O Content of Chloroprocaine Penicillin O.[31]

Accurately weigh approximately 168 mg. of the sample in a 25 ml. glass stoppered test tube and add 5.0 ml. of chloroform (previously washed with water) and 15.0 ml. of distilled water. Place the tube in an ice bath for five minutes and then add 1.5 ml. of 1 to 4 phosphoric acid. Shake the tube vigor-

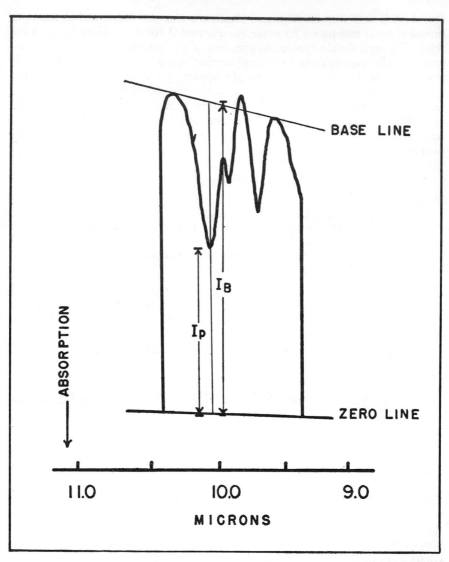

Figure 42

ously for two minutes, centrifuge for one minute to separate the layers, and withdraw the lower chloroform layer with the aid of a 10 ml. hypodermic syringe equipped with a 3 inch needle. Superficially dry the chloroform by filtering through a pledget of cotton, using a U-shaped funnel to reduce evaporation during filtration. Collect the filtrate in a 5 ml. glass stoppered bottle and use within an hour. Place this chloroform solution in an absorption cell (consisting of two rock-salt plates with a 1.0 mm. polyethylene spacer between them, clamped firmly in the cell holder). Adjust the amplification of the infrared spectrometer to full-scale deflection for 1 microvolt, set the slit opening at 0.300 mm. and record the spectrum from 10.7 to 9.4 μ, taking a zero reading (shutter closed) at the beginning and at the end of the run. Draw a base line from the transmission peak at 10.3 μ parallel to the zero line. Calculate the base-line optical density from the following formula:

$$D_B = \log_{10} \frac{I_B}{I_P}$$

where D_B = base line density.

I_B = distance from the zero line to the base line measured at the transmission peak at 10.3 μ.

I_p = distance from the zero line to the maximum absorption of the band at 10.1 μ.

The extinction coefficient of the sample in the particular cell being used is calculated as follows:

$$E = \frac{D_B}{\text{weight of sample in grams}}, \text{ where } E = \text{extinction coefficient.}$$

Using an accurately weighed sample of about 100 mg. of the potassium penicillin O working standard in this procedure, determine its extinction coefficient in the particular cell being used.

Obtain the per cent chloroprocaine penicillin O in the sample under test by the following calculation:

$$\frac{E_{sample}}{E_{standard}} \times 168 = \text{per cent chloroprocaine penicillin O.}$$

If potassium penicillin O is to be tested, use 100 mg. of sample and obtain the per cent potassium penicillin O by the following calculation:

$$\frac{E_{sample}}{E_{standard}} \times 100 = \text{per cent potassium penicillin O.}$$

Determination of Penicillin K.

At one time during the production of penicillin, the strain of mold being used produced fairly large quantities of penicillin K (n-heptyl penicillin). As the K type was not considered desirable, a limit (30 per cent) was placed on the amount of it in the commercial penicillin being sold at that time. By the use of precursors to guide the mold to produce penicillin G, penicillin K has been practically eliminated from the penicillin produced today. An approximate method for the determination of penicillin K is described in Method 11, in the event that one wishes to make such a determination. The method is based on the fact that penicillin K, when dissolved in one volume of pH 6 buffer and shaken with two volumes of chloroform, distributes itself so that about 31 per cent is extracted into the chloroform and about 69 per cent remains in the aqueous phase. Penicillin G under the same conditions distributes itself so that only about 1.5 per cent is in the chloroform layer and 98.5 per cent is in the aqueous layer. The formula used in the calculations is based upon average recoveries obtained with known samples of penicillin K and G. Penicillin X does not interfere in the method. Penicillins dihydro F and F interfere to some extent but the error introduced by the presence of these two types is small.

METHOD 11: The Determination of Penicillin K in Sodium, Potassium, or Calcium Penicillin.[32]

Dilute a weighed sample of the contents of a vial with 0.3 M phosphate (dibasic sodium phosphate and monobasic potassium phosphate) buffer pH 6.0 to give a solution containing approximately 1,000 units/ml. In the case of calcium penicillin where a precipitate of calcium phosphate occurs, remove the precipitate by filtration and use the clear filtrate. Place a 15.0 ml. aliquot of this solution in a 125 ml. separatory funnel, add 30.0 ml. of chloroform U.S.P., and shake for one minute. (Carry out all operations at room temperature.) Allow the mixture to stand, with occasional swirling to settle the droplets of chloroform until the top layer is clear (usually about 10 minutes). Draw off all but about 2.0 ml. of the lower chloroform layer through a small pledget of cotton into a glass stoppered flask. Take a 4.0 ml. aliquot of the original solution, a 4.0 ml. aliquot of the buffer solution remaining in the separatory funnel, and a 10.0 ml. aliquot of the chloroform solution and determine the mg./ml. of penicillin in each by the iodometric procedure described in section B, Chapter 2, using 4.0 ml. of the 1 N sodium hydroxide and 4.0 ml. of the 1.2 N hydrochloric acid for each of these aliquots. Make blank determinations on the same size aliquots. Calculate the per cent penicillin in the buffer layer and in the chloroform layer as compared to the original solution. The sum of these percentages should be 100 per cent ±2 per cent. The per cent penicillin K = (96.92 + per cent in chloroform − per cent in buffer) ×1.67. (The factors in this formula are based on distribution coefficients of penicillin K and G between chloroform and aqueous phosphate buffer at pH 6.0).

Determination of Penicillin K in Procaine Penicillin.

If it is desired to determine the penicillin K content of a water-insoluble salt of penicillin, such as procaine penicillin, it is necessary to extract the free penicillin acid into chloroform and then apply the distribution procedure. The details of this modification are given in Method 12.

METHOD 12: The Determination of Penicillin K in Procaine Penicillin.

Weigh from 30 to 35 mg. of the sample to be tested in a glass test tube or glass vial of approximately 10.0 ml. capacity. Add 2.0 ml. of chloroform U.S.P. and cool the mixture to 0 to 5 C. in an ice bath. Add 1.0 ml. of cold 1 to 4 phosphoric acid solution, stopper, and shake vigorously for about 15 seconds. Centrifuge to obtain a clear separation of the layers (approximately 20 seconds). After centrifuging, remove 1.0 ml. of the chloroform layer with a pipette or syringe equipped with a suitable needle. Immediately place the 1.0 ml. of chloroform in a 125 ml. separatory funnel containing 29.0 ml. of chloroform and 15.0 ml. of 0.3 M phosphate (dibasic sodium phosphate and monobasic potassium phosphate) buffer pH 6.0 at room temperature and shake for one minute. Allow the mixture to stand with occasional swirling to settle the droplets of chloroform until the top layer is clear (usually about 10 minutes). Draw off all but about 2.0 ml. of the lower chloroform layer through a small pledget of cotton into a glass stoppered flask. Take a 4.0 ml. aliquot of the buffer solution remaining in the separatory funnel and a 10.0 ml. aliquot of the chloroform solution and determine the mg./ml. of penicillin in each by the iodometric assay procedure described in section B, Chapter 2, using 4.0 ml. of the 1 N sodium hydroxide and 4.0 ml. of the 1.2 N hydrochloric acid for these two aliquots. Make blank determinations on the same size aliquots. Calculate the per cent penicillin in the buffer layer on the basis that the sum of the penicillin found in the buffer layer and in the chloroform layer is 100 per cent. The per cent penicillin K $=$ (98.46 $-$ per cent found in buffer) $\times 3.34$.

Determination of Mannosidostreptomycin or Dihydromannosidostreptomycin.

Mannosidostreptomycin (streptomycin B) or dihydromannosidostreptomycin (dihydrostreptomycin B), if present in quantity with streptomycin or dihydrostreptomycin, will affect the chemical assay methods so that correlation with the microbiologic assay will not be obtained. If the amount of these two substances is known, suitable corrections can be made in the chemical assay methods and agreement with the microbiologic assay can be obtained. A method for determining mannosidostreptomycin or dihydromannosidostreptomycin is described in Method 13. Methanolysis of mannosidostreptomycin or dihydromannosidostreptomycin gives, in addition to other products, methyl mannoside. Streptomycin or dihydrostreptomycin does not give methyl mannoside on methanolysis. The method described depends upon methanolysis of the sample, removal by ion exchange, of all products formed except the methyl mannoside, and colorimetric determination of the mannose as the dinitrophenyl osazone. It is apparent that any free sugar initially present as an impurity will remain with the mannose and give spuriously high values; a blank determination prior to methanolysis therefore must be made. In making the blank determination, it is necessary to remove streptomycin and its hydrolytic products quantitatively by ion exchange, as they react with the reagent.

METHOD 13: Mannose Colorimetric Method for the Determination of Mannosidostreptomycin or Dihydromannosidostreptomycin.

Reagents. METHANOLIC SULFURIC ACID. Dissolve 3.0 ml. of concentrated sulfuric acid in 100 ml. of absolute methanol. Prepare fresh daily.

DINITROPHENYLHYDRAZINE (DNPH) SOLUTION. Heat 25 mg. of reagent grade DNPH in 5.0 ml. of concentrated hydrochloric acid until completely dissolved. Dilute to 100 ml. with distilled water.

ALCOHOLIC SODIUM HYDROXIDE SOLUTION. Dilute 25.0 ml. of 2 N aqueous sodium hydroxide solution to 100 ml. with 95 per cent ethyl alcohol.

DILUTE ALCOHOL. Mix equal volumes of 95 per cent ethyl alcohol and distilled water. Isopropyl alcohol can be substituted for the ethyl alcohol.

ION EXCHANGE RESIN. For the methanolyzate use Amberlite MB3 or equivalent resin (resin A). For the sample blank, use analytical grade Amberlite MB3 or equivalent resin with the anion-exchange portion converted to the chloride form (resin B). To prepare this material, pass 2 liters of 2 N hydrochloric acid over 1 pound of the resin contained in a large column or percolator. Wash with distilled water (conveniently by a back-wash technique) until the washings are neutral. Transfer the resin to a large Buchner funnel, cover with filter paper, and draw a current of air through the resin for one hour. The product ready for use contains approximately 40 per cent moisture. After use, the mixed resins can be prepared for re-use with the anion resin in the chloride form by regeneration as previously.

Apparatus. ION-EXCHANGE COLUMN. A 200 by 25 mm. tube, with a stopcock at one end is used.

TEST TUBES. Borosilicate glass, 19 by 150 mm., are annealed after each use by heating in a muffle furnace to 600 C., maintaining this temperature for several minutes, and allowing tubes to cool slowly to room temperature. No soap or detergent may be used in washing the tubes.

SPECTROPHOTOMETER. Beckman Model DU or equivalent is used.

Procedure.[33] To 250 mg. of sample weighed into a 25 ml. flask, add 5 ml. of methanolic sulfuric acid and reflux in an all-glass apparatus for two hours. (Use of a larger aliquot in the conversion to the osazone will permit the use of a smaller sample.) Cool, make up to 100 ml. with distilled water, and transfer to a dropping funnel.

Place 30 Gm. of mixed ion-exchange resin A in a column, supported on a loose plug of glass wool. Run in sufficient distilled water through the lower stopcock to fill the column. Drain off the excess water until the level reaches the top of the resin bed; then add the methanolyzate at a rate of not more than 3.0 ml./minute, allowing the solution to run off from the bottom of the column at the same rate. Discard the first 90 ml. of effluent solution; this volume displaces and is diluted by the water initially on the column and therefore is not representative of the methanolyzate. Collect the remaining effluent for analysis.

For the sample blank determination, pass a solution of 250 mg. of the sample in 100 ml. distilled water over 30 Gm. of mixed resin B in the same manner.

Transfer a 2 ml. aliquot of the final effluent liquid to a 19 by 150 mm. test tube, and add 1 ml. DNPH reagent. (If the final reading indicates a content of more than 40 μg. of mannose, a smaller aliquot must be taken.) Immerse the tube in a steam bath to approximately one-third its length. Heat, using a vigorous flow of steam, until the tube contents are dry and the odor of hydrogen chloride is no longer detectable. In order to ensure completion, allow a period of a one-half to one hour of additional heating after dryness has been reached.

After the tubes have cooled, dissolve the contents of the tube in 2.0 ml. of the alcoholic sodium hydroxide reagent, running the reagent down the sides of the tube. Transfer to a 25 ml. volumetric flask, and make up to volume with the diluted alcohol. After a half hour, read the optical density at 556 mμ against a reagent blank. Subtract the value of the sample blank from the value of the methanolyzed sample. Prepare a standard curve using pure mannose solution.

Calculations. The following calculations are made.

$$\text{per cent mannosido-compound} = \frac{100 \times \text{wt. mannose found}}{\text{wt. sample}} \times \frac{100\ F}{\text{vol. aliquot}}$$

$$\text{where } F = \frac{\text{Mol. wt. of mannosido-compound}}{\text{Mol. wt. mannose}}$$

Compound	F
Mannosidostreptomycin sulfate	5.04
Dihydromannosidostreptomycin sulfate	5.05
Mannosidostreptomycin calcium chloride complex	5.40

Determination of Isonicotinic Acid Hydrazide.

A method was given in Section C, Chapter 3, for the determination of the streptomycin portion of the compound, streptomycylidene isonicotinyl hydrazine sulfate. As it is also important to determine the isonicotinic acid hydrazide portion of the molecule, a bromometric procedure for accomplishing this is described in Method 14. This same method may also be used to determine isonicotinic acid hydrazide in mixtures of this compound with streptomycin and dihydrostreptomycin.

METHOD 14: Bromometric Method for Isonicotinic Acid Hydrazide.

Reagents. The following reagents are used: 0.1 N potassium bromate—potassium bromide solution. (Dissolve 3 Gm. of potassium bromate and 15 Gm. of potassium bromide in sufficient distilled water to make 1,000 ml.); concentrated hydrochloric acid; 20 per cent w/v potassium iodide solution; 0.05 N sodium thiosulfate (accurately standardized against potassium iodate).

Preparation of Sample. Place an accurately weighed sample of approximately 250 mg. or an aliquot of a solution containing 250 mg. of streptomycylidene isonicotinyl hydrazine sulfate into a 250 ml. iodine flask. Add sufficient distilled water to give a volume of 25.0 ml.

Blank. Add 25.0 ml. of distilled water to a 250 ml. iodine flask.

Procedure. To each iodine flask containing the sample and the blank, add 25.0 ml. of 0.1 *N* potassium bromate—potassium bromide solution and 5.0 ml. of concentrated hydrochloric acid. Stopper the flasks and place distilled water in the well around the stoppers. Allow the flasks to stand for 15 minutes at room temperature and then add 5.0 ml. of 20 per cent potassium iodide to each flask. Titrate the liberated iodine with 0.05 *N* sodium thiosulfate, using starch as an indicator.

Calculations.

$$\text{Per cent isonicotinic acid hydrazide} = \frac{(B-S) \times N \times 3429}{W}$$

where   B = ml. of sodium thiosulfate required for the blank.
        S = ml. of sodium thiosulfate required for the sample.
        N = normality of the sodium thiosulfate.
        W = mg. of sample.

Determination of the Streptomycin Content of Dihydrostreptomycin.

When streptomycin is hydrogenated to form dihydrostreptomycin, there is usually a very small quantity of unchanged streptomycin that remains, since the conversion is not 100 per cent. The law requires not more than 3 per cent of streptomycin to be present in dihydrostreptomycin. The method used to determine this residual streptomycin is the maltol colorimetric procedure described in Method 1, Section B, Chapter 3, with certain modifications. These modifications of the maltol method are required because it has been found that the large amount of dihydrostreptomycin present prevents the maximum formation of maltol in the 10 minute heating period from the small quantity of streptomycin present (6 mg. or less of streptomycin per 200 mg. of dihydrostreptomycin).

In order to correct for the suppressing effect of the dihydrostreptomycin, it is necessary to add the dihydrostreptomycin being tested to the streptomycin standard used for the standard curve. A further complication lies in the fact that the dihydrostreptomycin sample added to the standard streptomycin also contains a small, unknown as yet, amount of streptomycin. To correct for this, the color developed from the dihydrostreptomycin being tested may be used as a blank to set the instrument at 100 per cent transmittance during the determination of the standard curve. This automatically subtracts from each point on the standard curve the amount of streptomycin in the dihydrostreptomycin. The absorbance reading obtained on the dihydrostreptomycin sample being tested, against a reagent blank, is then used to calculate its actual streptomycin content from the standard curve.

Another, and perhaps more convenient, way of correcting for the streptomycin content of the dihydrostreptomycin used in the standard curve, is to read both the standards and the sample of dihydrostreptomycin under test against a reagent blank. The reading obtained on the dihydrostreptomycin is subtracted from each reading of the standards. These differences are then plotted as the standard curve. The reading obtained on the sample under test against the reagent blank is then used to calculate the streptomycin content from the standard curve.

METHOD 15: Maltol Colorimetric Method for the Determination of Residual Streptomycin in Dihydrostreptomycin.

Reagents. The reagents used are: 10 per cent ferric chloride stock solution. (dissolve 5 Gm. of ferric chloride in 50 ml. 0.1 N hydrochloric acid); 0.25 per cent ferric chloride solution (dilute 2.5 ml. of the 10 per cent ferric chloride to 100 ml. with 0.01 N hydrochloric acid. Prepare the solution fresh daily); 1 N sodium hydroxide; and 1.2 N hydrochloric acid.

Preparation of Standard. Prepare a stock aqueous solution of the streptomycin working standard to contain 1.0 mg./ml. of streptomycin base. Store this standard solution in the refrigerator and use for no longer than two weeks. Also prepare a stock solution of the sample of dihydrostreptomycin under test, to contain 200 mg./ml. of dihydrostreptomycin base. Transfer 1.0, 2.0, 3.0, 4.0, 5.0, 6.0, and 7.0 ml. of the standard streptomycin solution to 25 ml. volumetric flasks. To each of these flasks, add 1.0 ml. of the dihydrostreptomycin solution. Finally add sufficient distilled water to each flask to give each a total volume of 10.0 ml.

Preparation of Sample. Add 1.0 ml. of the dihydrostreptomycin stock solution, as just prepared, plus 9.0 ml. of distilled water to a 25 ml. volumetric flask.

Blank. Transfer 10.0 ml. of distilled water to a 25 ml. volumetric flask as the blank.

Procedure. To each of the 25 ml. volumetric flasks containing standard, sample, and blank, add 2.0 ml. of 1 N sodium hydroxide and heat in a boiling water bath for 10 minutes. Cool in ice water for three minutes and add 2.0 ml. of 1.2 N hydrochloric acid. Add 5.0 ml. of 0.25 per cent ferric chloride reagent. Make to volume with distilled water. Transfer the colored solutions to a 2.0 cm. absorption cell. Using a suitable photoelectric colorimeter, set the instrument with the blank solution to read zero absorbance at 550 mμ. Obtain the absorbance readings of the standards and sample. Subtract the absorbance reading of the sample from each of the readings obtained on the standards. Plot these differences on graph paper as the ordinate scale and the concentration of streptomycin standard as the abscissa. This is the standard curve. Use the absorbance reading obtained on the dihydrostreptomycin sample to obtain the streptomycin content from the standard curve.

Chlortetracycline in Tetracycline.

Tetracycline may be made from chlortetracycline by catalytic reduction of the latter compound with hydrogen. It may also be prepared by fermentation methods. In either case, the amount of any chlortetracycline that might be present can be measured by the spectrophotometric procedure described in Method 16.

Tetracycline in alkaline solution demonstrates an absorption maximum at 380 mμ while chlortetracycline under the same conditions has practically no absorption at this wave length. Tetracycline in 0.1 N hydrochloric acid gives an absorption maximum at 355 mμ. Chlorotetracycline also absorbs strongly at 355 mμ. At this point, however, any chlortetracycline present in the tetracycline would have an additive effect on the absorption. By converting the tetracycline absorption obtained at 380 mμ to the equivalent absorption at 355 mμ, the difference between this and the absorption actually obtained would be the effect of the chlortetracycline. Knowing the extinction coefficient of chlortetracycline at 355 mμ, the chlortetracycline content can be determined. The method will measure down to about 2 per cent of chlortetracycline in tetracycline. As the absorbance of tetracycline in alkali changes with time as also does the absorbance of chlortetracycline in acid, all determinations of absorbancy are made six minutes after the addition of acid or alkali.

METHOD 16: The Determination of Chlortetracycline in Tetracycline. [34]

Accurately weigh about 100 mg. of tetracycline hydrochloride and transfer quantitatively to a 1,000 ml. volumetric flask with the aid of water. Add 100 ml. of water and mix until solution is complete. Make to 1,000 ml. with water. If tetracycline base is to be tested, use 5.0 ml. of 0.1 N hydrochloric acid to dissolve the sample and then make to 1,000 ml. with water. Transfer 15.0 ml. to a 100 ml. volumetric flask. Add 70 ml. of water and 5.0 ml. 5 N sodium hydroxide, make to 100 ml. with water, and mix well. Determine the absorbance at 380 mμ in a 1 cm. cell, using a suitable spectrophotometer, exactly six minutes after the addition of the sodium hydroxide. Transfer another 15.0 ml. aliquot of the 100 mg./liter solution to a 100 ml. volumetric flask. Add 70 ml. of water and 10.0 ml. of 1 N hydrochloric acid, make to 100 ml. with water, and mix well. Determine the absorbance at 355 mμ in a 1 cm. cell, using a suitable spectrophotometer, exactly six minutes after the addition of the acid.

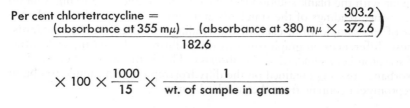

$$\text{Per cent chlortetracycline} = \frac{(\text{absorbance at 355 m}\mu) - \left(\text{absorbance at 380 m}\mu \times \dfrac{303.2}{372.6}\right)}{182.6}$$

$$\times 100 \times \frac{1000}{15} \times \frac{1}{\text{wt. of sample in grams}}$$

where 303.2 = specific absorbancy $E_1^{1\%}{}_{cm.}$ of tetracycline at 355 mμ in 0.1 N hydrochloric acid.

372.6 = specific absorbancy $E_1^{1\%}{}_{cm.}$ of tetracycline at 380 mμ in 0.25 N sodium hydroxide.

182.6 = specific absorbancy $E_1^{1\%}{}_{cm.}$ of chlortetracycline at 355 mμ in 0.1 N hydrochloric acid.

Methods for Moisture Determinations.

Many of the antibiotics are unstable in the presence of excessive moisture. For this reason, it is necessary to keep the moisture content at a minimum in these antibiotics and their various preparations. Two methods in common use for the determination of moisture in antibiotics are the oven drying method and the Karl Fischer titration method. The oven drying procedure is described in Method 17 and the Karl Fischer procedure in Method 18.

In the oven drying method, the sample is weighed before and after heating and the loss in weight is calculated as moisture. The drying is usually carried out in a vacuum oven at a temperature of 60 C. for a period of three hours. This temperature was chosen to avoid overheating of the antibiotic, which might cause degradation. It has been found convenient to use weighing bottles equipped with stoppers having a capillary tube. In such weighing bottles, the stopper is put on before placing in the oven. During the drying, the moisture escapes through the capillary. When removed from the oven, it is not necessary to replace the stopper, as is required with conventional weighing bottles, and there is no uptake of moisture through the capillary during the weighing operation.

The oven drying method may be used in general for all the antibiotics in crystalline or powder form and for products, such as troches and tablets, which may be reduced to a powder and then dried. There are some exceptions, for example procaine penicillin, which is a hydrate and may decompose at 60 C. The oven method is not generally applicable for the determination of moisture in ointments, oil mixtures, or suppositories, because the oils used in these preparations may oxidize during the heating and increase in weight thus leading to a false moisture value. The oven drying method may also give fictitious moisture results on any products that contain volatile flavoring agents.

The Karl Fischer reagent reacts with water and thus actually measures the water content of the sample being tested. This method thus permits determinations where the volatility, oxidation, or decomposition of samples prohibits use of the oven method. It will also measure water of hydration, as for example in procaine penicillin, in addition to the adsorbed moisture. It may be used on powdered samples or on ointments, oils, or suppositories. There are some compounds that will react with the Karl Fischer reagent and unless such compounds are eliminated or corrected for, true moisture values are not obtained.

The Karl Fischer reagent is composed of iodine, pyridine, sulfur dioxide, and methanol or methyl cellosolve. The main reaction of the reagent with water in methanol is believed to take place in two steps.

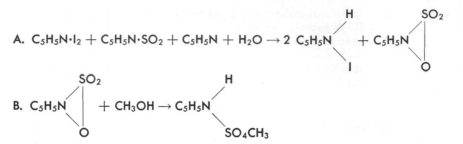

A. $C_5H_5N \cdot I_2 + C_5H_5N \cdot SO_2 + C_5H_5N + H_2O \rightarrow 2\ C_5H_5N\overset{H}{\diagdown}_{I} + C_5H_5N\overset{SO_2}{\diagup}_{O}$

B. $C_5H_5N\overset{SO_2}{\diagup}_{O} + CH_3OH \rightarrow C_5H_5N\overset{H}{\diagup}_{SO_4CH_3}$

For a most thorough and complete discussion of the Karl Fischer method, the reader is referred to the book by Mitchell and Smith.[35] This method has extremely wide application and is the method of choice because of its speed and accuracy.

METHOD 17: Oven Drying Moisture Method.

In an atmosphere of about 10 per cent relative humidity, transfer approximately 100 mg. of the finely powdered sample to a tared weighing bottle equipped with a capillary-tube stopper, the capillary having an inside diameter of 0.20 to 0.25 mm. Weigh the bottle and place it in a vacuum oven, without removing the stopper and dry at a temperature of 60 C. and a pressure of 5 mm. of mercury or less for three hours. At the end of the drying period, fill the vacuum oven with air dried by passing it through a drying agent, such as sulfuric acid or silica gel. Place the weighing bottles in a desiccator over phosphorous pentoxide or silica gel, allow to cool to room temperature, and reweigh. Divide the loss in weight by the weight of the sample and multiply by 100 to obtain the percentage of moisture.

METHOD 18: Karl Fischer Moisture Method.

Reagents. KARL FISCHER REAGENT. Preserve the reagent in glass stoppered bottles and use from an all glass automatic burette, protecting the solution from the moisture in the air. Directions for preparing the reagent are given in Chapter 21.

WATER-METHANOL SOLUTION. Use methanol containing approximately 1 mg. of water/ml. Store the solution in a glass bottle attached to an automatic burette and protect from moisture in the air at all times.

Standardization of Karl Fischer Reagent. Add a known volume of the Karl Fischer reagent to a suitable titrating vessel, which has been previously dried at 105 C. and cooled in a desiccator. Introduce a mechanical stirrer and two platinum electrodes which are connected to a suitable electrometric apparatus for measurement of the end point. Start the stirrer and titrate with the water-methanol solution until the end point is reached. Calculate the ml. of Karl Fischer reagent equivalent to each ml. of water-methanol.

Add an accurately weighed quantity of water (approximately 50 mg.) to a dry titrating vessel; add an excess of the Karl Fischer reagent and back titrate with the water-methanol solution. Calculate the mg. of water equivalent to each ml. of the Karl Fischer reagent. Standardize the Karl Fischer reagent in this manner daily.

$$e = \frac{w}{v_1 - v_2 f}$$

where e = mg. of water equivalent to 1 ml. Karl Fischer reagent.
   w = weight of water in mg.
   v_1 = volume of Karl Fischer reagent used.
   v_2 = volume of methanol used.
   f = volume ratio of Karl Fischer reagent to water-methanol solution.

Procedure. Transfer from 0.3 to 1.0 Gm. of the powdered sample depending upon the amount of water anticipated to a dry titrating vessel, add an excess of the Karl Fischer reagent, and back titrate with the water-methanol solution until the end point is reached.

$$\text{Per cent moisture} = \frac{(v_1 - v_2 f)\,(e)\,(100)}{w_s}$$

where w_s = weight of sample in mg.

In the case of oils, ointments, and suppositories, it is necessary to use a solvent, such as chloroform or chloroform-carbon tetrachloride or other suitable solvent, to dissolve the sample prior to the addition of the Karl Fischer reagent. In such cases it is necessary to correct for any water in the solvent used. The procedure for procaine penicillin in oil, for example, is as follows:

Transfer 1.0 ml. of the sample to a dry titrating vessel, add 10.0 ml. of dry chloroform and an excess of the Karl Fischer reagent, and back titrate with the water-methanol solution until the end point is reached. Transfer 10.0 ml. of the dry chloroform used to a dry titrating vessel, add an excess of Karl Fischer reagent, and titrate with the water-methanol as previously. Calculate the ml. of Karl Fischer reagent equivalent to 10.0 ml. of chloroform.

$$\text{Per cent moisture} = \frac{(v_1 - v_2 f - b)\,(e)\,(100)}{s\,(1000)}$$

where b = ml. Karl Fischer reagent equivalent to 10.0 ml. chloroform.
   s = volume of sample in ml.

21 MEDIA, SOLUTIONS, REAGENTS, AND APPARATUS

Section A: Culture Media

The ingredients used should conform to the standards of the U.S.P. or N.F. if applicable. Most of the culture media listed may be obtained in a dehydrated form from commercial sources which when reconstituted as recommended by the manufacturer should have the same composition and growth promoting properties as when made from the individual ingredients.

Medium No. 1	Peptone	6 Gm.
	Pancreatic digest of casein	4 Gm.
	Yeast extract	3 Gm.
	Beef extract	1.5 Gm.
	Dextrose	1 Gm.
	Agar	15 Gm.
	Distilled water to make	1000 ml.
	pH 6.5 to 6.6 after sterilization	
Medium No. 2	Peptone	6 Gm.
	Yeast extract	3 Gm.
	Beef extract	1.5 Gm.
	Agar	15 Gm.
	Distilled water to make	1000 ml.
	pH 6.5 to 6.6 after sterilization	
Medium No. 3	Peptone	5 Gm.
	Yeast extract	1.5 Gm.
	Beef extract	1.5 Gm.
	Sodium chloride	3.5 Gm.
	Dextrose	1 Gm.
	Monobasic potassium phosphate	1.32 Gm.
	Dibasic potassium phosphate	3.68 Gm.
	Distilled water to make	1000 ml.
	pH 6.95 to 7.05 after sterilization	
Medium No. 4	Peptone	6 Gm.
	Yeast extract	3 Gm.
	Beef extract	1.5 Gm.
	Dextrose	1 Gm.
	Agar	15 Gm.
	Distilled water to make	1000 ml.
	pH 6.5 to 6.6 after sterilization	

Medium No. 5   Same as medium no. 2 except the pH is adjusted so that it is 7.8 to 8.0 after sterilization.

Medium No. 6

Pancreatic digest of casein..............	17 Gm.
Papaic digest of soy bean..............	3 Gm.
Sodium chloride......................	5 Gm.
Dibasic potassium phosphate.............	2.5 Gm.
Dextrose............................	2.5 Gm.
Manganous sulfate, hydrous.............	0.03 Gm.
Distilled water to make.................	1000 ml.

pH 6.9 to 7.1 after sterilization

Medium No. 7   Same as medium no. 2 except the pH is adjusted so that it is 6.95 to 7.05 after sterilization.

Medium No. 8   Same as medium no. 2 except the pH is adjusted so that it is 5.6 to 5.7 after sterilization.

Medium No. 9

Pancreatic digest of casein..............	17 Gm.
Papaic digest of soy bean..............	3 Gm.
Sodium chloride......................	5 Gm.
Dibasic potassium phosphate.............	2.5 Gm.
Dextrose............................	2.5 Gm.
Agar..............................	20 Gm.
Distilled water to make.................	1000 ml.

pH 7.2 to 7.3 after sterilization

Medium No. 10

Pancreatic digest of casein..............	17 Gm.
Papaic digest of soy bean..............	3 Gm.
Sodium chloride......................	5 Gm.
Dibasic potassium phosphate.............	2.5 Gm.
Dextrose............................	2.5 Gm.
Agar..............................	12 Gm.
Distilled water to make.................	1000 ml.

Boil to dissolve the medium and then add 10 ml. of polysorbate 80.

pH 7.2 to 7.3 after sterilization

Medium No. 11   Same as medium no. 1 except the pH is adjusted so that it is 7.9 to 8.0 after sterilization.

Medium No. 12

Peptone............................	10 Gm.
Yeast extract........................	5 Gm.
Beef extract........................	2.5 Gm.
Sodium chloride......................	10 Gm.
Dextrose............................	10 Gm.
Agar..............................	25 Gm.
Distilled water to make.................	1000 ml.

pH 6.0 to 6.2 after sterilization

Medium No. 13

Peptone............................	10 Gm.
Dextrose............................	20 Gm.
Distilled water to make.................	1000 ml.

pH 5.6 to 5.7 after sterilization

Medium No. 14

Yeast extract........................	5 Gm.
Pancreatic digest of casein.............	15 Gm.
Glucose............................	5 Gm.
Sodium chloride......................	2.5 Gm.
L-Cystine...........................	0.75 Gm.
Thioglycollic acid....................	0.3 ml.
Agar..............................	0.75 Gm.
Resazurin, certified..................	0.001 Gm.

	Distilled water to make................	1000 ml.
	pH 7 to 7.2 after sterilization	
Medium No. 15	Brain, infusion from...................	200 Gm.
	Heart, infusion from...................	250 Gm.
	Proteose peptone.......................	10 Gm.
	Glucose...............................	2 Gm.
	Sodium chloride.......................	5 Gm.
	Disodium phosphate....................	2.5 Gm.
	Distilled water to make................	1000 ml.
	pH 7.3 to 7.5 after sterilization	
Medium No. 16	Heart, infusion from...................	500 Gm.
	Tryptose peptone......................	10 Gm.
	Sodium chloride.......................	5 Gm.
	Agar..................................	15 Gm.
	Distilled water to make................	1000 ml.
	pH 7.3 to 7.5 after sterilization	

Medium No. 17   Add 4 per cent sterile defibrinated sheep or rabbit blood to medium no. 16 which has been melted and cooled to 48 C.

Note: Cultures of the microorganisms used in the microbiologic assays described in the various chapters may be obtained from the American Type Culture Collection, 2029 M Street, N. W., Washington, D. C.

Section B: **Solutions**

Phosphate Buffer Solution No. 1, pH 6.0
Dibasic potassium phosphate..............	2 Gm.
Monobasic potassium phosphate...........	8 Gm.
Distilled water to make..................	1000 ml.

Citrate Buffer Solution No. 2, pH 6.3
Citric acid...............................	13.2 Gm.
Sodium hydroxide........................	7.06 Gm.
Sodium citrate...........................	97 Gm.
Distilled water to make..................	1000 ml.

Phosphate Buffer Solution No. 3, pH 8.0
Dibasic potassium phosphate..............	16.73 Gm.
Monobasic potassium phosphate...........	0.523 Gm.
Distilled water to make..................	1000 ml.

Phosphate Buffer Solution No. 4, pH 4.5
Monobasic potassium phosphate...........	13.6 Gm.
Distilled water to make..................	1000 ml.

Glycine Buffer Solution No. 5, pH 2.0
Glycine..................................	3.5 Gm.
Sodium chloride..........................	3 Gm.
Distilled water to make..................	1000 ml.
Adjust pH to 2.0 with hydrochloric acid	

Phosphate Buffer Solution No. 6, pH6, (10 per cent)
Dibasic potassium phosphate..............	20 Gm.
Monobasic potassium phosphate...........	80 Gm.
Distilled water to make..................	1000 ml.

Phosphate Buffer Solution No. 7, pH 6 (4 per cent)
Dibasic potassium phosphate..............	8 Gm.

Monobasic potassium phosphate...................... 32 Gm.
Distilled water to make.............................. 1000 ml.
Phosphate Buffer Solution No. 8, pH 6 (8 per cent)
    Dibasic potassium phosphate......................... 16 Gm.
    Monobasic potassium phosphate...................... 64 Gm.
    Distilled water to make............................. 1000 ml.
Phosphate Buffer Solution No. 9, pH 8.0
    Dibasic potassium phosphate......................... 167.3 Gm.
    Monobasic potassium phosphate...................... 5.23 Gm.
    Distilled water to make............................. 1000 ml.
Bovine Albumin Solutions
1. 7.0 per cent bovine albumin solution
2. 3.5 per cent bovine albumin solution

The bovine albumin solutions are prepared as follows: Dissolve 7.0 or 3.5 Gm. of bovine albumin powder (fraction V) from bovine plasma (Armour and Co., Chicago, Ill.) in phosphate buffer no. 3, *p*H 8, to give a total volume of 100 ml. Adjust the final *p*H to 7.4. Before use, filter through a Seitz filter. This sterile solution may be stored in the refrigerator and used for several weeks or longer.

Section C: Reagents

Karl Fischer Reagent. To prepare 3 liters of Karl Fischer reagent, transfer 254 Gm. (1 mole) of resublimed U.S.P. iodine to a 5 liter Pyrex flask, which can be tightly stoppered, and add 800 ml. (10 moles) of reagent grade pyridine (containing less than 0.1 per cent water). Shake for several minutes until the iodine has dissolved and then add 2 liters of ethylene glycol monomethyl ether (methyl cellosolve). Collect about 135 ml. (3 moles) of liquid sulfur dioxide in a cold trap immersed in a carbon dioxide and methanol bath, taking care to avoid absorption of moisture from the atmosphere. Add the liquid sulfur dioxide rapidly, but carefully, with shaking, to the iodine solution. Then stopper the flask and allow the contents to return to room temperature. Release the pressure (by momentarily loosening the stopper) and set the solution aside for a day or two before being put into use. The final reagent has a water equivalence of about 3.5 mg. and is stable for several months.

Penicillinase. The enzyme penicillinase, which is used to inactivate penicillin in various assays and in the sterility test, may be obtained from the following suppliers: Difco Laboratories, Inc., Detroit 1, Mich.; Baltimore Biological Labs., Baltimore, Md.; Schenley Laboratories, Inc., 350 Fifth Avenue, New York 1, N. Y.

Various methods have been proposed to measure the ability of penicillinase to inactivate penicillin. It is believed that the following procedure, although empirical, will provide a rapid and fairly reproducible means of evaluating the amount of penicillinase necessary to inactivate a given quantity of penicillin.

Method. PREPARATION OF PENICILLIN SOLUTION. Dissolve sufficient sodium or potassium penicillin in distilled water to obtain about 200 ml. of a solution containing 15,000 units/ml. This solution should be assayed by the iodometric assay method in Section B, Chapter 2.

PREPARATION OF PENICILLIN SOLUTION CONTAINING THE PENICILLINASE. Place exactly 100 ml. of the penicillin solution just prepared and 1.0 ml. of penicillinase concentrate or a weighed quantity of the dry penicillinase powder in an Erlenmeyer flask and mix well.

PENICILLIN SOLUTION BLANK. Place in an Erlenmeyer flask the remainder of the penicillin solution that is left after the 100 ml. has been used in the solution containing the penicillinase.

PROCEDURE. Place both the penicillin solution blank and the penicillin solution containing the penicillinase in a water bath at 37 C. At the end of a half hour, remove exactly 2.0 ml. of each solution, in turn, and pipette into 125 ml. glass stoppered Erlenmeyer flasks, prepared several minutes before needed, containing 10.0 ml. of 0.01 N iodine. Stopper the flasks, and exactly 30 seconds after the penicillin was added titrate, as rapidly as possible, with 0.01 N sodium thiosulfate, using starch as an indicator. Repeat this operation also at the end of one hour, one and a half hours, and two hours. At the end of the longer incubation periods, it may be necessary to pipette the 2.0 ml. of penicillin solution containing penicillinase into a flask containing 20.0 ml. of 0.01 N iodine instead of 10.0 ml. The need for this can be foreseen by the size of the preceding titers.

CALCULATIONS. Determine the number of units of inactive penicillin in each ml. of solution at each time interval as follows:

$$I = (T_b - T_p) \times \frac{\text{Potency of penicillin standard in u./mg.}}{F \times 2}$$

where I = units/ml. of inactivated penicillin.

T_b = ml. of 0.01 N sodium thiosulfate used in the blank titration.

T_p = ml. of 0.01 N sodium thiosulfate used in the titration of the solution containing penicillinase.

F = ml. of 0.01 N iodine absorbed by each mg. of the standard as determined in the iodometric assay method, Section B, Chapter 2.

2 = volume assayed in ml.

Then determine the rate of inactivation for each time interval as follows:

$$R_1 = I_{1.0} - I_{0.5}$$
$$R_2 = I_{1.5} - I_{1.0}$$
$$R_3 = I_{2.0} - I_{1.5}$$

The three time intervals serve as replicate determinations. Determine the average rate of penicillin inactivation per minute.

It has been found that the amount of penicillinase which will give an inactivation rate of 20 units/ml./minute as determined by this test is sufficient to inactivate satisfactorily 500,000 units in the sterility test described in Chapter 18. If 1.0 ml. of the enzyme solution has an inactivation potential of only 15 units/ml./minute then 1.3 ml. must be used in the sterility test. On the other hand, if it can inactivate 40 units/ml./minute, only 0.5 ml. is necessary. One may also easily calculate, from the inactivation rate already obtained, the quantity of penicillinase to be added to inactivate penicillin solutions for the microbiologic assay procedures.

Note that penicillinase preparations should be tested for sterility.

Standards. The following U.S.P. antibiotic reference standards are available and may be obtained by writing to U.S.P. Reference Standards, 46 Park Avenue, New York 16, N. Y.: penicillin G sodium, streptomycin sulfate, dihydrostreptomycin sulfate, chlortetracycline hydrochloride, oxytetracycline, chloramphenicol, tetracycline hydrochloride, bacitracin, polymxin B sulfate, tyrothricin, neomycin sulfate, and erythromycin.

Standards for carbomycin, viomycin, and anisomycin may be obtained by writing to Chas. Pfizer & Co., Inc., Brooklyn 6, N. Y. No official standards for these antibiotics have been established yet. The same applies to fumagillin manufactured by Abbott Laboratories, North Chicago, Ill., and to nystatin manufactured by E. R. Squibb & Sons, Division of Olin Mathieson Chemical Corp., 745 Fifth Avenue, New York 22, N. Y.

The Food and Drug Administration also maintains antibiotic standards that are available to manufacturers of antibiotics and antibiotic preparations. The majority of the FDA standards are identical with the U.S.P. standards, since the same batch of the antibiotic has been shared by both groups.

Antibiotic reference standards should never be used for routine testing work. Each laboratory should set aside a suitable portion of a good commercial lot as their "house standard," which should be used for routine day to day testing. The reference standard should only be used for standardizing the "house standard" at periodic intervals, usually once a month.

Section D: **Apparatus**

Cylinders (Cups). Stainless steel with an outside diameter of 8 mm. (±0.1 mm.), an inside diameter of 6 mm. (±0.1 mm.), and a length of 10 mm. (±0.1 mm.). These cylinders may be purchased from The Ericson Screw Machine Products Co., Inc., 25 Lafayette Street, Brooklyn 1, N. Y.

Filter Paper Discs. These may be purchased from Carl Schleicher and Schuell Co., New York, N. Y.; S and S No. 740-E, one-half inch (12.7 mm.) diameter.

Antibiotic Discs. Filter paper discs containing impregnated antibiotics for use in determining the sensitivity of microorganisms to antibiotics may be purchased from Difco Laboratories, Detroit, Mich., and from Baltimore Biological Laboratories, Baltimore, Md.

Petri Dish Covers. These may be either Coors porcelain glazed on the outside, unglazed on the inside, to fit 100 mm. glass Petri dish bottoms, or aluminum covers containing an absorbent cardboard inner liner. The porcelain covers are listed as a stock item in most all of the apparatus suppliers' catalogs.

The aluminum covers may be obtained from Baltimore Biological Labs., Baltimore, Md.

Special Petri Dishes. If only a small quantity of medium is to be used for the cylinder-plate assay, it is essential that there be as little variation as possible in the thickness of the medium and a specially made flat bottom Petri dish should be used. These dishes may be obtained from various apparatus supply firms and are listed in the Corning catalog as item No. 3162.

Cylinder Dropping Device. The device used for dropping cylinders onto the agar surface in the cylinder-plate type of assay used in our laboratories is described by Chandler and Shaw.[2] These devices were manufactured by Mr. Shaw, who is now deceased. Further information concerning the availability of the devices may be obtained by writing to Mrs. R. D. Shaw, Adams Road, Bloomfield, Connecticut.

Spectrophotometers, Colorimeters, and Other Instruments. No attempt will be made to list the various instruments available for use in turbidimetric assays, colorimetric assays, etc. There are many such instruments available that are satisfactory for such purposes. Several of these that have been used in our laboratories are mentioned in the various chapters. The operation of those instruments that are mentioned is described to illustrate the exact procedure to be followed and does not imply that other instruments will not work equally well.

Instruments for Reading Zone Diameters. The Fisher-Lilly zone reader is available from the Fisher Scientific Co. and is described in their catalog under item No. 7–906.

The overhead projector used in our laboratories and described in Chapter 1 is a Model BOH Balopticon which may be obtained from Bausch and Lomb, catalog No. 41–21–40–05.

REFERENCES

1. OSWALD, E. J., AND RANDALL, W. A.: A cylinder guide for use in plate assay of penicillin, Science *101:*99, 1945.

2. CHANDLER, V. L., AND SHAW, R. D.: Dropping device for cylinder plate assay of penicillin, Science *104:*275, 1946.

3. ALICINO, J. F.: Iodometric method for the assay of penicillin preparations, Indust. Engin. Chem. (Anal. Ed.) *18:*619, 1946.

4. MUNDELL, M.; FISCHBACH, H., AND EBLE, T. E.: The chemical assay of penicillin, J. Am. Pharm. A. (Scient. Ed.) *35:*373, 1946.

5. SCHENCK, J. R., AND SPIELMAN, M. A.: The formation of maltol by the degradation of streptomycin, J. Am. Chem. Soc. *67:*2276, 1945.

6. BOXER, G. E.; JELINEK, V. C., AND LEGHORN, P. M.: Colorimetric determination of streptomycin in clinical preparations, urine and broth, J. Biol. Chem. *169:*153, 1947.

7. HISCOX, D. J.: Spectrophotometric determination of dihydrostreptomycin, Anal. Chem. *23:*923, 1951.

8. SULLIVAN, M. X., AND HILMER, P. E.: Chemical studies of streptomycin, Am. Chem. Soc., Abst. of 109th Convention, Div. Biol. Chem., p. 4 B, April, 1946.

9. MONASTERO, F.: A colorimetric determination of streptomycin and dihydrostreptomycin, J. Am. Pharm. A. (Scient. Ed.) *41:*322, 1952.

10. MONASTERO, F.; MEANS, J. A.; GRENFELL, T. C., AND HEDGER, F. H.: Terramycin: chemical methods of assay and identification, J. Am. Pharm. A. (Scient. Ed.) *40:*241, 1951.

11. LEVINE, J.; GARLOCK, E. A., JR., AND FISCHBACH, H.: The chemical assay of aureomycin, J. Am. Pharm. A. (Scient. Ed.) *38:*473, 1949.

12. LEVINE, J., AND FISCHBACH, H.: The chemical determination of chloramphenicol in biological materials, Antib. & Chemo., *1:*59, 1951.

13. HAUSMANN, W., AND CRAIG, L. C.: Polymyxin B_1, fractionation, molecular weight determination, amino acid and fatty acid composition, J. Am. Chem. Soc. *76:*4892, 1954.

14. KUZEL, N. R.; WOODSIDE, J. M.; COMER, J. P., AND KENNEDY, E. E.: Spectrophotometric determination of erythromycin in pharmaceutical products, Antib. & Chemo., *4:*1234, 1954.

15. GARRETT, E. R., AND EBLE, T. E.: Studies on the stability of fumagillin. I. Photolytic degradation in alcohol solution, J. Am. Pharm. A. (Scient. Ed.) *43:*385, 1954.

16. FISCHBACH, H., AND LEVINE, J.: The identification of the antibiotics, Antib. & Chemo., *3:*1159, 1953.

17. SCUDI, J. V.; BOXER, G. E., AND JELINEK, V. C.: A color reaction given by streptomycin, Science *104:*486, 1946.

18. United States Pharmacopeia XIV, p. 650.

19. ANON.: Microscopic-Crystallographic Procedures for Identification of Drugs. *In:* Legal Medicine, St. Louis, C. V. Mosby Co., 1954, pp. 724–753.

20. HARTSHORNE, N. H., AND STUART, A.: Crystals and the Polarizing Microscope, Ed. 2, London, Edward Arnold and Co., 1950.

21. CHEMOT, E. M., AND MASON, C. W., Handbook of Chemical Microscopy, Vol. 1, 1938.

22. JACKSON, G. G., AND FINLAND, M.: Comparison of methods for determining sensitivity of bacteria to antibiotics in vitro, A.M.A. Arch. Int. Med. *88:*446–460, Oct., 1951.

23. MELENEY, F. L.: The close association between laboratory and clinic in the control of surgical infections, Proc. New York State A. Pub. Health Lab., *30:*19–26, 1950.

24. COLLINS, A. M.; CRAIG, G.; ZAIMAN, E., AND ROY, T. E.: A comparison between disk-plate and tube-dilution methods for antibiotic sensitivity testing of bacteria, Canad. J. Pub. Health *45:*430–439, Oct., 1954.

25. WELCH, H.; RANDALL, W. A.; REEDY, R. J., AND OSWALD, E. J.: Variations in antimicrobial activity of the tetracyclines, Antib. & Chemo. *4*:741–745, July, 1954.

26. REEDY, R. J.; RANDALL, W. A., AND WELCH, H.: Variations in the antimicrobial activity of the tetracyclines. II., Antib. & Chemo. *5*:115–123, March, 1955.

27. MADER, W. J., AND BUCK, R. R.: Chemical assay for crystalline benzylpenicillin, Anal. Chem. *20*:284, 1948.

28. SELZER, G. B., AND WRIGHT, W. W.: A method for the estimation of benzylpenicillin, Antib. & Chemo. *4*:1196, 1954.

29. CARR, J. C.: Commercial Solvents Corp., Terre Haute, Ind., personal communication.

30. JOHNSON, J. L.; STRUCK, W. A.; SCOTT, E. J., AND STAFFORD, J. E.: Determination of penicillin G in penicillin O, Anal. Chem. *25*:1490, 1953.

31. WRIGHT, W. W.: The quantitative determination of penicillin O by infrared analysis, Antib. & Chemo. *4*:71, 1954.

32. WRIGHT, W. W., AND GROVE, D. C.: The estimation of penicillin K in commercial penicillin, J. Am. Pharm. A. (Scient. Ed.) *37*:115, 1948.

33. LEVINE, J.; SELZER, G., AND WRIGHT, W. W.: The chemical determination of mannosidostreptomycin and dihydromannosidostreptomycin, Anal. Chem. *25*:671, 1953.

34. WOOLFORD, M. H., AND CHICCARELLI, F. S.: Lederle Laboratories Division, American Cyanamid Company, personal communication.

35. MITCHELL, J., JR., AND SMITH, D. M.: Aquametry, New York, Interscience Publishers, Inc., 1945.

INDEX

INDEX

Tissue
assays:
  of bacitracin, 80
  of chloramphenicol, 75
  of erythromycin, 103
  of neomycin, 95
  of penicillin, 32
  of streptomycin and dihydrostrepto-
    mycin, 46
  of tetracyclines, 64
Toxicity
  test for, 175, 176
  table, 178–185
Turbidimetric Method
  in chlortetracycline assays, 48–49
  in oxytetracycline assays, 50
  in streptomycin and dihydrostreptomycin
    assays, 36–38
  in tetracycline assays, 50
  in tyrothricin assays, 82–83
  in viomycin assays, 111–112
Tyrothricin
  assay methods:
    turbidimetric method using *Strepto-
      coccus faecalis*, 82–83
  chemistry, 83–84
  combinations:
    with bacitracin, 137
    with bacitracin and neomycin, 140
    with neomycin, 143
  preparations:
    alcohol or propylene glycol solutions,
      84
    gauze pads, 85
    mineral oil emulsions, 85
    mouth wash, 85
    nose drops, 85
    ointments or creams, 84–85
    otic (ear drops), 85
    powder, 84
    troches, 84
  qualitative tests:
    modified biuret test, 149

Tyrothricin *(Continued)*
  ninhydrin test, 147–148
  paper chromatography, 149–150

Ultraviolet Absorption Spectra
  of antibiotics, 157
Ultraviolet Spectrophotometric Method
  for determination of penicillin G content
    of benzathine penicillin, 200–201
  in chloramphenicol assay, 69–70
  in fumagillin assay, 114
  in oxytetracycline or tetracycline assay,
    55–56
Urine
  assays:
    of bacitracin, 80
    of chloramphenicol, 74–75
    of erythromycin, 103
    of neomycin, 95
    of nystatin, 119
    of penicillin, 32
    of streptomycin and dihydrostrepto-
      mycin, 46
    of tetracyclines, 64
    of viomycin, 113

Viomycin
  assay methods:
    cylinder-plate method using *Bacillus
      subtilis*, 109–111, 112
    turbidimetric method using *Klebsiella
      pneumoniae*, 111–112
  assays:
    in blood serum, 113
    in urine, 113
  chemistry, 112–113
  preparations:
    sulfate for injection, 113
  qualitative tests:
    modified biuret test, 149
    guanido test, 147
    ninhydrin test, 147
    paper chromatography, 149–150
  sterility test, 186